PENGUIN BOOKS

The Singing Whakapapa

Born in Auckland in 1932, C. K. Stead made his name as one of the new New Zealand poets of the 1950s and 60s, and developed an international reputation as a critic. He was also known during those years as a short-story writer and editor. His novel *Smith's Dream* appeared in 1971 and was filmed as *Sleeping Dogs* in 1977, starring Sam Neill in his first film role. In the same year appeared Stead's Penguin selection of Katherine Mansfield's *Letters and Journals*, which continues in print.

In 1986 the author took early retirement from the University of Auckland Professorship of English he had held for twenty years. He holds a doctorate from the universities of Bristol (PhD) and Auckland (LittD) and was awarded the CBE in 1985 for services to New Zealand literature. He is the only New Zealand writer to have won the New Zealand Book Award for both poetry and fiction.

The Singing Whakapapa is C. K. Stead's sixth novel. Others include *All Visitors Ashore* and *The Death of the Body*, the latter currently available in Swedish, French and Portuguese language editions, with translations into German, Italian and Spanish pending.

Stead is married with three children and several grandchildren.

The Singing Whakapapa

C. K. STEAD

PENGUIN BOOKS

PENGUIN BOOKS

Penguin Books (NZ) Ltd, 182–190 Wairau Road, Auckland 10, New Zealand
Penguin Books Ltd, 27 Wrights Lane, London W8 5TZ, England
Penguin USA, 375 Hudson Street, New York, NY 10014, United States
Penguin Books Australia Ltd, 487 Maroondah Highway, Ringwood, Australia 3134
Penguin Books Canada Ltd, 10 Alcorn Avenue, Toronto, Ontario, Canada M4V 3B2

Penguin Books Ltd, Registered Offices: Harmondsworth, Middlesex, England

First published in 1994
3 5 7 9 10 8 6 4
Copyright © C K Stead, 1994
All rights reserved

Editorial services by Michael Gifkins and Associates
Typeset by Egan-Reid Ltd, Auckland
Printed in Hong Kong

The assistance of the Literature Programme of the
Queen Elizabeth II Arts Council towards the production
of this book is gratefully acknowledged.

To my family
near and far,
early and late

The author's thanks go to the
Arts Council of New Zealand
for the award of the Scholarship in Letters
in 1992–93

THE
SINGING
WHAKAPAPA

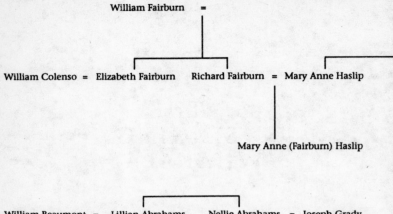

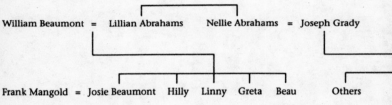

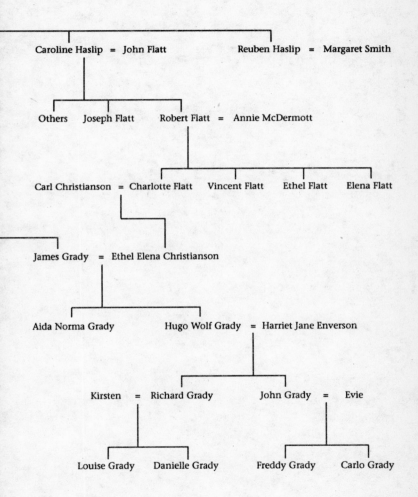

PART
ONE

IT WAS AT FRANK MANGOLD'S burial that Hugh Grady had
his moment of recognition. His interests had shifted away
from *real* history, which was, so to speak, in the public
domain, in favour of his family story, his 'singing whakapapa'; and it was the young librarian, Jean-Anne Devantier,
the one he jokingly called his research assistant, who had
brought this about. The recognition took him by surprise,
coming as it did at this moment of watching the coffin
poised over the sheered clay, old soldier Frank's eighty years
of life under review, Hugh's own sixty also, not to mention
the lives that went before, shading back through time and
across seas.

Round about and rolling away into brown and purple
distances were the pastures, rich now, but remembered as
they had been in his childhood, still pocked with holes left
by gum-diggers (Serbs were they, or Croats? Dalmatians
everyone called them) who had worked over the landscape
with their shovels and spade-handled spears to find and take
up the deposits of gum, all that remained of the kauri forests
under the wasteland the loggers had left.

Sometimes what the digger's long fine spear touched on
proved not to be gum but stone — an adze, a mere — a
reminder of the tribespeople who had once passed through
the kauri forest travelling from coast to coast, or perhaps southward on one of those raiding parties by which the northern
tribes, the first to get muskets, ravaged their southern enemies.

Years later, when the Dalmatian diggers had moved
on and were making themselves or their sons over into

prosperous fishermen and vintners, some small deposits of gum had remained, and a boy, two boys, Hugo and Wolf, had walked over ploughed fields finding pieces the shares had turned up, sometimes fine and clear, translucent amber, with bubbles, sometimes crumbling and opaque, 'sugar gum' it was called, but it all went into the sack and in Auckland the factory paid a shilling a pound.

Trees milled, gum mined, Dalmatians departed, and what had been left then in this neck of the North but a desolation for cow-farmers? Sixty years, and turning a moment from the graveside, locking on distance, Hugh admired it, pasture and crops rolling away to the hills, a vast green garden.

They were lowering Frank now, the straps taking the strain of the small weight his eighty years had left him, and the local pharmacist who had conducted the service throughout (he had been firm to the last, Frank Mangold, his send-off, he had ordained, was to be 'truthful', by which he meant secular) was reciting, 'Our revels now are ended, these our actors as I foretold you were all spirits and are melted into air, into thin air . . .'

Under Hugh Grady's taking in of the familiar words he was aware still of the landscape, impressing itself with the dual vividness of memory and of something seen for the first time.

'And like the baseless fabric of this vision, the cloud-capped towers, the gorgeous palaces, the solemn temples, the great Globe itself, yea all which it inherit shall dissolve . . .'

Yes Hugh knew those lines by heart, as dairy-farmer Frank Mangold had known them, half a world and several centuries from that place where, that time when, a writer unimaginably real had first scratched them down. By heart — and *at* heart. There was something to be explained in that fact, by God there was, and that meant (Hugh thinking again as historian) grappling with it, not explaining it away, moralising it out of existence, as if it were enough to say their forebears, his own and Frank's, had blundered into this place (as they had), destroyers (as perhaps they had been), and there was an end to it (as there was not).

'. . . and like this insubstantial pageant faded, leave not a rack behind. We are such stuff as dreams are made on and our little life is rounded with . . .'

. . . with a bump as his box hit bottom and with the thud of the first clods on his lid. But the Returned men had still to be allowed to pay and exact their soldierly tribute, so there was the playing of their old bugle tape of the Last Post, and the recital by a voice less eloquent than the pharmacist's (more of the gumboot than the white coat in it) of 'They shall not grow old as we that are left grow old'.

'"They shall not grow old . . .",' Hugh murmured to Hat. 'Frank was *eighty*, for Godsake.' She smiled down at the red earth underfoot, and shushed him.

And now it was over, Frank Mangold was down and out, they were standing in the little churchyard with its family graves, looking at the little timber church overshadowed by a macrocarpa already boy-climbable half a century ago, at the fence now falling in slow mime-rape under the loving weight of honeysuckle, at that vast green garden of a landscape dipping down and running away and lifting at last to far blue hills, when a cousin Hugh hadn't seen these past four — no, not years (life on this occasion working to the larger scale) but decades — greeted and embraced him, calling him Hugo.

Hilly. She was unrecognisably large and unmistakably the child with whom he had ridden bareback through fern and manuka, and he was moved, as if someone had handed him back, solid and real, what seemed to exist only in fading recollection, like a piece of that perfect orange-brown kauri gum in which an image had been fixed for ever. That she was telling him she was now a grandmother, was divorced, had found God, had taken Him into Africa for Africa's good — none of this touched quite on the feeling Hugh Grady had of a recovery out of the deeps of himself. And at that moment he looked and saw that they were standing beside her parents' graves — William Beaumont (old Bill), Lillian Beaumont (young Lill). He stared at the dates as Hilly told him of Christ in the Congo or the Virgin in the Upper Volta, and calculated that she, ninth child and eighth daughter, must have been three when her mother died (age forty-six), ten when her father followed (age seventy-three); and as they rode, together again in his remembering, he forgave her her rare moments of petulance. He had never at that time thought of her, brought up by her big sisters, one of whom was Josie, Frank Mangold's widow, as an orphan.

HUGH AND HAT GRADY had driven up from Auckland to Kaiwaka, then taken the back road to Hakaru, past the Mangold farm that had been the Beaumont farm, past the fields where Hugh, and his sister Aida, and their cousin Hilly, had ridden bareback; where he had trapped rabbits and hawks, fished for eels, fed pigs, milked cows, helped the dogs to slip their chains. Past the gate where half a century before he had ridden Bos'n to collect the meat, and bees, unseen, had swarmed in the box; and as he stretched an arm around to the front of the box, which pointed towards the road, reaching for the parcel in its brown paper, out they came at him, up reared Bos'n and away, and he was borne saddleless, headlong, elbows knees tight against neck and flanks, over fields, through manuka and gorse, along the ridge mirrored in the brown waters of the dam, bees in his hair and swarming behind in furious pursuit. That picture would be on his coat of arms if he had one, his insignia, his emblem, a boy in pain on a horse in panic, trailing behind them a widening plume of bees. Life since had seen repetitions of that moment — the blind reaching for something, the fury of the response, the wildness of the ride, the tranquillity of the dam and the vastness and indifference of the sky. Next day, and for days afterwards, the stings ached and burned and itched, and his eyes looked out of holes small as nostrils in a moon of a face.

So they drove, Hugh and Hat, past the Mangold house; past those familiar, benignly bee-humming folds and slopes and ridges, the same fields, plusher now, more richly yielding, where twelve years before he was born, twenty-five before the hot-pursuit bees were tangling in his hair, his father, James Grady, eighteen-year-old rabbiter pushing his shotgun ahead of him through a fence, had blown away most of his right biceps and shattered the bone, and had lain alone out in the damp fields, night coming down, bleeding, so it seemed, to death. So James Grady's clawed right hand, for ever paralysed from the damage done to the arm, a hand which he might, who knows, have secretly chosen for his emblem, as Hugh took for his that plume of bees — it, too, had its origin in this place.

The name Hakaru was known to Hugh, but hardly the place, except that he remembered the timber church, and climbing once in that macrocarpa pretending to be Young Jack in his favourite novel of those years. But his father and his father's Beaumont cousins must have spoken of dances there, because the name conjured images of young men and women coming on horseback or in gigs through rain and mud, shedding boots at the door and putting on best shoes to go into the lantern light and dance to the music of fiddle and accordion. But now Hugh had no idea what to expect. Would it be a settlement, as they used to call such places? A village? A cluster of shops?

In fact there was nothing. Hakaru was a point where two roads met 'in brief embrace of dust', a conjunction of the aimless and the insignificant, a map-reading in an empty landscape where people gathered now as if word had gone around that all should meet at the blasted oak — except that a building which might have been a barn or a woolshed or a sharemilker's modest accommodation proved to be the local RSA Memorial Hall, built after what someone explaining to Hugh its provenance called 'the second show'. He and Hat were in good time but already friends were gathering for Frank Mangold's send-off. And how could that unpeopled landscape have produced so many? Where did they hide in it, or how far had they travelled?

It was a rural crowd. This was the 1990s but it struck Hugh, already sensitised by the occasion and the fact of his old mentor's death, as a scene from another time, a stage set, a movie mock-up for some docu-drama of the long ago; except that here among the actors were the cousins first and second and once or twice removed, the faces so long lost, so familar of feature and voice, but so unfamiliarly old. Frank's funeral was real, with the wonderful and terrible nearness of a dream.

Indoors they took their places on chairs set up in a space cleared by moving the pool table back and stacking it with the trestle tables that would come forward later. The pharmacist spoke of the Frank Mangold who had been in and out of his shop these forty and more years. A cousin of Hugh's who had been like a second son to Frank offered reminiscences. A neighbour spoke, his feeling, pure gold, not finding its feet, or only feet of clay, in a public language. There was the reading of a poem. There was a hymn, not for any promise of Things to Come but for the words and the music, which Frank had liked. There was the further recital of facts and dates. Another poem.

Hugh listened, he sang, he remembered, he thought of Frank just back from 'the second show' with his ginger-blonde handlebar moustache that had given him the nick-name 'Binder-twine'. He read the notices around the walls. Balls and cues were to be returned to their clips and cupboard. Bad language would not be tolerated. The bar would only be unlocked by a Committee Member. There were photographs of the Hakaru lads who hadn't come back, mates of these old mates of Frank Mangold's now leaning forward on their sticks, cupping an ear, coughing, blinking, nodding off, in their suits and RSA badges and service ribbons.

And then, as the coffin was carried out to the hearse followed by Frank's widow Josie, his children and grand-children, his sisters-in-law and their children and grand-children, two lines formed up to give him a guard of honour, the beribboned Returned men on one side standing to attention, on the other the women of the Bowling Club in their strange white uniforms and strange grey hats, standing at ease.

And so they were in their cars foll
down the road, a mile or a kilometre dep
and disposition more than on the mea
churchyard, the recital of 'Our revels n
lowering on straps, the playing of the ra
reading of the 'They-shall-not-grow-ol
shall-remember . . .', the clods and flowe
and then their conversations, desultory among family grafts,
their recovery of distant shared pasts.

to leave
run f

Hugh had wanted so often to come back, but it had
meant too much, couldn't be casual, was feared for its
potency. Frank's death had given him his excuse, and now
here he was at last, back in the fold that was not quite his
but one in which his foot (one of his feet) had a place,
listening to Cousin Hilly who had taken God into heathen
Africa.

JOSIE IS STANDING in that central cluster close to the heaped
earth and the mounded flowers, surrounded, supported, by
children and grandchildren. Hugh belongs, if after so long
a lack of due family diligence he belongs at all, here on the
periphery, among the second rank of cousins. Over Hilly's
shoulder he sees an aquiline face, a tall slim elderly figure, a
woman who walks with difficulty, helped by her two
daughters, but who manages still to look about her with the
air of one who is 'treading the boards'. She smiles at him
enquiringly. Does he remember her? she wants to know. It
is an absurd enquiry. Isn't it only a brief half-century since
they last met — a mere flash in the pan of history, a blink in
the eye of Time? She was twenty then: Linny, another of the
Beaumont sisters.

He is trying to reconstruct the Beaumont farmhouse
kitchen as he knew it. It is summer, 1942, summer holidays,
and he is up from Auckland, five hours by train to cover sixty
miles, much of it spent shunting into sidings and going back
on their tracks, every minute of it loved by Hugh, aged ten,
a boy (or two boys, as he likes to think, Hugo and Wolf) glad

behind the older sister and the eccentric parents, to
ree, a not-quite-colt turned loose.

Old Bill Beaumont is dead. Hilly is there and not there,
sometimes, perhaps, sent to other sisters for parts of the
holiday. Josie is married to Frank Mangold but he has gone
away to kill Japanese and grow his binder-twine handlebars.
The only Beaumont brother, Boy, or Beau, has joined the air-
force. So the farm is run by three young Beaumont women,
Josie, who is the housewife, Greta, who milks the cows and
gets the cream to the gate and fights a half-hearted losing
battle against gorse and blackberry and manuka, and Linny
whose unspecified role might be to add style, to bake cakes
and knock up batches of scones, to dress, entertain, say clever
things and strike useful theatrical poses.

The big farm kitchen is where all the indoor life goes on.
It runs across almost the whole width of the house, at the
back, with a wood-burning oven in heavy black metal at one
end, and at the other the big scrubbed table around which
must formerly have sat old Bill, and Lilly his young wife who
was to die before him, and their nine children, eight of them
girls. Up the centre of the house to the front verandah runs
the hallway, bedrooms opening off it, and one room kept as
the 'sitting room', the parlour, no longer (if it ever was) used.
Beyond the black iron oven at one side of the kitchen opens
a pantry to the left, with its bins of flour and sugar and rice
and salt, and to the right the bathroom with tin bath and
linoleum floor. At the back of the kitchen you step down into
a porch where the mud-caked gumboots and the wet oilskins
are shed on entry.

It is warm weather, but the fire is going, burning pine
cones Hugo has gathered and manuka Greta has chopped,
heating the oven for scones because there is to be a
haymaking on a neighbour's farm and they are to deliver a
batch on their way to the store. Josie, who is always tranquil
and has a lovely speaking-voice, is standing at the window
smiling at nothing, or at something in her head that pleases
her. Linny is making a sackcloth Indian head-dress, sewing
Black-Orpington feathers along the trailing sides, and at the

front, feathers of the cock pheasant. She is making it for Hugo, who is sitting on the couch at one end of the room reading *Alf's Button*, a story about a soldier whose button was made from Aladdin's lamp and so produced an obliging genie every time he polished it. ('Well strike me pink!' said Alf at the genie's first appearance, and on the instant turned an embarrassing salmon colour.) Greta is angrily out searching for the dog that once again and inexplicably has slipped its chain, and which can't be relied upon to stay out of the hen run. If you fed them better, Hugo wants to tell her, instead of expecting them to survive on chop bones and skim, the hens would have less appeal. She makes the dogs run on three legs, one front paw hooked into the collar. Whenever he gets the chance Hugo releases the paw and lets the dog run free. There is this small war between them. With Greta, Hugo becomes Wolf. He takes the dogs' part.

The doors and sash windows are open allowing big blowflies to rush through the house, in one side and out the other, or in the front door, down the hallway and out the back, without turning or crashing on glass. That zooming through, and Greta's voice up on the ridge calling the dog's name down into the back paddock, and the summer cicadas in the garden, and the occasional tingling of neighbours' signals on the party line, and whatever small noises come from the oven fire burning Hugo's cones and Greta's manuka to make Linny's scones, are the only sounds. It's only now, half a century later, it occurs to Hugh that there is no radio.

There is no car either. The young Beaumont women don't move much about the district, and when they do it's on horseback. But to entertain Hugo, Linny has embarked on a project, at first resisted by Greta, and then gradually accepted by her too. It's to bring the old buggy out of its retirement, oil its moving parts, grease its leather straps, patch its upholstery and touch up its paintwork, harness the horses and drive it the five miles or so to Jacques' store. On and off for most of a week now they've been working at it, and today Bos'n and Rusty are to be put in the shafts.

So we give the blowflies time for another two or three

hundred fast sweeps, during which Josie smiles out vacantly into the vacant garden (dreaming, it may be, of Frank Mangold in Jap-infested jungles with bayonet in his teeth and a hibiscus flower in his hair), and Greta corners, kicks and kennels the missing dog. And now the scones, tied up in teatowels, are steaming on the back seat, to be delivered somewhere down the road; the horses are shuffling, not altogether willing, in their collars and shafts; Linny is in the driving seat holding reins in one delicate hand, whip in the other (the one with two missing fingers); Hugo is on one side of her and imagined Wolf on the other; Greta is holding the five-barred gate open that lets them into the front paddock and on to the track rutted deep by the twice-daily traverses of the cream-sledge; Josie is waving an absent-minded handkerchief from the front verandah — and they are on their way.

But the wheels don't fit those sledge-ruts, and long before they reach the road the buggy has set up a rolling motion, Hugo up, Wolf down, Hugo down, Wolf up, while Linny-in-the-middle in silk scarf and pretty hat waves her whip and makes a noise in her throat, *Aaaaargh*, which Rusty and Bos'n, making their own way in their own time, understand is more than anything an expression of their driver's theatrical temperament. Through the last gate, past the meat-box, past the cream-stand where this morning's can and a shivering bobby in a cage still wait for the collection truck, out on to the clay road — and still that rolling motion, Hugo up, Wolf down, down Hugo, up Wolf, continues, and he can see, looking at himself across Linny's lap or behind her back where her scarf floats out and faints, his other face, Wolf's, a mirror image growing green-pale.

Who vomited first over the side, Hugo or Wolf — or was it in unison? Their (his) first seasickness, anyway, was on land, and so Linny, determined to drive on to Jacques' store for what her cousin, having listened while she cranked the phone handle and whispered down the party line, knew was to be an assignation, put him down with scones at the haymaking two or three miles from the Beaumont farm, where he was given work on top of the stack, tramping down the hay as it was thrown up. It was to be a day all dusty and golden under a borrowed straw hat, with bread and cold chops and lime juice for lunch as well as the scones with butter and jam, and a long after-sundown tramp home, among the scarecrow silhouettes of stumps and cabbage trees, learning a sinister new language in the creak of gates.

PIANO WAS THEIR MOTHER'S forte, music her religion. In a fit of Verdi-and-Bellini mania Ethel Elena Grady named her daughter Aida Norma; and when the little girl came home from school upset because some Plymouth Brethren school-mates had said that *their* names came, as all names should, from the Bible, she was instructed to explain that *hers* came from 'Grand Opera'. Hugh is sure their mother thought this would settle the matter. That the Bible might be more sacred than the works of the great European composers was not a proposition she would have entertained. She was also a singer, though her voice wasn't as strong as her own mother's, and at the time of her second pregnancy she had developed a passion for the songs of the German Hugo Wolf, which suited very well both her northern European inherit-ance, with its temperamental swings from short dark winter days to long light summer nights, and also her less than full-operatic voice. So Aida's brother and his twin or doppel-gänger were named Hugo and Wolf after the composer whose eerily brilliant blending of note and word, piano and voice, they had learned first *in utero*.

Or so the boy liked to pretend when he found himself alone with the landscape. In truth he was the one who got it all, both barrels. There was only one of him, and he was named Hugo Wolf Grady.

They were the Gradys (the Greedys, as their Irish grand-father said when he came to Christmas dinner, or the Degradys, as their mother made it when the Celtic and the Scandinavian came in conflict) and the Gradys were Catholic. But James, their wounded father, was his Cornish mother's as well as his Irish father's son, and his mother not being Catholic except in name and for convenience, it was a religion James had been able without noticeable trauma to set aside, saying only that if its God or His Virgin Mother should ever heal the severed tendons and nerves of his blasted arm and restore mobility to the fingers of his paralysed hand, he would reconsider. He was not, however (he would go Irishly on), able or willing to travel to Lourdes where these Greatnesses were said to operate a Clinic of Intercession, so the matter was never put to the test. His weekdays rolled by without confession, and his Sundays without the bread and the wine.

Sister and brother, therefore, who might have been, let's say, Mary Carmel and Joseph Patrick, were Aida Norma and Hugo Wolf. Through primary school little brother was stuck with Hugo. There was no choice. But when he reached secondary school he shortened it to Hugh. From that time on schoolmates, friends, library colleagues, everyone would call him Hugh. Only here at the graveside, talking to Hilly, Linny, others — and finally to grieving Josie — he is taken back to that old time when he was Hugo. The name in their mouths has a curiously soothing effect, as if restoring something he gave away and later couldn't take back.

Now it's raining, not heavily but enough to send them all back to their cars, back along that mile-or-kilometre to the Hakaru hall where the trestle tables have been brought forward, the cakes and sandwiches and scones and sausage rolls are uncovered, the big enamel teapots, held in the strong brown hands of the ladies of the Bowling Club, are pouring strong brown tea into strong white cups. Goodbye, Frank Mangold! At some moment, and the rain has brought it forward, they have to turn their backs on you and your box, leaving it to these our actors who are not at all spirits but two good men with one shovel, to heap over you the local clay. Haere ra, Binder-twine with the blue-eyed laugh. You are not forgotten.

And so they are back where we began; and it's here, over the tea and among the trestles that Hugh finds Greta. She hasn't been at the burial, has remained here in her chair, her two sticks crossed over her lap, her hat pulled down over her imperfectly aligned eyes. Cousin Mary and her brother Jack, cousins to the now elderly Beaumont sisters and to deceased James, point her out to Hugh. Now it's his turn to ask is he remembered, and Greta heaves herself around in her chair, bristling to confront him, with a strange excitement that hits like a bow-wave, and with the lovely fullness of that voice which comes back to him as if she'd been calling continuously over the decades, down from the ridge into the back paddock, or up from the swamp to the ridge, 'Getin-behindthereyou- mongrel. GET IN BEHIND!' And what she says is, 'God, I've had to wait *all these years* to tell you what *a little bugger of a kid* you were.'

GRETA ROSE BEFORE DAWN to bring the cows in for milking. It must have taken her two to three hours to get through the herd. She slept after lunch and milked again in the evening.

Hugo used to go down to the milking shed after breakfast and help her hose down the concrete floor and wash the separator. She'd been at it a long time by then, but it still seemed to him early as he walked along the ridged slope and heard in the distance the chug-and-huff of the machine and the clap of its belting, the opening and shutting of a bail and the lowing and cow-patter of the herd. Down in the swampy lowland between milking shed and bush there was a square well with timber sides, its water green with weed and loud with frogs. Over nearer to the edge of the bush was another timber shed, weathered-grey and lichen-rough, where the buggy was housed together with mildewed harness, forgotten hay bales, and old broken horse collars shedding straw. If he didn't stop to catch tadpoles or play in the buggy shed he was usually in time to help milk the last of the herd. He'd learned to put on the leg-rope, wash the udder, apply the cups; and when the machine had done its work, to 'strip' what was left into a bucket. The two hands alternated, right, left, right, left, and the sound as each stream hit the bucket was always different, *pshew, pshaw, pshew, pshaw* — or the other way about, *pshaw, pshew*. In the back room, beyond the dairy, the heavy leather machine belt that had once whipped two of Linny's fingers right off, leaving her with a stumpy hand, whisked and clapped around, sagging and bouncing, turning the separator and driving the pump that sent skim up to the pigsty. The yard, which might once have been paved, was broken up and churned into mud, and the cows stood hoof-deep, lifting their tails from time to time and adding copious streams to it, amber-crystal. Hugo liked the herd smell, the piss-and-shit smell, the smell and taste and feel of milk squirted hot from the teat. He liked the bristle feel of the cows' bony backs as he slapped them into their bails, the softness and roundness of their noses, the dreaminess of their eyes. He liked the horn-hoof-on-concrete sound, slipping and stamping as they kicked against the leg-rope, or made for a bail, or were slapped out of it into the race. He like the head-tossing and flank-heaving that you could get in among in the yard; the chewing and snorting and grass-breath and farting.

Cows didn't have beautiful dispositions, nor ugly ones. Each was a grass-processor, a big leather gas-bag, containing two (or was it four?) stomachs and a uterus, and hung on a crude bone frame with an oversized milk-sack like a set of bagpipes underneath. But that wasn't quite all. Up front they had faces, and temperaments of a sort, by turns bewildered, panicky, and vacant. They were even kin of a kind. Kine-kin. He liked their bigness and their clumsy unpredictability, their freedom to move with or against you — just as he liked the feel and smell and independence of horses and dogs.

The pigs were different. Low to the ground, they lived in mud and seemed to like it. They stank, ate anything, and seemed vaguely lawless — even dangerous. He disliked their squeals too; and the best you could say for their nose-in-the-trough grunting and slurping was that there was nothing half-hearted or mean-spirited about it. But their deepest oink-notes, like a double-bass in an echo chamber, were incomparable and thrilling.

He didn't have much idea about Greta's body except that it wasn't small. She wore mostly fawn-brown trousers tucked into her gumboots, or khaki dungarees, with a plain shirt. She had cross eyes, red-brown hair, and a beautiful speaking voice, which, with her stature, gave her a certain unmistakable authority. She seemed to welcome him in the mornings, not generously, but warmly enough to bring him back next day.

When milking was over they drove the horse-drawn cream-sledge, first to the sty where Hugo helped her bucket skim from drums to troughs, then on out to the road to leave the can on its stand for the dairy-factory truck. Sometimes, as he left her to drive back to the house without him and went to explore the bush, Greta would ruffle his hair that was stiff with mud and dust. He looked up at her then, into one of her eyes, and noticed how firm and full her flesh was, how healthy she seemed, how good she smelled.

In the evenings he seldom went to the shed, but he would not have been able to say whether that was because he felt he wasn't needed, or wasn't wanted. Willis Handy, a second or third cousin of the Beaumont women (once or twice removed) had lately taken to riding over to help Greta with the evening milk. Neither Josie nor Linny, nor Greta herself, ever commented on this in Hugo's presence, and so he gave it no thought. But 'riding over' meant from the coast, ten miles there and ten back. Each afternoon around four, the lean brown figure on the lean brown horse would appear in the distance. Moving at an unhurried pace, his boots and hat and oilskin would come into focus down the far hill, up the long slow rise to the house, and on past it — saluting Hugo at the gate, or Linny in the garden, or Josie at the window — towards the milking shed.

There was an early afternoon, whether before or after Willis Handy's visits began Hugh can't now be sure, when the boy ran out of the house on to the front verandah where he stopped to think. There was no one in the garden, but if we place ourselves there we will see him hesitating, then returning indoors. After a minute or two he comes out again and this time comes down the steps and along the path until once again he pauses and ponders, and returns indoors. Now he is gone for some minutes. We have time to take in the garden, enclosed on three sides by trees and on the fourth by the house. Its beds of flowers and flowering shrubs are unweeded but in profuse bloom, and in the sheltered stillness of this warm afternoon, they buzz with insects and glitter with wings.

Now the boy comes a third time through the open front door, a look of panic on his face — down into the garden, along the path to one of the big macrocarpas which he climbs effortlessly and high, beyond our view, to look out across the rolling-away landscape until the farms come to a stop at the mountain.

That old wooden verandah where he hesitated and turned back is every farmhouse verandah in early New Zealand. You sat out there when the sun was too hot, walked up and down when the rain was too heavy. The smallest kids rode their rocking horses on it and later, in more modern times, their trikes. Beer was drunk there, pipes and cigarettes were smoked. Deals were done to buy or sell horses, stock, pigs, hay — anything that was surplus or in short supply. Opinions were aired there, plans made, stories told, quarrels begun or ended. On the verandah marriages were proposed, seductions begun or, in the dark, completed. And it was there the boy called, let's say for the moment, Wolf, Hugo's twin and doppelgänger and alter ego, stopped to consider what it was he had seen from the hallway outside Greta's door in the early afternoon.

Whatever it was, this much was certain: it was large and white and pink and red; and it wasn't a cake. The door was ajar and Greta was sleeping with just a sheet over her, which had fallen aside. By the time the boy had reached the verandah after seeing it that first time he was unsure, so he went back and looked again. It was a breast, of course, a big one, bigger than he'd ever seen before, if indeed he ever had seen one. He stood as long as he dared, taking it in, feeling something unfamiliar and too strong to be entirely pleasant. Greta stirred and sighed, and he ran out into the garden. But he needed to see it again, needed to reach out across the space between it-in-the-bed and him-in-the-hall, not to touch, that would be impossible, but to imagine touching — and back he went. He stood at the door staring at that big firm white-and-pink mountain with its red crest, wanting whatever unknown thing it is you want when you are a healthy growing lad looking at a healthy full-grown breast.

Greta's eyes opened. One of them looked at him. He ran, and this time didn't stop until he reached the macrocarpa and climbed it and stared away into the distance, ashamed to have been seen seeing, thinking nostalgically, for the first time that summer, of home.

Nothing was said, much was imagined.

IT WAS MOST LIKELY LATER, after the fact of what was hidden under Greta's shirt had been so starkly made known to him, that Hugo set out one evening for the milking shed. Willis Handy had long since appeared out of the blue-green distance and gone brownly by, saluting his cousins and their cousin, on his way to the shed. As the boy approached along the ridge he could see that the yard was almost empty. The usual sounds, bovine and mechanical, came up from it, and from beyond, those special last calls with which tuis make the edge of the bush seem like the end of the world, signalling the last accelerating downward slide of the sun. He bumped his way down the ridge, from cow-track to cow-track, until he came to the yard, fenced by rough-sawn rails. He climbed, threw one leg then the other over the top rail, and dropped down among the last of the cows, which he slapped aside. There was a cow in each of the six bails, no one attending. One of the cows stamped and a cup came loose, sucking on nothing.

They were in the doorway to the dairy. She was against the wall, partly obscured by tall lean Willis, still with his hat on, bending over her, one brown leather hand inside her shirt, some of the white and pink exposed under it, his other hand elsewhere, lower, obscurely searching.

That cup hanging loose and sucking noisily on emptiness distracted them. Willis's head turned, giving Greta also a line of sight, straight to Hugo. Three eyes met his, which he knew were wide with surprise. He stepped back a pace and felt a hard hornless cow-head nudging at the small of his back. He turned, clambered over the yard-rails, and with a brave determination to save himself and them embarrassment, walked slowly away towards the old well, whistling as a boy who has seen nothing, or nothing significant, whistles on his way to hunt for tadpoles, but uncharacteristically for one who learned the songs of his namesake *in utero*, making two or three sounds that were not in the middle of the note.

'WHAT A BUGGER of a little kid you were.' Unfair, Hugh wants to reply, remembering innocence and how it felt, but he says nothing beyond a vague sentence or two of distant-cousinly demur, and moves away.

There must be a committee member present because calls on the bowling ladies' big enamel tea pots are slowing down. Another door beside the kitchen fold-down-fold-up has opened, and from a small cubicle-counter the hard stuff is being dispensed, these men with their ribbons and their memories needing something of the alcohol kind to unlock feelings and unleash tongues. Frank Mangold was small of stature and great of heart, not one who can be allowed to slip away soon or easily into silence. There is a great deal of talking to be done.

But now it has occurred to Hugh that they are only a few miles down the road from the farm, and that all who belong there are here at the hall, and will be for some time. He consults with Hat, checks with Frank Mangold's son, Frank junior, says a few goodbyes, and soon he and his wife are driving back along that road from Hakaru to Kaiwaka, the one on which (if he is to so divide himself) Hugo-up and Wolf-down lost their breakfast over the side of the buggy. The family fields come into view, their layout, their rises and falls, distantly familiar. To the left, close to the road, is the house

Frank Mangold built after Hugo visited the farm for the last time.

They turn in, pass the Mangold house, and follow the drive, once the sledge-track, through and over fields to where the old Beaumont house stood, the one Hugh still visits in dreams. Here Frank Junior has built a modern house. It is on two levels in a beautiful garden in which a small black piglet, a Captain Cooker, runs up to greet Hat, squealing for attention. Here a single chimney stands, all that's left of the old house, an acknowledgement, a memorial.

There are places Hugh would like to rediscover — the site of the old milking shed, the well, the buggy shed, the giant kauri in the bush, places along the stream where he fished for kokopu, a waterfall in the bush that had drilled into the rock making a centuries-deep smooth-sided hole. He and Hat walk over fields, scramble through undergrowth, walk some way into the bush. His funeral trousers are creased and dirty, his best shoes scraped and mud-stained. They come upon a cow in a drain, thoroughly dead and loud with flies.

Away from this place he carries its map in his head; but in fifty years everything has changed. The present reality imposes itself. That interior map, which can't be made to match it, fades. It will come back, but only when he removes himself. Somewhere on these acres his Grady father destroyed his right arm, Linny lost her fingers, bees pursued him. There were births, there were deaths. The present doesn't deny these facts, but won't confirm them either, remains indifferent to everything but the silent growing of grass and trees, the behaviour of weather, the persistence of birds and eels, fish and frogs, lizards and mice, cows and dogs and pigs and horses. It is life without language or law, without consciousness or conscience. It is life without history.

Hugh remembers the recognition at Frank Mangold's graveside of how far his interests had shifted from public to family matters. It had seemed at that moment a move away from the study of 'History'. But why *away*? Why not *towards*? Hand-to-hand history. History as close encounter.

It is with a renewed sense of purpose that Hugh Grady, retired librarian, climbs with wife, District Court Judge Harriet Enverson, into their big city car and drives away.

TWO

WE MUST IMAGINE Hugh Grady's great-great-grandfather, young (youngish — still on the near side of thirty) John Flatt one evening less than a week after his arrival in the Bay of Islands. It was January 1835. He was a man, if not quite of humble origins, certainly only of modest yeoman stock. His family had been farmers for some generations, their home villages Methwold and Feltwall in Cambridgeshire, and Flatt had first learned farming there, on his home ground, and subsequently in Norfolk and Nottinghamshire. Proud to be described by the Church Missionary Society as its agriculturalist, he had been sent out to assist with the Society's farm run by Mr Richard Davis at the Waimate mission.

Since their arrival at the Bay of Islands John Flatt and his fellow-catechists, William Colenso and William Wade, together with Wade's heavily pregnant wife, had recovered from the near-disaster of their crossing from Sydney, during which their ship the *Blackbird*, under the command of Captain Crook who lacked all skills in navigation, had been briefly run aground by its drunken mate on the way out of Port Jackson, and as a later consequence had sprung a leak in a mid-ocean storm, causing the travellers (apart from Colenso, too sick to do anything but wait for death) to pray fervently for salvation, but more importantly and usefully, to take turns manning the pumps.

Now they had had time to admire the lovely setting of the mission at Paihia which looked down to a beach where the pohutukawas were at present in bloom, and to enjoy dry land and warm calm weather. They had been twice back and forth along the fifteen miles of new road inland to Waimate, seen the fields cleared of fern where more wheat was to be planted, the pasture land, the stands of tall kauri that supplied building timber for the mission and spars for flagpoles and schooner masts, and the mission schools where the children, native and European, were taught to read and write, and even sometimes to play cricket. They had drunk tea with the missionary families at Waimate, seen the gardens, the beds of potatoes, peas, beans, cucumbers, asparagus, rhubarb, the orchards of apples, pears, peaches, figs, apricots, the grape vines with their bunches forming. They had been shown the stables, the threshing barn with its winnowing machine, the blacksmith's forge, the pigsties and poultry runs. They had admired the mission houses, so airy and spacious and light, such a contrast to their four-month shipboard accommodation, and to the smoky native whares clustered close to the ground along the way. These sights, and the cheerful civility of the missionary families, had given the young newcomers hope and confidence, caused them to feel a further lift in their spirits, the worth of their Christian enterprise clearly demonstrated.

They had delivered documents and letters from London, and verbal messages from the Rev Samuel Marsden in Sydney with whom they had spent some days during their stopover. Their sealed envelopes from the London headquarters had been opened, revealing that Colenso and Flatt were to receive £30 per annum plus single man's rations measured as for convicts at Port Jackson — 'flour, tea, sugar, salt, and lamp oil, also pork and potatoes'. They had watched Colenso's Stanhope press, New Zealand's first, on which the first parts of the Bible in Maori would soon be printed, brought ashore on a platform lashed between two canoes, and carried up to a lean-to on one of the missionary houses. At Waimate John Flatt had handed to Mr Richard Davis new varieties of grape cuttings sent by the Rev Marsden from his farm in Parramatta. These last, however, like Flatt himself, had been received by Mr Davis with something less than enthusiasm.

In fact through all of these encounters and explanations

and excitements Flatt had detected, under the politeness of his superiors, ordained and otherwise, a tone that seemed calculated to put a damper on the eagerness he felt and, expecting it to be welcome, had constantly expressed, to begin the work he was there to do. Now, at last, the truth which for these first days had been hidden from him had been revealed. Mr Davis did not want his help, had all the help he needed from his own son, did not need an 'agriculturalist', and would not have one.

Alone, confused, conscious of eighteen thousand terrible sea-miles between himself and arbiters who might be disinterested and fair, alternately angry, self-critical and unhappy, John Flatt was standing in the evening light on a small rough-hewn jetty in an estuary where river and sea met, a green calm enclosed on either side by mangroves, and beyond the mangroves, steep tree-covered bluffs. There was a sound from the water of a deep voice chanting something that sounded like 'Hoi-*uh*! toi-*uh*!', rhythmically accompanied by a firm splash on the '*uh*!', then silence, another splash, then silence again. He looked in the direction from which the sound came and saw a canoe manned by two dozen paddlers. A bronze old man in a cloak sat against the carved stern-post, seeming almost to be a part of it, looking away into the distance as if nothing near at hand was so real to him as his image of himself, a figure of power and authority. Near to him, leaning over the side, a young man plied the special paddle which served as rudder. Amidships a warrior holding a carved spear decorated with white feathers was the one giving the chant by which the paddlers kept time. As the canoe skimmed towards him in half-light, John Flatt could see the tattoo patterns on their faces. There was an impulse to call to them or salute in some way rather than simply stare. But as it came closer something steely and forbidding came to him from that death-ship — a challenge which his body wanted to meet. The muscles in his arms and neck tightened. He felt himself alert, wary, strong, as if an eternal warrior had momentarily stirred beneath the Christian cloth.

He was reminded in that moment of one of the first words he had learned of the native language — utu. Mr Baker, at whose house he had shelter, had explained to him that utu — revenge, or payment for a wrong or a slight — seemed to him almost chief among the motivators of this warrior society. 'They have great and sensitive pride,' Baker had said. 'Turning the other cheek is to them the act of a coward or a worthless person.'

The canoe was close to Flatt now, passing quickly. He could see their expressionless faces clearly in the fading light. He knew they saw him there, but they paid him no attention, and were gone.

These paddlers were what he had referred to, in the first of the notes he was required to keep for report to his superiors in London, as 'poor ignorant heathens'. That was not how they seemed to him. They were formidable — not to be dismissed in a clap-trap phrase — and he reproached himself for an insincerity he knew would persist because it was expected of him and was therefore a necessary part of his determination to advance himself in the world. Why else should he have come so far?

And now it seemed he must travel further — south to Hauraki, thence to the end of the estuary that had been called the Firth of Thames, fourteen miles up-river to the station at Puriri recently set up by Mr William Fairburn, and beyond again, inland across the plain of Waikato, to assist the Rev Alfred Brown in the establishment of a new mission in a place where natives, some of whom had not yet seen a European face, would be given the opportunity to come to God. There John Flatt was to serve as catechist, learn the native language, teach reading and writing, assist in the construction of the mission and see to the making of its garden. This had been decided by the Committee and explained to him by the Rev Henry Williams, who in his crisp unyielding naval fashion had described it as an opportunity, a challenge, a chance to show the willingness to serve and comply which God required of His servants.

But was Mr Richard Davis showing compliance to what

amounted to instructions from their principals in London, the Church Missionary Society, who had engaged Flatt specifically for the post of agriculturalist at Waimate? And were the Rev Williams and his committee showing firm leadership, or only a reluctance to cross the man on the spot, Davis, who seemed determined to reserve that post for his own son?

These questions put by Hugh Grady's forebear in the course of an interview had incurred the fierce displeasure of the Rev Williams. Williams had set his tight mouth tighter, glared reproachfully through his small wire spectacles, and reminded 'young Flatt' that God and not the Church Missionary Society was his first employer.

'Are you afraid?' he had asked in a contemptuous and bullying tone. Receiving a negative answer he had said, 'Go, then, and do your duty.'

The jibe had been unfair. Flatt was not fearless, and did not pretend to be. But his reluctance to go far into the interior had nothing to do with fear. What he had felt was disappointment; and resentment at what seemed to him a wrong done at such distance from those who could right it. Colenso had come as printer, Flatt as agriculturalist. Colenso's press was ashore. Yesterday he had been cheered by the natives when they were told that he was to print the Bible in their own language. Everyone in the little community, English and native, was waiting to see him work it. Flatt too had brought special skills, but they were unwanted, rejected. That was how it felt.

And now, as a further consequence, he must say goodbye to the friends made at sea, good Colenso, and the amiable Wades.

The canoe was gone; the sound of the chant had faded with the light. Darkness closed down on Flatt; colours merged into degrees of shadow. He hoped he could find the track back to the house of Mr Baker who was his sympathetic host, a member of the committee who seemed unhappy at his own acquiescence to the dictates of Richard Davis, but unwilling to speak out. A night-bird — some kind of owl —

called from the woods. The last faint light from the sky was picked up on the glassy surface of the water. John Flatt felt the beauty of the place, and its loneliness, and its danger.

DRIVING BACK IN THE HALF-LIGHT of a spring evening from Frank Mangold's funeral, Hugh Grady registered images that to him represented 'the North' — cabbage trees, mangrove swamps, salty estuaries, the long line of Orewa Beach seen from its northern upland — beautiful in themselves and with the added flavour of nostalgia. So often, at sixty, one had 'been here before'. Life without memory, without record, was that cow in Frank Mangold's drain, fly-loud and vanishing.

Hugh went over it in his head, his antecedents, his New Zealand whakapapa, and how it had joined him there with Hilly beside her parents' graves at Frank's burial: John Flatt, who had been in at the beginning, here in the North before the signing of the Treaty, begat Robert Flatt who begat Charlotte Flatt who married Carl Christianson; and it had been Charlotte and Carl's daughter, Ethel Elena, who married James, son of Irish Joseph Grady and Cornish Nellie Abrahams, naming their children Aida Norma and Hugo Wolf. Nellie's sister Lilly had married Bill Beaumont and given him eight daughters. One of them was Hilly; another, Josie, had married Frank Mangold . . .

That was how their families were joined. But now that he had begun to study it, Hugh, or to give credit where it was due, Hugh and his voluntary assistant, Jean-Anne Devantier, had found other connexions. For example (to take Jean-Anne's latest discovery) Frank Mangold's earliest progenitor on his mother's side, Gilbert Mair, had been in charge of the whale boat that arrived by chance when the *Blackbird* was finally becalmed outside the Bay of Islands, 30 December 1834. So it was Frank's forebear who had brought Hugh's ashore for the first time in New Zealand . . .

It was almost dark now. They were on the motorway, coming in to Auckland. There, ahead, across the full tide of Big Shoal Bay, the glass towers of the central city were catching the last of the light, pretending to permanence. In imagination Hugh turned on his microfilm reader and watched coming into focus the handwriting of John Flatt, sometimes big and spidery, flashing with impatience or haste, sometimes copybook — those letters from New Zealand, reports that had also been oblique appeals (pious, yes, but with a faint whiff of insincerity, and a barely concealed impatience for justice) addressed to the Rev Mr William Jowett, Church Missionary Society House, Salisbury Square, Fleet Street, London.

As they had worked on it, Hugh regularly in his retirement, a few hours every day, Jean-Anne as she was able to find or steal the time from her regular work at the university library, they had been able to fill many of the gaps from the time John Flatt left the Bay of Islands at the beginning of 1835 to the dramas that occurred in the Bay of Plenty in 1836 — events which were to send him back for a brief time to England, there to appear before a Select Committee of the House of Lords set up to look into 'the Present State of the Islands of New Zealand'.

Flatt's disappointment at being denied the post of agriculturist had been expressed often in his letters and reports, and his anger with Richard Davis had not been concealed. But what of Davis himself? His letters, Hugh had found, were so full of piety and reports on the spreading of the Word, there had been scarcely room for anything else. No mention of the arrival of Flatt, whose assistance Davis had so firmly rejected. None of Colenso, despite the fact that Colenso's press had attracted such interest and anticipation. In March Davis had sent to London 'the first fruits of our mission press at Paihea — namely, the Epistle of St Paul to the Ephesians and Philippians in the Maori tongue', still without any mention of the young printer, as if this first publication had been just another part of his own missionary work.

It was notable, however, or seemed so to Jean-Anne when she came upon it, that within weeks of Flatt's arrival in the Bay and the decision to despatch him south, Davis, who wrote seldom of anything but giving the Word to another eighteen, or thirty-five, or sixty-nine natives in a single day, and of coaxing them towards and coaching them for their baptism, was reporting that his son James, a farmer like his father, had found that his calling was in the work of the Church, and that it was important he should be ordained:

'The Lord hath blessed my son James and called him to the knowledge of Himself. But I can only consent to his union with the Church Missionary Society as an ordained missionary, because he would be more at liberty in the mission field as an independent settler, than as a catechist.'

'. . . only . . . as an ordained missionary'. Hugh had shaken his head over the phrase when Jean-Anne had pointed it out. There was, it seemed to them both, such a leap in those two sentences from other-worldly piety to worldly self-interest. All the catechists had wished for the security and privilege of full ordination. Few had received it, because they were not gentlemen.

And then there was Mrs Davis. Her few letters were less guarded, more (if inadvertantly) frank and forthcoming, speaking of her husband's anxiety, and of the anxiety she felt for him: 'I am much alarmed for my poor husband', (she had written). 'He has laboured for the society early and late. His trials have been many and heavy. His mind has been on the rack.'

Why this mental torment? What had slowly become clear to Hugh and Jean-Anne was that Richard Davis had worked hard, but in his own interests, and that he had feared the disturbance newcomers and 'prying eyes' might cause. All the catechising and proselytising he had boasted of in his reports and letters must have been done (they were sure of it) over ploughshares, across the backs of cattle, above the banging and blowing of the blacksmith's forge and the grinding of the millstone; done, in other words, in the course of labours and trading which scarcely figured in his reports. Davis had made for himself a profitable and comfortable place in the wilderness, and he was not going to let his and his son's hold on it slacken, nor permit the way he allotted his time and the use he made of the farm's profits to be watched over by some young upstart 'agriculturist' unloaded upon him by the Society in London.

And had the Rev Henry Williams felt a similar, if secret, anxiety — that the new man, who showed himself to be of independent mind, might spy on them? They were both aware, Davis and Williams, that they were as far from London as it was possible to go, a separation which, at times frightening, was also a freedom. Why, they must have asked one another (a question settlers would echo down the years and decades until the colony became a nation) should these matters be decided in London? What should be done with this egregious, enthusiastic, superfluous Flatt? What else but send him, as catechist, well away south into those regions yet to receive the benefits of the Blood of the Lamb? Let him proceed first to Puriri, where there would be work for him; and then let Alfred Brown have his services in Matamata. That was as far south as the Society's arm at present reached from the Bay of Islands.

So for some time, and not for the last time, John Flatt faded into the general picture. Jean-Anne had found his name on the 1835 list of subscribers for the building of a church at Kororareka — £3 3 shillings, or rather more than ten per cent of his first year's salary — and then it seemed he vanished from the northern mission.

IT WAS TWO DAYS AFTER Frank Mangold's funeral and Hugh was sitting at the place Jean-Anne had reserved for him. She had arranged access to archives and to the Glass Case collection, and use of microfilm reader and photocopier. Sometimes she came in to ask how the work was going, and to exchange ideas and discoveries.

At this moment she was leaning over the back of his chair, her belly, just beginning to reveal her pregnancy, warm against his upper arm, one hand lightly on his shoulder. Yesterday Hugh had received from Miss Gladys McDermott, an elderly cousin of his grandmother's to whom he had written enquiring about John Flatt, some family documents which she said 'might be of interest'. If they were, she had more.

There was shared excitement and a need to focus on it, to fit it exactly into what they knew already, made difficult for Hugh by that warm pressure against his arm, and by the fact that Jean-Anne had called him Hughie.

The new document consisted of unbound pages from a diary, unsigned, but beyond a doubt in John Flatt's hand. It was January 1836. Flatt had been one year in New Zealand. In that time he had sailed south on the missionary schooner *Columbine* into the Hauraki Gulf and the Firth of Thames, then up-river to Mr William Fairburn's mission at Puriri. After a time there he had gone on into the interior as instructed by the Rev Henry Williams, to assist the Rev Alfred Brown in the establishment of a new mission at Matamata. He had learned the native language, supervised the building first of raupo huts with wooden floors, later of two small mission houses, paying his native labourers in 'duck trowsers', shirts, slates and pencils, razors, and occasionally blankets; and in the mornings, at first light before work began, teaching them to read and write.

But now he had once again come north, as far as the Tamaki isthmus. How he had got there and what deliberations had brought him were unrecorded. There he stood among a group of his fellow missionaries, facing a group of Maori elders and chiefs. A land deal was about to be completed.

'I was assured' (Flatt wrote) 'that the elevated ground we stood upon was of volcanic origin, though very old, worn down by time and weather, and consequently not high and fortified like others in this region; but sufficient to afford us good views of the surrounding countryside, which sloped one way towards tranquil eastern beaches, and rolled away to the north and west, fern-clad, with little visible forest cover until it reached the blue mountains of the Waitakere range. Between them and the mountain range rose, here and there, the tawny volcanic hills of the isthmus — Maungakiekie, Maungawhau, Owairaka, and others — their step-down slopes indicating that they were once native fortifications, and could be again. To the south-east the near land ran almost level, then dropped to a broad tidal estuary, with mangroves on either side.

'The chiefs who were making the sale pointed out its boundaries, marked in the far distance by rivers, hills and coastline, but so far away it seemed to me they must be uncertain or imprecisely defined, and enclosing an area so extravagantly large it impressed me as being almost the size of an English county. The documents of sale which had been drawn up were as insignificant as the area was grand, consisting of two sheets of foolscap, one in English, the other in the native language. There was no map.

'Speaking in their own language the chiefs reiterated their eagerness to sell and their understanding that the purchaser, mission catechist Mr William Fairburn, would engage their people to work the land, which at present, because enemy tribes dispute ownership, lies idle. That was the agreement upon which the sale was made, and once it was understood and accepted they were impatient to have it completed so peace could be established and their employment commence. Mr Fairburn confirmed that this was indeed the arrangement, but added that the land was being purchased partly for the future, and for his children. They, at least — the children (this being said with a laugh) — "would not be working it tomorrow, or next week".

'Payment had been discussed, but now it was raised again by the Rev Williams. To the direct question of what payment they expected the chiefs replied with what I have observed to be their usual formula: "It is your thought, not ours."

'And then, as the matter of payment was circuitously canvassed, I was taken aside by two of the lesser natives, chiefs of a sub-tribe, who explained to me that they were troubled by this transaction. I did not at once understand, because they spoke figuratively, one, an old man with a heavily tattooed face, kicking the ground with his toe, saying repeatedly something that means roughly "She is not faithful", or perhaps "She is an adulteress". At last it became

43

clear that he meant this piece of land had given itself to more than one owner. It had been disputed back and forth between two or three tribes. And it had been sold already, some years ago, to another European who had gone away across the seas but might return, in which case they — my informant and his friend — would be embarrassed and not know what to say to him because they had been recipients of part of the payment.

'This explanation took some time, and when I returned the price had been settled. The land, written down on the foolscap sheets as being of an estimated 40,000 acres in extent, would be sold for goods already brought for the purpose — two cartloads of blankets, a very large number of axes, adzes, chisels, hammers, razors, scissors, knives, tobacco and pipes, together with shirts and trowsers, needles, nails, fish-hooks, tins and boxes. The chiefs who were urging the sale seemed quite satisfied, and while they looked the goods over, trying the blankets on their shoulders, testing the weight of axes and the sharpness of knives, I explained to the missionary group what I had been told.

'But the Rev Henry Williams was unwilling to give it any countenance. Indeed, I believe he was displeased with me for reporting it. These men I had spoken to, he assured me, were troublemakers. I tried to say what is quite true, that this was not the first time I had heard that this tract of the Tamaki isthmus had already been sold; but I found his back already turned to me.

'When the two sheets had been signed by Mr Fairburn, and the chiefs had added the marks of their respective moko, it was the turn of the Rev Williams and another, a Mr Preece, to add their signatures as witnesses. Then it was that Mr Williams turned to me saying that a third witness was needed, and inviting me to sign.

'I was surprised, for there were others present; and though it seemed a gesture of conciliation, as if he felt ashamed of having turned his back on me, the thought was also in my mind that he perhaps wished to make me a party to the sale, and in that way to silence me.

'I signed willingly enough, thinking to myself that to witness is not to approve. Indeed, should the matter ever come into question, my signature will confirm that any report I make is not mere hearsay.

'That same day when our party returned to the anchorage where the *Columbine* rested, the Rev Williams set up a committee, consisting of the Rev Brown with catechists Hamlin, Chapman, Preece and Fairburn, to decide what should be done with this vast tract of land. Mr Williams insisted that he should not himself be a member of the committee, and nor should I, since I was the youngest of the party.

'But I was present at their deliberations, and heard their decisions. It was resolved that Puriri, being damp, low-lying and unhealthy, was not a suitable location for missionary work, and that Mr Fairburn should close up his houses there and bring his native workers north to this newly acquired land, to open a mission on a beautiful beach called Maraetai, for which timber and other supplies were already being unloaded from the schooner. The Rev Brown and I, on the other hand, would be delivered back to the Thames and make our way once again southward into the interior, to carry on the work of the mission at Matamata.

'I am setting down these recollections a week after the event. Mr Fairburn and I are on board the *Columbine*, he returning to begin the closure and transfer of the mission at Puriri, which will take many months, I returning south towards Matamata. But for the moment we are becalmed on a hot day somewhere between Tamaki and Thames. As I write I am not able to set aside questions which I know it is not my business to ask. Where did Mr Fairburn, a catechist in the north since 1819, a man of no personal fortune subsisting on the bare living provided by his missionary work, all at once acquire the means to lay out for the purchase of land goods worth at his own estimate not less than £150, and by other estimates a great deal more? I find it hard not to suspect that the money came from the Church Missionary Society; or even from the Rev Williams himself. Why else should the use of land acquired as a private purchase have been decided by a missionary committee? Why was the *Columbine* already laden with timber and goods for the establishment of a mission at Maraetai, if it had not been decided in advance that there should be one? And what was the usefulness of the pretence by which the Rev Williams, who was so clearly the author of the committee's decisions, ruled himself out as one of its members?

'These events, these thoughts and questions, I store up, to my shame, for my revenge, if the time should come, for that wrong which has been done me by Mr Davis and the Rev Williams. Or let me call it, in the thought of the native New Zealander, my utu — something owed to me.'

A day later there was a postscript: 'But not to my shame. For how shall I have what I foolishly call my revenge unless Providence shall put the means into my hands? — and as at this day, 30 January 1836, I see neither means nor likelihood that it ever shall be so. The Lord's will be done!'

THE HARBOUR BRIDGE is the road north. It wasn't always so. In Hugh's childhood, when he was only and always Hugo, cars crossed the harbour by vehicular ferry to Devonport, or drove twenty-five miles around it to join the main road north at Riverhead. The railway took you through the western suburbs, west of the upper harbour, through Swanson and Waitakere, and then on north through Taupaki, Kumeu, Huapai, Waimauku, Rewiti, Woodhill, Wharepapa, Helensville, Kaukapakapa, Kanohi, Tahekeroa, Ahuroa, Woodcocks, Kaipara Flats, Hoteo, Wellsford, Te Hana, Topuni and Kaiwaka. These words, run together by young Hugo Grady, made up a romantic sentence which, loosely translated, meant 'It's summer, school's over, and I'm on my way to the Beaumont farm.' But in those days the sentence was always articulated slowly. Those trains, pulling goods and passengers together, seemed to stop at every shed-sized station (attached, most of them, to nothing but a name, a dusty road and an empty landscape) sometimes to shunt into a siding and wait, fuming, while a man walked down the line hitting the big metal wheels with a hammer to see that each was properly tuned for the next movement. Five hours sometimes, for sixty miles, like an opera by Wagner, and as Hugo's mother would say of an opera by Wagner, never too long.

Ethel Elena Grady, née Christianson, could not ever have been present at the performance of such an opera, because at that time none was ever performed in New Zealand — or to be exact (and Ethel had sought out the facts) the last performances had been by George Musgrove's Grand English Opera Company in 1901 before she was born (*Lohengrin*), and in 1907 when she was a baby (*The Flying Dutchman* and *Tannhäuser*). But at the height of her Hugo Wolf enthusiasm she had read all she could find about him in public libraries and learned of his role in the Viennese musico-culture-war between the Wagnerians and the Brahmsians.

Loyalty to Wolf caused her to revise her previously high regard for the works of Brahms, whose supporters had been Wolf's detractors and enemies, and try to learn all she could of Wagner, since it was the Wagnerians who had been Wolf's allies. Like everyone of her generation Ethel had walked to the altar to the strains of the wedding march from *Lohengrin* ('Here comes the bride / Fair, fat and wide', children used to sing to it) without thinking about who might have composed it or what its larger context might have been. She knew the 'Ride of the Valkyrie' as she knew the 'Flight of the Bumble Bee'. The 'Siegfried Idyll', transcribed for piano by Liszt, was somewhere in her piano repertoire with, and hardly distinguished from, 'In a Monastery Garden', as 'Forest Murmurs' was with 'Rustle of Spring'. But under the influence of Hugo Wolf she set about correcting this ignorance. Not only the names of Wagner's operas (*Tannhäuser*, *Parsifal*, *Rheingold*, *Götterdämmerung*, *Walküre* and the rest) but also the names of places and people, some real others fictional (Sieglinde and Sachs, Brunnhilde and Beyreuth, Cosima and Kerwenal, Wotan and Wahnfried, Minna, Tauber, Hanslick, Faffner) — in young Hugo's ears these were like rain on the roof or wind in the trees, pure sounds enjoyed for, and meaning nothing but, themselves, as familiar and as obscure as those names along the railway line north. What lay behind or beyond each of them was to him largely unknown.

Later came stories which remained in his mind as images — for example his namesake Hugo Wolf, aged seventeen, being shown into Wagner's hotel suite, its couches and floors strewn with thick furs, and telling the master how deeply he admired his work, while Cosima, Listz's daughter whom Wagner had stolen away from the conductor Bulov, displayed her irritation at the intrusion by marching from the room.

Or the image of Wolf, now an established composer, staying the night on Humperdinck's couch and, unable to sleep, studying the score of *Parsifal* by the light of the moon.

Once, quarrelling with his mother, Hugo had remembered a story about Wolf kissing Brahms's doorknob, and had asked why she had named him after a fool. Her reply had been swift and sure. If she had named him after a fool he would have had nothing to reproach her for. Unfortunately, she had named him after a genius.

And the story about the doorknob, she added, was untrue, put about by the Brahmsian camp to discredit the songwriter.

On the whole James Grady was patient, even indulgent towards his wife's enthusiasms, though given to jokes about Wagner and his music, mostly when Ethel was elsewhere. *Parsifal*, Hugh remembers his father saying, was about a king with a nasty flesh wound who spends the first hour of the opera running his bath, and the second having it. And Wagner's Wotan was the sort of no-nonsense father who, when his daughter argued with him, put her up on a mountain surrounded by lighted gas-jets. But then, Ethel would point out when her husband's jokes were brought to her notice, James Grady couldn't even sing in tune. What else would you expect of a man with such a disability?

Hugh has not lost his interest in music. Indeed he has been through phases not unlike his mother's. There was a time — he was thirty-six, and in love, and not with his wife — when the second movement of Brahms's Fourth

Symphony seemed to gather up and give beautiful and agonising expression to the central emotion of his secret life. At the time he knew next to nothing about Wagner except those names and titles remembered from childhood. Wagner lay ignored in the back of his mind, part of the sometimes sad comedy of his mother's life, one of her musical crazes, connected with the one that had given him his name.

And then, as a means of getting over the emotional interlude of the love affair that had disturbed their marriage, Hat had suggested he should take unpaid leave and they should take the children on a world tour. So Hugh, in his late 30s, found himself for the first time in London, and one day, without knowing why, but perhaps out of some sense of piety towards his mother, he joined a queue in the snow outside the English National Opera where tickets for a Wagner season were being sold. The opera for which he obtained seats high up and far back in that vast auditorium, the Colosseum, was *Götterdämmerung*, the last of the Ring cycle.

Hugh likes to tell the story of that experience — how he had no clear or continuous idea about what was going on but was simply drawn in, like a long rope pulled hand over hand, every chord, every bar, seeming to bring with it the full force of all that had gone before, until after five hours, when Brunnhilde seemed to be bidding farewell to her flying horse, sending it away into the heavens, he knew he had to stop listening for a moment or he would faint. Nothing in all his years of listening to music had left him so disturbed and exalted. Hugo Wolf Grady had become a Wagnerian.

Now, at sixty, talking to Jean-Anne, whose interest in music (she is singer as well as librarian) is what first made them acquainted, judicious Hugh is able to stand back from it all. Brahms, he tells her, still seems to him 'master of plangent yearning, nostalgia, regret'. But Wagner, for all that the comic spirit must see him as grandiose and absurd, is 'master of everything'.

'When you hear a love duet of Sigmund and Sieglinde and compare it with the best that Brahms can do, you know,' Hugh insists, 'however cruel it may have been, why it was that Wagner called Brahms the eunuch of music, and why Nietzsche said that he expressed the melancholy of impotence. In Wagner sex is fulfilled, in Brahms it is defeated.'

Hugh is in full flight now — it happens sometimes with this Jean-Anne Devantier. 'Wagner calls to our human strengths,' he tells her. 'Brahms to our weakness. That's why no one speaks ill of Brahms, and few speak well of Wagner.'

JOHN FLATT FELT the breeze pick up as the firth narrowed and the *Columbine* approached the river entrance. Ahead he could see calm water vanishing into lowlands, with grey-green mangroves absorbing light on one side and on the other an army of shiny dark-green flax spears.

Beside him at the rail William Fairburn sniffed the salt smell of the marshland around the rivermouth at low tide and said he would not be sorry to be saying goodbye to Puriri. His wife didn't like it and their children had been unwell in the winter months. Flatt sighed and said he envied Fairburn that beautiful north-eastern slope down to the beach at Maraetai, which might be good for growing grapes.

Ahead for him, beyond the navigable part of the river, lay a canoe journey up smaller rivers followed by a trek across the swampy edge of the Waikato plain under the morning shadow of the Kaimai range. And then, arrived at Matamata, it would be back to hard labour, rising early and working late, making the station more habitable, and teaching the young natives to read and write.

There had been stirrings among the tribes, he told Fairburn, arguments back and forth, with emissaries coming from the lakeland area further west and after koreros lasting through long days and nights, leaving grim-faced. There had been a murder, and now all the talk was of utu. The Rev Brown believed that unless the mission intervened it must mean war.

Fairburn nodded. It usually did, he acknowledged; and intervention seldom helped, though it had to be tried. 'You plead with them, you tell them many will be killed and eaten and many more made slaves, and that it will all be for nothing. You tell them God loves them and wishes them to love one another; and that it is the peacemakers who inherit the earth and go to heaven. They are polite. They listen. They agree with you. And then they go away and consult their tohungas and prepare for battle.'

THREE

I T WAS FRANK MANGOLD who said to the boy Hugo, 'That house is New Zealand history. Nobody writes it any more.'

Two summers, three, four had passed. The war ('the second show') was over and the trio of Beaumont sisters no longer ran the farm. Frank had returned and he and Josie were the farmer and the farmer's wife. They had one little blonde daughter, then a second, soon there would be a third before Frank junior was engendered, as if there was something in the soil or air or water, not inimical, but resistant, to sons. Males on that farm, as in doorways everywhere, and when the lifeboats were lowered, had to stand back and let the females go first. Greta, whose big vanilla-and-cherry coloured secret had once been revealed to pre-pubescent Hugo, was married now to leathery Willis Handy, with two children. Linny, it was said, though exactly how and where Hugo wasn't sure, had 'gone on the stage'. Hilly, who would one late day in her life take God into Africa, was training to be a nurse. The only boy of the family, Beau Beaumont, also known as Boy, back from the war had no wish to be a farmer and was working as a Rawleigh's Man out of Dargaville.

It was the evening of a day when Frank and Hugo had been over to the coast to see felled and brought out of the bush a kauri which was to provide timber for the building of a new house for Greta and Willis. For years the Handy brothers, Willis and Gren, had occupied as much as they needed of the old homestead, letting the rest make its accommodation with time and landscape and weather. There were rickety brass bedsteads, locked chests, chipped ewers, broken pots, old family albums, Maori adzes and meres, mildewed books, trays of butterflies and moths with frayed fading wings and fractured legs, collections of kauri gum, framed photographs of men in bowlers with bowyangs and gum spears and of women in high-collared embroidered dresses with flowers in hair piled high or hanging low — hair that had been brushed one hundred times before bed and fifty before breakfast. Most interesting to Hugo, there were cups won by the Handy brothers in their younger days when they had been competitive axemen and Australasian champions at the crosscut saw.

Gren, the elder by some years, was content to stay there; but for the new house one last kauri would be felled, brought out by bullock team and pit-sawn by the brothers. It was as if, Frank said, they had decided to step back in time.

So today, up in the bush hills above the Handy farm, the great crosscut that won them their championships had gone into action along with their best competition axes. Wedges had been driven, axe blows and the creaking of centuries-hardened timber had echoed through the bush, the canopy had trembled and heaved, hillslope and valley had held their breath while the tree teetered as if making a difficult decision, and at long, very long last down it had come, crashing, bole bouncing, branches splintering, revealing to that part of the forest floor a new abundant colour — blue — and a new intensity of light. When branches had been stripped, Gren had brought his bullocks, harnessed for one last time, up as near as possible, ten of them in five square-fronted short-legged pairs under heavy wooden yokes. A long steel hawser had been tied around the huge log, leather whips had cracked while the animals tossed their horns and rolled their eyes, the hawser had stretched and tightened overhead on a steep angle to the fallen tree, rollers had been put under and wedges at the sides, and slowly, inch by inch, foot by foot it had been hauled around in line with, finally manœuvred into, what remained of the old wooden slipway used in the days when timber-milling had been a part of their way of life.

Now Frank and Hugo were back at the Kaiwaka farm, sitting over the remains of their meal at the long kitchen table under the Tilley lamp. The little blonde girls were asleep, and drowsy Josie, who today had had to get the cows in and begin the evening milk before Frank was back, had taken a candle and her third pregnancy to the big bedroom at the front of the house.

In the early days, Frank was saying, the settlers used to write history while it was happening. Now nobody wrote it. The Handy house was like New Zealand's past, slipping away from us, letting itself be forgotten. 'When I left school I'd won a scholarship to go to the university, but there was a depression. I had to find work. I'd wanted to study history, but now — I don't know that I regret it. They don't study our own history. It's all my eye and the War of Jenkins' Ear. England and Europe and the British Empire. You should go to university, Hugo. Maybe by the time you get there they'll know we've got a history of our own. Or you could be the one to make it known. You could be the first.'

THAT MUST HAVE BEEN Hugo's last visit. Already he was becoming Hugh. His boy-voice that went with the Hugo-name was showing signs of breaking, but he still sang soprano — in the school choir, and to the landscape at large when he was far from the farmhouse riding Bos'n into the Unknown. When the choir sang in the Town Hall, his sister Aida, sitting in the gallery, said she could pick his voice among the sopranos. Frank heard it two gullies away, and remarked on it, quoting 'The isle is full of noises, sounds and sweet airs which give delight and hurt not'; and Hugo, embarrassed, denied knowledge of what the eerie music might have been.

But soprano or incipient baritone, Hugo along with Wolf, his shadowy Other, was put to work that summer. He was glad of it. No one before Frank Mangold had ever set him serious tasks and left him alone to carry them out, trusting him, risking it. That year the war on rabbits, suspended while the world one had left the farm unmanned, and still not fully resumed, was his to wage. He flinched at what a gin trap did to a rabbit's leg, but to set and clear the traps was his job and he did it, late afternoons planting them in light soil where there were signs the rabbits had scratched, early mornings taking each animal that danced and clanked like a dog on a chain, releasing the broken foreleg from the iron jaws, holding it by the back legs so the head hung down, and with the single blow of a heavy stick to the back of the head, despatching it. Some of the meat went into Josie's stews and pies, while the skins, stretched inside-out on bent pieces of fencing wire, were put out to dry and kept with the sacks of collected kauri gum for sale in Auckland.

Soon Hugo was brown with sun and singed with fire. Above the new dam the slopes had been overgrown with gorse and manuka. He was given a primitive oil-burner shaped to a point like a dunce's cap, shown how to cut firebreaks with a slasher, warned to watch the wind, and left alone to burn it off. For his mistakes, if he should make any, there were only wet sacks and a bucket at the edge of the dam. Three days later a perfect segment, wide at the top of the ridge and narrowing down to the dam lay black and smoking, and no pasture had been lost.

WHY DID THOSE VISITS to the farm come to an end? Hugh is not sure. Because he was now a Grammar boy who played sport summer and winter? Because he was preoccupied with movies, dancing, girls? Because his father, who was fond of saying 'business is booming', bought a Rover car upholstered in green leather with pockets, and the family went on summer holidays to Rotorua, where Hugh learned fly-fishing? Are these 'causes'? Must everything that happens have one?

'The Causes of the First World War', Hugh was to find when he got to university, was the title of a popular course in the History Department. He would enroll for it, and learn that certain things happened, and then certain further things, followed by more, and others, and yet more; and at the end of all this a war was declared, men and guns were mobilised, many, and more, and other, and further (including his great-uncle Vincent Flatt) were killed, and then it came to an end. How many (Hugh was to wonder) of those things listed as 'causes' would need *not* to have happened for the First World War not to have happened either? Or for it to have been so different as to be something else? And what were the causes of the causes?

Hugh got a B+ for that course — the first of many. He was not destined for academic greatness, but his degree, when he finished it, was better than respectable. It took him into the library world where he prospered, and even made his mark as an historian of sorts, not in the professorial class, but certainly not amateurish either — good enough to give occasional lectures to senior students of (Frank Mangold's prediction had been right) New Zealand history, and to run a few tutorials. Quirky, Hugh Grady was sometimes called — a man with bees in his bonnet.

He sits now at his desk looking out at the sun setting behind the Waitakeres, and then down at three photographs side by side under the anglepoise lamp. One is a close-up of a white wooden cross, with the inscription

TARORE
aged 12 years
whose Maori Gospel of St Luke brought peace to the
tribes of Aotearoa
daughter of Ngakuku . . . & great-niece of Te Waharoa of Matamata
died at Wairere Falls 19th October 1836

The second photograph shows the back of the cross, inscribed 'This Memorial was unveiled by Dame Te-Ata-i-Rangikaahu, 16th October 1977'. In the third Jean-Anne Devantier, librarian, singer, and Hugh's unofficial research assistant, stands beside the little white picket fence surrounding the grave, and looks towards the mountains of the Kaimai range where, ten or twelve kilometres away, the white slash of the Wairere falls can just be made out.

Did Tarore's death 'cause' peace to come to the tribes of Aotearoa? All these years and decades since his student days Hugh is still sceptical about the idea of historical 'cause'. But if his great-great-grandfather, John Flatt, was present at a death which was *said to be* a cause, therein at least lay a story, a piece of our history worth unfolding.

AT MATAMATA IN 1835–6 John Flatt worked under the direction of the Rev A. N. Brown. They were there at the invitation — it might almost have been described as the insistence — of the old warrior chief Te Waharoa, whom one hundred and more years later historians of the plains would blandly celebrate as 'the Maori Napoleon, conqueror of the country from Waikato to Rotorua and the Bay of Plenty, and father of Wiremu Tamihana the Maori Kingmaker.' On hearing that there was to be a mission at Rotorua and one at Tauranga, Waharoa had pointed out to the Rev Brown that his territory lay between the two. 'I will see your people passing from Rotorua to Tauranga, and from Tauranga to Rotorua. They will want to stop along the way and they will be ashamed to have no missionary here with me. How will I know which day is the Sabbath? How will I and my people learn the Christian lesson of peace?'

His point was not quite correct, since there was another route from Tauranga to Rotorua which the missionaries preferred; nor had there been much evidence of Waharoa's wish to learn the lesson of peace. Some on the missionary committee saw his complaint as a veiled threat. The Rev Brown chose to see it as a genuine wish for the improvement of his tribe. His request was acceded to, and in return Waharoa provided workers for the establishment of the station, and children for its schools.

It was set up close to the pa, which was spread out along the edges of a bluff below which the river curled and twisted on its way north to join the Piako. The land beyond the river was swampy, difficult for strangers who had not been taught its intricate pathways, so the pa was easily defended against attack from that side. To the east the land ran away more or less flat to the Kaimai range. Defence on that side was by a system of strong palisades and trenches, behind which the community could be withdrawn if an attack was threatened.

THE PARTS OF JOHN FLATT'S journal which Miss Gladys McDermott had found and sent down from her home in Whangarei were not continuous and not all legible; the sheets were unbound, or the binding had come unstitched. Some pages were missing and others were water-stained and difficult to read. But there were sections which offered glimpses of Hugh's great-great-grandfather's year in Matamata, and he had transcribed them:

' . . . and my task it has been to supervise the making of this fence enclosing land, ten acres we estimate, given us by the tribe, also the clearing for gardens, and the planting which begins tomorrow. Work proceeds apace but that is not to say we are without problems and difficulties. Yesterday it was Wiremu's turn to complain about his day's wage, and when I told him (as I have told them all) it was the same for all, he replied that the *work* was not the same for all — he was strong and had done more. Refused further payment, he flew into a violent rage and began to tear down his section of the fence. I remonstrated, not taking quite seriously his anger, which at first I thought more theatrical than deeply felt. My mistake was at once clear to me when I found myself threatened with the small axe we had been using to cut stakes. My blood froze and I stood still and silent, waiting for the blow to fall — upon which Wiremu ran off taking the axe with him.

'Now I was the one in a rage. It was a matter I felt I could not let rest, and without seeking the Rev Brown's permission, I went at once to the pa to make a complaint to Waharoa whom I found sitting behind a flax-woven wind-break, eating pork and potatoes hot from the hangi. The chief listened, offered food which, perhaps mistakenly (but in truth I am often hungry), I accepted. Waharoa asked after the Rev Brown, spoke of the weather and the flax trade, and responded not at all to my complaint about the axe. I began to understand, or to suspect, that this was no matter to bring before a mighty chief. I thanked the old man for his time and went away. Wiremu has not returned, and I suspect the axe will not be recovered.

'Today my work on the fence was interrupted while I accompanied the Rev Brown on a visit to the widow of Paringaringa. Since P's death three days ago she has been wailing constantly, and it was thought some Christian comfort should be offered the poor soul. She told us she had pains in the chest to which the Rev B. responded (perhaps injudiciously, but his intention was for the best) that she might be harming herself with this ceaseless lamentation. Her reply was surprising. Did we suppose that she enjoyed making so much noise? she asked. But if she stopped, her tribe would tell her she was lazy . . .'

. . .

'The laying down of flooring in the two southernmost of raupo huts is complete and yesterday, determined that none of the land allotted to us should lie idle, I saw to it that more potatoes and corn were planted out. But my work has been interrupted, first by the necessity that I should carry a small gift together with the mission's apologies to the chief of a sub-tribe some miles away because we have not fulfilled a promise he claims we made to buy kumara of him; then by a visit (a welcome one, I should add) from the flax-trader, Mr Clementson; and finally by the need to accompany the Rev Brown many miles in rainy weather through the swamp to attend a sick chief, a journey which proved to be fruitless because the chief's illness had rendered him tapu — untouchable — so we were unable to minister to him.'

. . .

'. . . difficulty waking and rising before first light, as I am required to do, to lead my young natives in prayers before teaching commences, and I have asked Tarore, my best pupil, who cleans and keeps house for the Browns, to call me if I fail to stir.

. . .

'. . . intensely difficult, a drowning having caused the river to be declared tapu, which means I am not able to take a party to collect nails and wire and other supplies unloaded at Puriri from the *Columbine* and much needed for our present labours. There is also a tapu on the Native Boys' House, because Paringaringa in his final illness was not put out of doors, as is their way, but permitted to die there. The tohunga who has brought down this tapu could lift it at any time but asks payment; and because B believes it would be wrong to pay Christian money for a pagan ceremony, it remains and the boys will not enter. Yesterday, however, the tohunga told me he wished to exchange a pig for a blanket, and I believe we may be able to make the lifting a part of the bargain.'

. . .

'Last evening I returned from Puriri accompanying the much-needed supplies previously obstructed by the tapu on our river. I travelled with Messrs Fairburn, Preece, Maunsell, and Wilson. This is to be Mr F's last trip to Matamata before his removal to Maraetai, and he permitted his son Edwin, now eight years old, to travel with us. We stopped for a night at a raupo house along the way, and after our meal sat around the lantern discussing the grammar and pronunciation of the native language, calling one of them in now and then to settle disputes. There was much talk of the prospect of war between the tribes, which every day seems more likely; and indeed while we talked we could hear the war drum which Mr Fairburn explains is beaten to ensure wakefulness when an attack is feared. It frightened young Edwin, of whom I have a great fondness from my time at Puriri; and no sooner was he settled of that, and the lamps extinguished for our sleep, than an owl flew in at his window frightening the poor boy once again.

'It is as a consequence of the murder of a relative of Waharoa's on Christmas day at Rotorua that war is said to be almost certain. Since I have been away it has become more difficult to get labourers at the mission as more and more of the people at the pa are occupied in cutting and scraping flax to be traded for guns. The Rev Brown remonstrates with Waharoa, tells him that he will not be received into Heaven if he dies fighting in a war of vengeance, but the chief tells him the war must be fought, after which he "will believe like an English soldier, and go to Heaven". Brown offers this as an example of the simplicity of the native mind. Perhaps he is right, and I do not argue. But my suspicion is that in this, as in much else, we may be being teased, that being the thought which came to me on hearing an exchange in which Waharoa, having asked Mrs Brown what food he would eat in Heaven, and having been told that a spirit needs none, pointed out that the Rev Brown had preached the resurrection of the body. Mrs B considers this a merry example of what she too calls the simple uncivilised mind, which has no notion of a spiritual body. I have not much idea of it either, and so am left unsure of how to read the thought of our chiefly host.'

.   .   .

'The Browns believe Tarore's father, Ngakuku, who has been planting kumara and maize for us, to be their best current prospect for baptism, though he once had among his tribe a reputation for ferocity in battle. Yesterday he rushed at, and seemed to threaten with death, the trader Clementson whose "fault" was that he was travelling on the Sabbath! This inclines me to the view that Ngakuku, a man of anxious temperament, is in a state of mental confusion, pressed on one side by his new faith and on the other by his native ways.

'Tarore, however, has been my best scholar, and the Browns have given her a copy of the St Luke Gospel in Maori done on Colenso's press. There is no doubt she prizes it. She has a small flax kit in which she takes it with her wherever she goes, and Mrs Brown believes this to be a sign of great piety. Tarore is certainly a thoughtful and intelligent young woman, sometimes playful, always energetic, with much vividness of life.

'Last evening she stood with me looking down from the bluff to where her younger brothers and sisters were swimming in the river. Wearing her best mat, and with her thick dark hair oiled in the way of native women, she was impressive beyond her years, which I take to be fifteen or sixteen. She told me that one of her uncles who had been baptised had given up three of his four wives, and that because of this her father was thinking of giving up his second wife. I could see no sign that this pleased her, and wondered whether her mother was the first or the second wife. I suspect the second, but did not like to ask.

'I should mention that though I have heard the natives refer to me by the name, Paratee, their language makes of Flatt, she has been the first to address me thus — a fact which gave me pleasure, I suppose because it is a signal of trust.'

IF THE MISSION AT PURIRI was to be closed then it was decided Matamata should have its small dairy herd. At first the animals were carried on board the *Columbine* to Tauranga, and it was to be John Flatt's task to bring them across the mountains. Brown, who had been in Rotorua trying to prevent the war that threatened between the tribes, met up with Flatt in Tauranga to arrange the unloading. But the local chief required payment if the herd was to be brought ashore on his land, and the amount requested was unreasonable. At the end of three days he remained adamant, and Brown's patience was at an end. The schooner was sent back to Puriri still with the animals on board, and the missionary party returned across the mountains to Matamata.

A month or so later, with preparations for war going on all around them, it was decided that the matter of the herd had become urgent, and that Brown would go to Puriri by the usual route, which meant a good deal of it by canoe, while Flatt would travel on foot with Maori guides, assessing whether it might be possible to bring the animals overland.

Late in the evening of the day after Brown's arrival at Puriri, Flatt reached the station, soaked to the skin. He reported that they would have to get the herd across one sizeable river, and there might be difficulties around the worst edges of the swamp, but it was certainly possible. The greater problem might be a sub-tribe whose chief had declared he would want payment if cattle were to cross his territory.

They decided they would face that when it arose, and next day Fairburn, Brown and Flatt set off driving the herd south, aided by a group of mission Maori who referred to the three missionaries by something in their own language meaning 'Big, Middle and Little', Fairburn being tall, Flatt of middle height, and Brown so small it was said he preached standing on a box so his head might appear over the pulpit. They were in high spirits. Fairburn, whose health had not been good, and who, in the depression that had invaded him before the decision to move his mission to Tamaki, had been, as Brown wrote in his journal, 'sorely tried by our great Adversary', or as Flatt put it, had been 'sampling too much of the communion wine', was more cheerful than he had been for many months. As they went along the easier parts of their journey they talked nostalgically about their favourite parts of England and sang the songs of their childhood.

Flatt's journal continued:

'It was late afternoon, we had just passed by the soda springs where mission picnics sometimes take place, and were descending towards the river when we heard shots from behind and to the left and saw rushing down at us a taua, or "fight" — not a large number, but naked as is their way in battle, except for cartridge boxes strapped around their waists. Bodies oiled and faces blackened, they appeared indeed warlike and I was full of fear. The Rev Brown and Mr Fairburn, however, appeared more irritated than afraid.

'A korero followed. The leader of the taua said he required payment for his tribe. He would get none, Mr Fairburn told him bluntly.

'We were told we were unwelcome. The Rev B said on the contrary we travelled at the invitation of the great Te Waharoa.

'The warrior pointed out that this was not Waharoa's territory, which the Rev Brown acknowledged, but suggested that Waharoa might make it his if they displeased him.

'The warrior took offence at the threat thus gracefully implied, and began (or so it seemed to me) to bluster. Since we would not pay, he said, he would kill us all and swallow our eyeballs, to which Mr Fairburn answered, half to the heavens, half to our brown and naked interlocutor, that it might be safer to chew on a fern root.

'There was now a fearsome haka, at the end of which B, perhaps feeling he must for safety's sake appear conciliatory, acknowledged it to have been very fine, but said it could make no difference. We could make no payment — had none to offer. We would therefore return to Puriri with the cattle so no offence would have been given and none taken.

'At this the taua leader gathered his men around him. After a few minutes talk he came smiling and holding out his hand to us. He and his men would join us in prayer, and share our meal.

'The Rev B agreed. Prayers were said, a meal prepared and eaten, and the taua departed into the gathering darkness while tents were put up.

'I think we all supposed that this was an end to the matter but so it proved not to be. Next morning they were back, again demanding payment. Told yet again that they would get none they began to drive the cattle back towards Puriri. Resistance on our part seemed neither wise nor indeed possible, and we followed behind, I thinking that we would never achieve our desire of adding the herd to our Matamata establishment, and that my promise to teach Tarore how a cow is milked was to remain unfulfilled. But after a mile of this the taua seemed to accept that they would get no payment. I think they would have taken the cattle had they known how to handle them or what to do with them, but it was clear they did not. So, not daring to break the tapu which protects the tohungas of the white man's religion, they shook hands with us once again and went on their way.

'Now at last the path was open. When the worst of the journey was over Fairburn said his goodbyes to us, and turned back with his natives towards Puriri. Next day (yesterday) we had the herd safely behind fences here at

Matamata, and this morning, with much laughter which I am afraid occasioned stern looks from Mrs B, Tarore had her first lesson in the art of the dairy maid.'

KAIWAKA, TOPUNI, TE HANA, Wellsford, Hoteo, Kaipara Flats, Woodcocks, Ahuroa, Tahakeroa, Kanoki, Kaukapakapa, Helensville, Wharepapa, Woodhill, Rewiti, Waimauku, Huapai, Kumeu, Taupaki, Waitakere, Swanson . . . And then Mt Eden? Sitting at his desk, looking westward from his house on the lower slopes of the hill, the photograph of Tarore's grave lying under the anglepoise lamp, Hugh Grady rolls the names backward that brought him, tanned and reluctant, home for the last time from the Beaumont farm. Didn't the train go through Mt Eden on its way to central Auckland? There was a little station there, but now he can't remember ever having got off at it. He remembers only getting on and off at central Auckland, and that when he was a child that station was his idea of a big building. One you could run about in. Vast. Grand. Echoing. That and the Auckland Museum, where the name of his grandmother's brother, Vincent Flatt, was engraved in marble among the names of those who 'fell' in the First World War. At his grandmother's house, also in Mt Eden, he remembers there used to be a small round bronze plaque, beautifully engraved, with Vincent Flatt's name on it under an image of a woman with an olive branch and the inscription 'He Died for Freedom and Honour'. Even so many years later, and with another war ('the second show') being fought, that plaque could bring tears to Charlotte Christianson's eyes because, she said, in the patriotic folly of the first days of that earlier war she had encouraged her young brother when he said he wanted to 'join up'. Vincent died in France. Once when they were visiting his grandmother, Hugo's mother told him, in a terrible whisper while the old lady was out of the room, that Uncle Vincent's head was 'blown clean off his shoulders'.

Hugh has never strayed far from Mt Eden —

65

Maungawhau, as the local tribes called it — hill of the whau tree. He lived there as a child, settled with Hat in Epsom when they married, still in walking distance of the hill, and later, after their post-affair- recovery tour of Europe, bought an old cottage, on the slopes above Mt Eden Road, which has recently been taken away, replaced by this neo-Art Deco town house in which he sits watching the sun go down in flames beyond the Waitakeres.

Hugh's sons, Richard and John, grew up on the slopes of the hill, broke an arm each doing daring sledge runs down into the crater, learned to swim at the Mt Eden pool, went to Mt Eden Primary School and Auckland Grammar. They are downstairs now with their wives and children — Richard and Louise with their little girls Daniella and Kirsten, John and Evie with boys Freddie and Carlo. Richard is a lawyer in Parnell; John a beekeeper, living not far from Maraetai. Every Monday evening they come. Last week Hugh asked Hat whether she thought it might be a good idea next time to invite Jean-Anne and her husband Philip Devantier to meet the family. Hat's reply — 'Jean-Anne?' and then, 'Oh yes, of course — if you like' — contained such a huge unspoken 'But why?' he took it no further.

He gets up and goes downstairs. The four small children are being fed first, at the kitchen table. Their parents talk and joke over their heads. In the dining room the glass-topped table is laid with tapa placemats and red candles. The wine is uncorked. Hat is putting around individual bowls of salade niçoise.

Over dinner Hugh doesn't talk much at first. There's so much to listen to. But asked about his research he tells a story Jean-Anne has pointed out to him in the journal of the missionary Morgan, about a young Maori woman suckling a dog. When asked why she was doing this she said, with a sort of bravado, it was because her baby was dead — strangled. Appalled, Morgan wanted to know who had done this terrible thing? She told him she had done it herself. It had been necessary. She had been cold at night and a tohunga had lent her his mat. It had been full of fleas and lice, which kept her awake, and to be rid of them she had picked them off and eaten them. But a tohunga's mat was tapu. Nothing should be eaten from it. She and her baby had become ill, and then very ill. To save herself it had been necessary to end the tapu by sacrificing her child.

Louise wants to know whether he believes this dreadful story. He says there is no reason to doubt it. It rings true. And why would Morgan invent it?

Across the corner of the table, while Hat discusses with Richard and Louise the depositions hearing in a recent case of rape and murder, Hugh talks to John, who has inherited his passion for opera, about a new recording of Strauss's *Ariadne auf Naxos*. The talk rouses memories of the music, sets some of its Wagnerian phrases ringing in his head.

He is surprised by a momentary and quite unfocused feeling of loneliness and regret.

'SINCE MY LAST LETTER,' Hugh's great-great-grandfather wrote to the Rev Mr Jowett in September 1836, 'war, bloodshed and cannibalism have raged in this part of New Zealand.'

In his pyjamas that Monday evening after the family gathering, Hugh stood out on the balcony that opened off their bedroom, while Hat, in what current real estate pidgin called 'the ensuite', could be heard cleaning her teeth. The lights of those modest suburbs, lower Mt Eden, Balmoral, Sandringham, Mt Albert, Avondale, glittered as bright in the clear air as the royal and patrician associations of their names suggested they should.

Hugh was still trying to get straight in his mind the inter-tribal alliances and antagonisms, the hatreds and long-preserved determinations to revenge, the plots and counter-plots, which were the background to Te Waharoa's last war, and which were his responsibility in this part of his joint research project with Jean-Anne Devantier. There was little about it, he had told Louise at the table, that was glorious or noble or inspiring. It was mostly cold and cruel, dupli-citous, heartless and violent, like the internecine wars of the

Mafia, or the murders and revenges of the IRA and the UDA. But it was exciting; and much more interesting if it wasn't sentimentalised.

Hat's teeth were done now, and she sat up in bed looking at some 'forensics', wearing the half glasses over which every day she looked down with impartial severity on accuser and accused. Hugh decided he would try to tell it to her as a story. Telling sorted it out in your mind — reduced it to essentials. Hat took off the spectacles, put aside the half dozen colour photographs of the naked body of a stabbed and strangled woman, and listened.

The place where it was simplest to begin, Hugh told her, was with the murder of Hunga by Huka on Christmas Day 1835.

Huka was of the Arawa tribes of the Rotorua area, and considered himself to have been wronged by his own people. Part of the problem was a share of profits which he claimed to be his due, and which he had not received, from the sale of flax to the Norwegian trader Tapsell, who was himself married to an Arawa woman, and traded under the protection of that tribe. The other wrongs Huka had suffered were more shadowy. There was, John Flatt said in his evidence to the House of Lords in 1838, something about an adultery; and there was an associated insult — something to do with the violation of a tapu. Huka acknowledged that he could not have revenge by making war against his own people; but he could bring war upon them. This was his purpose in murdering Hunga.

Hugh has found two differing accounts of how it was done. One has Huka greeting Hunga on Christmas morning, hongiing with him. As their noses touched a second time, pressing gently and warmly above their smiling lips, Huka's son clubbed the unsuspecting Hunga in the approved Maori manner, behind and below the ear. A second blow was not necessary. In the other account Huka struck the blows — more than one — catching Hunga as he was emerging, bent double to come through the low entrance to his whare.

Whichever way it happened the end was the same. The

great Te Waharoa's cousin fell to the ground, twitched and jerked in dusty sunlight, and died. It was an act certain to bring retaliation.

Maori convention demanded that Huka's tribe, however they might regret what he had done, had to accept it as their own doing, even in some degree honouring him for an act of warrior daring and bravado, while at the same time preparing for the consequences. Hunga's body was beheaded, gutted and quartered, and pieces sent around to be eaten by various related sub-tribes, as a modern farmer might butcher a sheep and divide it among his neighbours. The tribe made some conciliatory gestures towards Waharoa, but only as far as pride and honour would allow. They also accepted that to attempt some kind of revenge was his duty as a chief, and that he would have no choice. They hoped, however, his actions might be limited and soon over.

So during the early months of 1836, while the Matamata missionaries travelled to and fro attempting to make peace, Waharoa, in his own way and at his own pace, prepared for war. Less attention was given to crops and more to flax, which was harvested in huge quantities, scraped, and sold or exchanged for weapons. Emissaries were sent to other tribes — Ngatikoroki, Ngatimaniapoto, Ngaiterangi — who could be expected to join their Ngatihaua cousins and share the spoils. Tohunga and matakite were consulted for prophecy and spells. Hakas were danced and karakias chanted. Sometimes the Rev Brown and his helpers were confined to the mission station, and spies posted along the tracks to ensure they didn't travel; sometimes they were told the tracks were open to them, and they could go to Rotorua and Maketu, if they wanted to, and pursue the cause of peace. When Flatt suggested to Brown that they might be let out only because Waharoa wanted news, possibly false news, carried abroad, and that they might be acting as his carrier pigeons, he was told that such thoughts were not helpful. If unwittingly they carried the chief's message, wittingly they carried God's, which was more potent, and they must do His work as and when opportunity offered.

For a long time it was not clear whether Waharoa's attack would be made at Rotorua, the Arawa heartland, or on their coastal settlement at Maketu, where there was an Arawa pa, and where Tapsell had built a store protected by cannon. But in the early days of March all the signs were that Rotorua would take the onslaught.

On 19 March four hundred men of the Ngatimaniapoto and Ngatikoroki arrived at Matamata to join Waharoa's taua. Two days later Brown went to the pa and made a final attempt to reason with the chief. He found there what he described in his report home as 'a high war fever'. To his appeals Waharoa said only, 'How sweet will the flesh of Arawa taste to me with the new kumara.' On the 22nd the mission station woke to an uncanny quiet. Long before sunrise a thousand warriors had moved silently away. All the signs that Rotorua would be the point of the attack had been deceptions. They were heading for the coast — for Maketu.

It was several days before the missionaries dared leave Matamata. First Brown went, with a new man, Mr Maunsell, leaving John Flatt with Mrs Brown. Next day, however, Mrs Brown insisted Flatt follow, thinking he might be needed. Meanwhile Brown and Maunsell had met up with Captain Levington of the *Columbine*, and later with Mr Wade and Mr Wilson who were at the Tauranga mission station. By the time the party of Englishmen were all in one place the battle was over and they were able to piece together what had happened.

Reaching the coast, Waharoa had first captured a group of fourteen Arawa, together with Tapsell's agent, James Farrow. Mr Wilson had interceded on behalf of the captives and had been assured that they were only being held so that they could not take news to Maketu of the coming attack. But when Wilson had gone, the fourteen were killed, cooked and eaten. Next day Farrow, who had escaped and been recaptured, was released. He was told to go to Tapsell and warn him that if he wished to live he should not fire his cannon.

By now, with the addition of coastal allies, Waharoa's

force numbered 1600, and the attack on Maketu went ahead. Sixty-five Arawa were killed and later eaten; 150 others, mainly women and children, were captured as slaves. The remainder fled, and the pa was destroyed. Tapsell, watching the battle from a nearby hill, had taken into his house a wounded Arawa chief and hidden him under the bed. Only minutes before the attackers arrived the chief died. In Tapsell's house they cut off his head and outside on the lawn warriors fought for pieces of his body, which they ate raw. Blood was splashed over a pile of watermelons, and those who could not taste the chief's flesh ate the bloodied melons. In the frenzy that followed Tapsell's store was broken into, stripped of everything, and burned to the ground. The grave of his infant daughter, buried in his garden, was dug up, the little corpse thrown into bushes, and the coffin taken away.

Because he had not fired his cannon Tapsell was protected by Waharoa. He and his Arawa wife escaped with their lives — but that was all.

Now the expedition was over and the warriors were making their way home, carrying the spoils of war, including baskets of human flesh. They were in dangerous high spirits, the blood lust still up, and when they stopped for the night at Tauranga, Waharoa put his sleeping mat across the door of the mission house and slept there, knowing that if he did not protect those inside with his tapu, some hot-head would be likely to break in and kill them for sport.

But the missionaries had now to think of the retaliations that would follow. For them the worst danger in the future lay in the fact that Tapsell's store had been stripped and his property destroyed by Waharoa's men. Since the Matamata mission 'belonged' to Waharaoa, as Tapsell's trading station 'belonged' to the Arawa, in any retaliatory raid the Arawa would think it their right to strip and possibly destroy the mission station. It was this, Hugh explained to Hat, which would bring about the closing of the Matamata station, and the most terrible of John Flatt's adventures.

Hat was close to sleep now. Hugh picked up her 'forensics', stacked them on the bedside table with her glasses, and turned out the light leaving the curtains open so he could drift asleep looking out at the western sky.

IN ONE OF HIS JOURNAL ENTRIES, transcribed with great difficulty by Jean-Anne Devantier from water-damaged pages, John Flatt lies with his hands crossed behind his head staring out through the open tent flap at the unfamiliar patterns of the southern stars. The mission group are making their way back from Tauranga to Matamata. Flatt is tired from the day's walk, but his mind is full of images which hold sleep at bay. Or when a sort of half-sleep comes, still those straggling lines of warriors with their captive slaves tramp through his head, laughing, good-natured, ill-natured, unpredictable, volatile, dangerous, cruel. One carries a human heart on a pointed stick, the organ singed with fire because it has belonged to the first-killed in a battle and has been offered as a tribute to the war-god Te Whiro. Another shakes a severed head at him, held by the hair, and laughs. He notices the cartridge box strapped around the waist of a naked warrior is lined with tattooed human skin. Everywhere the flax kits, fat with flesh, drip blood, fingers, whole hands poking through or sticking out at the top. A child pulls faces at the severed head of a chief. Once Flatt comes upon a corpse being eviscerated in preparation for the ovens.

He thinks again of the peace of the mission at Waimate, and the position of agriculturist in charge of the gardens there which the Society in London appointed him to, and which he travelled so many thousands of miles to fill. The sense of an injustice, a wrong done to him by Mr Davis who has clung to the post for his own son, and by the Rev Henry Williams who sent Flatt south to be rid of him, is still strong. But now it is complicated by other feelings. He could hardly admit it to Brown, whose distress and disgust at what has happened are so genuine and humane, but Flatt knows he is not sorry to have been involved in this adventure. It is something that will live with him for the rest of his life.

It has also changed him. More and more he has felt

during these past weeks that he and his fellow-missionaries have been compromised — gathered into, and made part of, the ways and doings they are here to deplore and the society it is their role to 'convert'. Brown's scolding, though deeply sincere, cannot conceal the reality, which is that they have moved when Waharoa has said they may, and been confined at his will; have become, in fact, inadvertently, 'his' missionaries. Finally their attempts to make peace have placed them, helpless, in the company of a cannibal war party now returning triumphant to a home which is also their home.

He remembers how nobly the image of the Maori warrior with his code of pride and utu impressed itself upon him that night down by the river when the canoe glided by into darkness, the splash of paddles in unison accompanied by the chant, Hoi-*uh*, toi-*uh*. Now he has seen what it means — the heartless blood-letting. And yet in Waharoa, the master-mind of all this horror, there can be seen also something gentle, thoughtful, wise, strong.

Sleep comes. When he wakes it is after midnight. Brown is shaking his arm. Maunsell is at the tent flap. There is a swishing sound through grass and the pad of bare feet. The three Englishmen on their knees at the tent door, peer out into the moonlight. It is the taua going by, tramping through the night. Without Waharoa across their doorway they know they are unsafe. Better to travel with them than to lie asleep. They dress, pack, and in the moonlight trudge on across the plain with what Brown, angry and depressed by what he has not been able to prevent, calls 'this company of murderers'.

As the sun rises they come on Waharoa's party who have made a fire and are cooking food. Success in battle has left them full of good humour and bravado, which only increases Brown's fury. He begins to address them, telling them that unless they believe and repent they will go to hell, will burn for ever; and that if they want to know what awaits them after death they should put a hand in their cooking fire and hold it there.

Even while Brown is speaking, a warrior picks him up bodily and places him on a rock, saying he needs to eat 'long pig' and grow tall — they can't see him when he stands on the ground. Brown ignores the insult and will not be silenced. Flatt admires his courage, the faith he always shows that 'every of our hairs is counted', but thinks that now is not the time for sermonising. These men have risked death in battle and survived, some with wounds. Better to wait until the excitement is over and they have had time to think soberly about the revenges their own revenge will inevitably bring.

The most threatening of Waharoa's men is asking Brown why he is complaining. 'We are bringing you slaves for mother Brown's school.'

Waharoa offers Brown a human rib. Furious, Brown holds up between them a small plain cross, closes his eyes, and quotes in English in his strong voice, 'Yea though I walk through the valley of the shadow of Death I shall fear no evil, for Thou art with me, Thy rod and Thy staff they comfort me . . .' Maunsell and Flatt join him in completing the psalm.

Now Waharoa is standing. He no longer looks amused. There is no doubt he fears the power of the white man's religion, especially those parts of it he does not understand. He stares hard at Brown. 'If you are angry with me,' he says, 'I will kill and eat you — you and all your missionaries.'

'I don't fear you,' Brown says. And Flatt, who does, believes him.

FOUR

VOICES. VOICE. JEAN-ANNE'S crooning in the stacks. Practising at lunch-time down in the university Music Department. At the piano once, singing Schubert lieder to Hugh's accompaniment. At the wheel, driving him home. In the Town Hall, full-throttle, full-dress, when she took a solo part with the university choir. And once, unaccompanied, in the archives room. That was when, as a surprise for his birthday (it was his sixtieth), she sang his namesake's 'Nimmersatte Liebe', and he pretended not to understand the lines

> So ist die Lieb'! So ist die Lieb'!
> Mit Küssen nicht zu stillen:
> wer ist der Tor und will ein Sieb
> mit eitel Wasser füllen?

It meant, she told him, 'Love's like that — it can no more be satisfied with kisses than a sieve can be filled with water' — and gave him a swift, fragrant, birthday kiss.

Yes Hugh Grady has heard all of these. He and Jean-Anne Devantier have worked together now for most of a year. In the library. At her home. At his. They have driven south together to discover Tarore's grave; and north to visit his aged relative, Miss Gladys McDermott in Whangarei, who has supplied, not all at once, but section by section as their enthusiasm has seemed to earn it, the tattered remnants of John Flatt's journal. It is because Hugh has heard Jean-Anne's many modes and registers, and because he is confident he knows a Voice from a voice, that he tells her he deplores, at

75

the same time that he celebrates, her pregnancy. He tells her that he himself comes from a long line of wasted voices, the last his own. Boy soprano became young man tenor-baritone in Grammar school shorts, and sometimes hoped that someone might tell him he must not stop singing, must go on, learn more, study, travel, win fame, sing at La Scala, Covent Garden, the Met. No one did. His mother, who named him Hugo Wolf and his sister Aida Norma (a disappointment — songless, like their father), never thought of it, only lamented the passing of his Hugohood which had given him the (transient, alas) gift of golden sopranodom.

In his teens, his Hugo-name contracted to Hugh, he learned to sing like Nat King Cole ('Too Young', 'Unforget-table') and the young Frank Sinatra ('I'll Be Seeing You', with the Tommy Dorsey Orchestra), and to play the saxophone in a dance band. Later there was a sense of regret, not at the certainty of a talent wasted, but at the uncertainty of one left unexplored. Libraries, he discovered, had that effect, especially through the middle years of his life when they expanded, were rehoused, becoming modern, upmarket, technological. Hugh has thought of himself sometimes as the little clerk in the story by Katherine Mansfield who compares himself to a moth or an insect crying, 'The shortness of life! The shortness of life! I've only one night or one day, and there's this vast dangerous garden waiting out there, undiscovered, unexplored.' Once — and once only — he, or his Wolf-self, flew out into the garden; and as quickly the Hugo-self flew back again. Darkness has its own ways of singeing your wings.

Does Jean-Anne think that he is impertinent telling her she should not neglect her voice? If she does, she shows no sign of it. She tells him the pregnancy wasn't intended but never mind. She has no regrets. Mothers can be singers. Or let her baby be the singer. Philip, her husband, has his medical work here in Auckland. She couldn't go abroad to study — wouldn't want to. There's nothing more to be said.

A WIND, A WELLINGTON WIND — sweeping along the valley floor and across the hills that rise on the far side. This is the suburb of Ngaio. Not real Ngaio, but Ngaio remembered after nearly four decades, and so it has become a place Hugh would not expect quite to exist in reality. It lies in his mind somewhere alongside the reality, a shadowy otherwhere, very close to the real, but distinct. Not an otherwhere he has conjured often. Tucked away, brought out now for the first time in so long that the last inspection is like the memory of a memory, faded, vague. You get here by a train called 'the Unit' from central Wellington — or so memory tells him. It goes through a hole in the hills that rise encircling the beautiful harbour, where the winter sun may be shining. The harbour is left behind, and you are in this valley where always the rain rains and the wind blows. That is part of its unreality. It has only one weather; and more strangely, this is a combination of slanting, hail-laced rain and moaning, driving wind, which suits his mood of that time and which he finds romantic. There must be houses on the opposite slope enclosing the valley, but perhaps not; what he remembers are hillsides covered in scrub — he supposes manuka, but which, for the good reason that the family who occupy this house are Scottish immigrants, his imagination converts to heather.

The station is somewhere down there below the house. You arrive in the rain, push up the street to the house to be greeted by the family who are billeting you for the duration of the universities winter tournament, and sit looking out at the slanting showers moving up the valley like battalions, bent double, and at the double. There are the mother, the father, and two daughters, one still at school, the other, your own age, perhaps a year older, working in a chemist shop in town.

Names? They have no names; they hardly have faces. The parents are presences, warm, encouraging, faintly anxious. Is there some purpose in their offering a billet? The schoolgirl has a schoolgirl's face. Her sister — is she dark? Fair? He remembers how much he liked her, felt liked by her, how exciting it was to pass by her in the half-dark hallway, coming and going from their bedrooms, and how terribly their shynesses were compounded. One evening over the family meal he told them — cannot have volunteered it, it must somehow have fallen into the conversation, like something pulled down on one's head from a high shelf — that he had no one to take to the Tournament Ball. In the silence that followed, the mother's smile, her looking from Hugh to her daughter, from the daughter to Hugh, said clearly what was obvious, that he need look no further. He had thought of it often, and lacked courage to ask. But if he could not bring himself to say it when alone with her, how could he ask now, in front of others? The embarrassment of it, of that silence, as on a stage when an actor misses his cue, must finally have brought something — anything — from one of them, probably the schoolgirl, to pick up the conversation and carry it on, forward, away. Down at the station the Unit moved off along the valley to another hole in the hills, another romantically windswept rain-sodden heather-clad glen.

It remains with him, not, or not especially, as an opportunity missed, but as an embarrassment, and as the sense of harm done, the memory of the pain of inflicting pain; because though young Hugh could seldom act, he could always see; and what he saw was that though the older daughter accepted the disappointment, and would not show it now or later by any display of sulks or self-pity, to her it could mean only that she was unattractive to him, that he would be looking for more splendid company. Worse, this had been demonstrated in the presence of her family. How else could it be read? And yet none of it was true. He wanted nothing more than to take her to the Ball; lacked not the wish, not at all, but only the courage.

It was also one of those moments when, as Hugh believes, not the Presence of great Gods but their terrible Absence, determines our future and our fate. If the subject had not come up over the dinner table he would surely have found a way to broach it. After that meal it was too embarrassing ever to be mentioned. He went alone to the Tournament Ball, and it was there he and Hat first met. A law student in the company of another so drunk he could scarcely stand, Hat abandoned her partner for the solo Hugh. While he was asking himself whether, given that she had arrived with a partner, it would be thought wrong to ask if he could see her home — a question he might have gone on debating with himself until it was too late — Hat asked him to see her home. When he was thinking about the possibility, and really the impossibility, of kissing her at her gate, she kissed him. Hat — Hattie, as she was then to her friends, Harriet to her family — took such a liking to him, the pain of decision and direct action was thenceforth, and almost for ever, lifted from his shoulders.

HUGH'S WIDOWED GRANDMOTHER, Charlotte Christianson, had lived only a few streets away from the Grady household. Sometimes she had talked to him about her own grandparents, John and Caroline Flatt, but in those days the subject interested him hardly at all, and so he retained little except a memory of it being said that John Flatt had ceased to be a missionary, and had fallen out with the Church which first sent him to New Zealand because he criticised the missionaries' acquisition of large tracts of Maori land.

The impressions of his grandmother which he carried away from childhood had more to do with music than with history. Charlotte had been the one with the Voice. She sang opera — yes; but like some of the great divas of the present day, and to the distress of her daughter Ethel Elena, who had a smaller voice and a finer sensibility, she sang anything at all — except, it should be said, Wagner and Hugo Wolf, whose music she considered tuneless and boring. While he was still singing soprano, young Hugo had learned from his grandmother some of the great soprano arias by Verdi, Bellini, Gounod and Puccini, and joined her in singing them. But he had learned also, simply by listening to her while she was grating carrots or peeling potatoes or bottling peaches

in her kitchen, some of the popular songs of her youth. These
included

> I've got a motto,
> 'Always merry and bright'.
> Look around and you will find
> That every cloud is silver-lined.

Or 'Waltz Me Around Again, Willie', about a girl called
Madeline Moony, which included the lines

> Waltz me around again Willie,
> Around, around, around.
> The music is dreamy
> It's peaches-and-creamy
> Oh don't let my feet touch the ground.
> I feel like a ship on an ocean of joy,
> I just want to holler out loud, *Shipahoy*!
> Waltz me around again Willie,
> Around, around, around.

When James Grady was visiting his mother-in-law's
house he encouraged her in these displays of bad taste, partly,
Hugo was sure, because they caused his wife a certain delicate
anguish, and partly because any bizarre contradiction, such
as banality and nonsense issuing from a great voice, suited
the Irish in him. His favourite among the songs Charlotte
could call up from the distant regions of her youth was one
he used to refer to as 'the Darwin number'. 'Give us the
Darwin number, Mother,' he would say, and if the mood and
the moment were right she would sing,

> Down in Jungle-Town
> A honeymoon is coming soon
> When you hear a serenade
> To a pretty monkey maid;
> And the chimpanzees
> Sing in the trees
> Sing in the trees
> She'll be true to Monkey Doodledoo
> Way down in Jungle Town.

He got on well with his mother-in-law, James Grady always said, because they were both atheists; but he like to recall Charlotte's missionary forebear, saying that he, James, was a *Catholic* atheist; Charlotte's atheism was low church Anglican.

Later Hugh was never sure whether his grandmother quite liked Hat, but there was no doubt she approved of her as his wife. Long before marriage had been quite spoken of, Charlotte was telling him that Hat would be good for him, was what he needed, was decisive as he was not. He would be able to leave his head in the clouds, where he liked it to be, because Hattie would have her feet on the ground. 'There has to be someone to know what day of the week it is,' his grandmother told him; and Hugh, who believed he coped perfectly well with such facts, felt mildly offended, but kept it hidden, pleased that she approved of his choice.

Not that then, or even later, he ever quite made a choice. It — whether by Hat, or circumstances, or the passage of time — was made for him. The summer after that winter tournament when he was billeted in the suburb of Ngaio, Hat came to Auckland where she spent the months of the university vacation, and they went everywhere together. Long before there had been any serious suggestion of marriage she would look at him, arriving to take her to the pictures, and say, 'When we're married the first thing I'm going to do is teach you how to dress decently'; or returning from a party, 'If we're going to spend the rest of our lives in Auckland, we're going to have to make some new friends.' Did he ever propose marriage in the old-fashioned way? He has no recollection that he did. He was swept off his feet, appropriated, groomed, and married by Harriet Jane Enverson, not only unresisting, but glad of it. She possessed then and, after so many years of marriage, retains now, the power to make him very happy.

BUT SO DOES JEAN-ANNE DEVANTIER, especially in her enthusiasm for their project, and for the hope that when it is completed they may publish something together, an article at least, perhaps a pamphlet, even a book.

This morning, like many mornings, she is keen to bring him up to date. In the open library there are constant interruptions — phone calls, user enquiries. But now, alone with him in the archives room, she is able to take her part of the story forward. It has to do with the unpublished letters and journals of Thomas Chapman which, in dividing the work, they have assigned to her, and which she has been struggling through on the microfilm reader.

Chapman was one of the missionaries at Rotorua in those years of the 1830s that interest them; and what Jean-Anne tells Hugh now is that they haven't — or she, anyway, has not — sufficiently understood how many disasters fell all at one time upon the missionary community in what was referred to from the Bay of Islands as 'the southern region'.

First there were simply the physical hardships in that part of the island — constant travelling on foot through swamp and forest, across mountains, down rivers and sometimes along dangerous storm-swept coasts; frequent drenchings and cold; raupo houses that could not keep out wind and water; hard, sometimes heavy, practical work: all accepted as part of their undertaking, but made more arduous-seeming by contrast with life on the balmy northern shores where their notion of life in New Zealand had been formed. These were hardships they could rise above — even, in some degree, enjoy. They were still young. The land which so buffeted them was vast and beautiful. There was a freedom in their way of life; a confirmation of individual powers, of Christian vocation, and of the strength it gave them. But still, Jean-Anne says, it was hard going.

Harder to cope with was the sense of failure, or at best of small success, in their work among the natives. They had gone into the region of the lakes and plains to propagate the Gospel, but also to make peace, and instead they had been gathered into a tribal war. They were even identified with one side, and could not easily disentangle themselves from Waharoa who had tricked them into something like complicity by seeming to promise that he and his tribe would one day 'believe'. This was something none of them, except perhaps John Flatt, ever quite faced up to.

They lived with fear — for themselves, for their wives and children. And by way of illustration Jean-Anne reads Hugh a passage in which Chapman writes, 'During the whole of one year I hardly ever laid me down without feeling I might be aroused by the cry of war, often watching and waiting for the morning with no small anxiety.'

But worse — much the worst for them, she insists — was the recognition of how successfully their 'great Adversary' was at work among them. Over them all hung the spectre of the missionary Thomas Kendall, who had found himself unable to resist the availability of native women, and who had brought disrepute upon the New Zealand mission. Among themselves now, Fairburn's drinking, his depressions, his occasional extravagant or outrageous outbursts, were well known — and there were other and worse rumours about him. It was said that in Rotorua the catechist Henry Pilley had been accepting sexual favours from native women; and though at first he protested his innocence, it was not long before the Rev Brown was writing to London, 'I fear another trial awaits the Society in the iniquity of Mr Pilley. He is now residing to the southward as a flax collector and has taken a native girl for wife; but these things are as nothing compared with the wickedness of which he is said to have been guilty while a member of this Mission.'

And finally, while Waharoa's war still raged around them, had come a visit from the Rev Henry Williams bringing news that William Yate, ordained missionary at the northern station, had been found to be engaging in homosexual practices with young native boys under his protection. 'There was a time,' Brown wrote, 'when the title of a New Zealand Missionary was an honourable one, but we shall soon, I fear, think it a disgrace.'

Jean-Anne has found Chapman's journal entries upon hearing the news of Yate, part of which she reads to Hugh in the archives room: 'Into what insignificance did all we had gone through sink when compared to that now laid upon us. Truly we seemed "to stink" — wretched man! Wretched apostate! If he be guilty? Yes, yes — so many circumstances, so many proofs — sad, sad — May the Lord keep *us*. May the Lord pardon our iniquities, for they are many and great — and this great Sin! O Lord pardon us, for truly Thou knowest we knew it not. Truly, truly is our most blessed Saviour wounded in the house of his friends!'

Jean-Anne's newest discovery is that news of the charges against Yate led the missionary committee in New Zealand to release all those men in its employ who were unmarried, allowing them to return to England, there to find wives, if they wished, before returning, or if they preferred, to stay.

'The distressing circumstances alluded to,' (Chapman wrote) 'induced the Committee to pass Resolution 2 at their meeting of November 6 1836. They could not but feel that our Great Enemy would in all probability take advantage of the fall of Mr Yate to spread prejudicial reports relative to our single brethren — from the simple circumstance that they were single — and that therefore it was but an act of justice to allow these brethren the privilege of withdrawing from the land.'

In the same month John Flatt wrote that the news about Mr Yate has reached them and that 'a special Missionary Committee has recommended that all the single men should leave. I had been in hopes that there should be no occasion for me to tread the Frozen Decks around Cape Horn, and I shall leave New Zealand with a heavy heart.'

THE REV ALFRED BROWN, returning from a late afternoon walk down to the river with his wife, discovers five chiefs standing in what might be called, if the house were less primitive, its parlour. He asks the grave tattooed men, wearing mats and carrying their meres like badges of rank, what they want in his house, but they signal him to be silent. Their heads are bowed but they seem to be listening, not praying. Now they look up and speak to one another, nodding in agreement. And leave.

Brown follows them to the gate; asks what has been the purpose of their visit. The youngest of the chiefs turns back to explain that three nights ago the moon cast an unusual light and that consequently they must attend to portents. They have been listening to the insects which live in the reeds and which come to sing in the walls and roofs of raupo houses. If they sing on the roof, it means the house will be burned down when the enemy attack. If they sing on the walls, the house will survive.

The chief turns to go, and Brown has to pursue him through the gate to ask what portent they have discovered, explaining that he is not himself able to hear these creatures. The insects, he is told, are singing on his roof. When the raid comes his house will be destroyed.

It is said with such flat conviction, as if it were the result of a scientific analysis, Brown has to struggle with himself to achieve the disbelief his own belief requires. He decides he will not tell Mrs Brown, and then at once, on returning indoors, tells her, and is glad, because she laughs so freely and merrily at the natives' superstition it releases him from his uncharacteristic moment of fear.

FOR BROWN, 1836 was a bad year. He was proud of the mission station at Matamata, liked its location, believed they were making some progress with the Ngatihaua, and in the face of difficulties tried to keep a level head. On waking each day he rose, washed his face at the pump, said first his own fervent prayer of thanks for another day of life, and went out to look from his verandah eastward towards the Kaimais beyond which in good weather the light welled up like water, seeming to shine and magnify; and then, walking to the back of the house, looked south and west over the still shadowy plain where earthbound flax and toetoe steamed and reached heavenward, competing to be first to get fingers into the light as it came over and down from the hills.

Tarore, Ngakuku's daughter and their young house-keeper, was always up and doing before he was, and had usually to go across the compound to call John Flatt, who had yet to learn the art of waking early — a fact which caused Brown more concern than it warranted, and which consequently and absurdly, because he had sometimes to control unreasonable irritation while he waited for her return, could spoil his morning sense of peace and equanimity.

Thenceforward the day went according to God's plan, every hour and every minute filled with work, extending the station and carrying forward its purposes. Alfred Brown was energetic and cheerful. He tried to put behind him the horrors he had witnessed after Waharoa's attack on Maketu. It was not the facts of war and death which had disturbed him most deeply, though they had been horrible, but the sense of his own involvement — the knowledge that these were 'his' natives who had brought back baskets of human flesh, hearts on spikes, heads on poles, and slaves whom they might at any time despatch. Even Ngakuku, one of their best believers, had kept several prisoners whom he could probably be trusted never to kill but could not be persuaded to relinquish.

And although the little missionary group had returned to its established routine, running the shool, attending to the sick, teaching agricultural methods, preaching the Gospel, they all noticed a change. Even their most loyal natives now behaved differently. John Flatt was finding his morning classes, which had been so full of eagerness and lively intelligence, dull and lifeless; and at his Sunday services Brown found his parishioners often inattentive, and sometimes boisterous and ill-behaved. A respect for the mission, which must have come first from Waharoa, who had asked them to establish there, was diminishing. Its tapu held, but less securely. There were petty thefts. Waharoa had to declare that the mission's cabbages were, each of them, his head in order to prevent his people from stealing them. There were even occasional threats of violence; and although Brown did not believe they would be carried out, he knew that they represented the crossing of a barrier not crossed before.

What hung over the inhabitants of the pa, making them nervous, querulous and unpredictable, was the knowledge that the success of their raid on the Arawa at Maketu could only mean that they themselves would suffer an attack. And because a chief from the Thames area had been killed at Maketu, there was a strong chance that his tribe would now join with the Ngatihaua's enemies. So fortifications were being strengthened and extended. Rumours spread. Young men came to the classroom or to church bearing their carbines, unwilling to be parted from them.

One evening Arawa spies were seen in the swamps, but escaped. Next morning shots were heard and the word went up that a taua from Rotorua was close. All that day women and children flocked in from surrounding land to the protection of the pa; but nothing happened. Having sowed fear and disorder, the taua withdrew. As Waharoa had done, they were perhaps signalling an attack at one place when it was intended at another. Soon came news that they had attacked Waharoa's allies in Tauranga, had taken the pa there with great slaughter, and that two senior chiefs had been killed and eaten.

There was nothing the missionaries could do but carry on their work, and pray. As winter came on Brown took his wife and Mrs Chapman into the Waikato region where the wife of the catechist James Hamlin was about to give birth. But first, and for reasons not yet clear to Hugh and Jean-Anne, he despatched John Flatt to the mission house at Tauranga where he was to remain alone for five weeks. In his official letter to London of that period Flatt spoke of being 'alone, yet not alone whilst I could enjoy sweet communion with my Heavenly Father'; but his private journal recorded that he had found company among the local tribespeople, and had 'recovered old delights and pleasures while lying in the fern bathed in winter sunlight'. In both official and unoffocial records he mentioned that he had preached to the Tauranga natives from the St Luke Gospel Chapter 12, and quoted in particular, 'Beware ye of the leaven of the Pharisees, which is hypocrisy.'

Storms and Mrs Hamlin's health delayed the Browns in the Waikato, and when they returned it was to learn that

Waharoa had decided he would no longer wait for the Arawa to move against him, but would attack them in their heartland, Rotorua. He and his warriors had already left to take the fight to the enemy.

It was now August. Rains were heavy, rivers high. Or if the sun shone the nights were cold, and in the morning frost made the ground crunch underfoot. News came that Waharoa's raid had been successful — he had lured his enemies into an ambush, killing sixty; but in the skirmishing afterwards the Rotorua mission station had been burned down and the missionaries there robbed and beaten.

A few days later Waharoa and his warriors returned. It was not the boisterous triumph Brown had expected. They arrived, he recorded in his journal, 'dirty, squalid, wretched, bearing their wounded on their shoulders'. Waharoa, himself wounded, was more than ever obsessed with the attack that must come against his own pa, and for the first time suggested it might be best if the mission were closed. It was as if the war had caused the old chief to regress entirely into his native ways of living and thinking, and the mission he had wanted, and had got by a subtle mix of blandishment and threat, was now an irrelevance to him, an irritation, a distraction.

Still Brown wanted to keep the foothold they had established. With the Rev Wilson he visited Rotorua to see the damage done to the mission there, to consult with the brethren who had been harmed, and to talk peace. He returned through Tauranga, depresssed by the evidence he had seen everywhere that the tribes were living 'in suspicion and dread — hateful, and hating one another', and by the recognition of how little the Christian message had done to change anything. Added to that was the horror of having come upon the site of the feast that had followed Waharoa's victory, where sixty human carcases had been cut up, cooked and eaten. Bringing Flatt with him, Brown returned to Matamata, while Mrs Brown and Mrs Wilson were sent to the relative safety of Puriri.

By late September Brown was ready to give up the

Matamata station, at least for as long as the war went on. On 11 October John Flatt set off with a small group of natives and two horses to drive the mission herd over the mountain range to Tauranga. There is no report of the difficulties this must have entailed; only that he succeeded and was back at Matamata four days later. Two days after that James Hamlin, John Wilson and James Preece left the station for Puriri. On 18 October Flatt took the one remaining horse and led a group of twenty mission natives towards the Kaimais and the route to Tauranga, bearing valued church and household items that Brown did not want left to be pillaged after the station was closed. They were to camp below the Wairere Falls, and press on to Tauranga next day.

A BODY IN A BOX. Brown's. Not Brown's body. Brown's box. Much blood, dry now, or drying. Tacky, black blood. A brown body in Brown's box. Dead. Heartless. That's to say breast chopped open, ribs dragged apart, heart torn out. So a cavity — a big dark hole, a cage opened, the bar-beating bird gone, set free. Also, the back of the head removed.

How to cope? Shuffle. Heave. Turn away. Sob — or anyway gasp. Insuck of breath. So much noise. All around, this wailing and shrieking, tearing of hair, scratching of face . . .

A gentle hand, his own, as if it did not belong to him, reaching into the box, brushing the black, still-shiny hair back from the closed eyes. Stroking the bruised brow.

Brown had seen such things before. Why was this worse? Why so shaken — as if sky had darkened, ground trembled, earth opened, doubt crept in . . . As if the pillars, the tabernacles of light . . .

Because she was a Christian Innocent? Others such had died. Because she was beautiful? All souls may be beautiful in the eye of God. Because she had lived in their house and served them? Because she was Ngakuku's daughter? Because she was Tarore?

Yes, all of that; but more particularly because there had always been about her, even while she was still a child, before the disturbance of young womanhood came suddenly upon her, something Brown responded to almost in spite of himself, a sense of fun, but more than fun, a cleverness, something like wit that seemed to mock him, a quality that sparkled like the best morning light across the plains and that would therefore, and for as long as his life lasted, be confused in his mind with the landscape which was her tribal territory.

It was the box Brown's mind fixed upon — incidental, irrelevant. As if the whole present agitation of his mind and heart had its source there. It was his own box, had been packed with chasuble and surplice, crucifix and candle, framed pictures, household items, odds and ends, prized irrelevancies brought here to the world's end for the comfort of . . .

Things Henry Williams would tell him they should not have concerned themselves with. A missionary, Williams liked to say, should travel like a soldier, with no more than he can carry in his kit. Williams who travelled thus, but whose own houses and land were safe in the north . . .

They were valued things. All gone, tipped, stripped, robbed, removed. Everything taken. Also Flatt's tent, saddle, bridle, even his clothes, except two shirts, his horse, and a halter — and this box in which her father, returning to their campsite after their escape from the attack, had laid her ruined body. Tarore, her young heart gone, burned to the glory of Te Whiro, the back of her skull taken off, to be displayed, proof of success, of a kill . . .

Ngakuku, the father, inconsolable. No not inconsolable; anxious rather. Wanting to know would she go to Heaven — or to Reinga? It was a strange time to ask such a question. Brown tried to pull himself back from his own confusion, to meet the needs of the father who grieved. The Christian Maori.

Her gospel according to St Luke was gone, taken by her killers.

FIRST, AT SEVEN IN THE MORNING, had come three of the young men, mud-spattered, out of breath, distressed. Their camp below the Wairere Falls had been attacked before first light by a taua from Rotorua. They had been woken by the barking of their dogs, had heard the taua coming, had shouted to the others to wake, had run off into the bush, hidden. They had heard gunshots, shouting, screams, Parati's (Flatt's) voice, Tarore's, then silence. They had seen nothing of the others and had run back through the swamps, fearing they might be the sole survivors.

Brown lived now through two hours of restless agitation until Ngakuku arrived with three others, bearing Tarore's body which set up such a wild lamentation in the pa it was difficult still to discover what had happened. But in the afternoon came the remainder of the party, all except John Flatt. Flatt had found them in the bush and decided they should make their way back to the safety of their own pa while he would press on to Tauranga.

When the attack happened, Brown now learned, the native party had been in a raupo hut by the river, Flatt in his tent only a short distance away. They had run away into the bush and he had been left to confront the attackers, who had caught and murdered Tarore. They had stripped everything he had, and all the goods they were carrying — all except a horse, a halter and two shirts. It was the long-threatened utu for the stripping and burning of Mr Tapsell's store at Maketu. The attackers had danced their haka and left with their spoils, and with Tarore's heart.

TWO DAYS LATER, Tarore was buried at the pa. Again Ngakuku asked Brown would his daughter go to Heaven or Reinga. Brown assured him she would go to Heaven. She had received the Christian message. Everywhere she had carried with her that copy, stolen by her murderers, of the Gospel according to St Luke, in which it was recorded that Jesus had said to the one who believed, 'Verily I say unto thee, today shalt thou be with me in Paradise.' Why should Ngakuku continue to doubt?

It was because, the father explained, 'she has heard the

Gospel with her ears, and read it with Mother Brown, but I do not know whether she has received it in her heart.'

Brown was puzzled, then deeply moved when, over the open grave, Ngakuku spoke to the tribe. They had asked these Christian teachers to come among them, Ngakuku said, and now were driving them away by engaging in wars of revenge. God was punishing them for this. Let utu be set aside. Let peace be made. He, Ngakuku, forgave the murderers of his daughter. He would seek no revenge. The cycle of vengeance had to be broken.

Brown wept. Almost for the first time he felt it had been demonstrated conclusively that it was possible for the Christian message to penetrate, suffuse and irradiate the pagan heart.

Three days later, 23 October, it was Sunday, and Brown conducted his last service at what had been the Matamata station. Contrary to his hopes, it would never re-open.

JEAN-ANNE AND HUGH are meeting over lunch on the deck outside the Art Gallery café, their folders of notes and xeroxes on the table among plates and cups. They have gone over it so often — that turbulent year which preceded John Flatt's return to London — they feel they have a grip on it. But it has left them with unanswered questions.

There are two accounts by Flatt of the events of 19 October. One, a letter to the Rev Jowett of the Church Missionary Society in London, is written one week later, 26 October, and describes how Flatt and his party of about twenty made camp for the night at the Falls where there was a raupo house for the natives.

'My tent being fixed, supper prepared by the natives, horse made fast and provided with food, all before sunset, after supper I called them together to family prayer as usual. After singing an hymn with them I read part of the third chapter of St John's Gospel and concluded by a prayer, all in their own language.'

They then (he goes on) all retired for the night, he to his

tent, they to their raupo house. He slept heavily after the
exertions of the day, and was half-woken in the morning
before first light by the barking of the dogs and shouts from
the native house, after which everything happened with such
speed he was helpless to prevent it — the attack, the escape
of all the natives except Tarore, Tarore's murder, and the theft
of everything including his clothes.

Tarore, he writes, 'fell victim to their ferocity in front of
my tent. One of the enemy fired at her and she fell wounded
but did not cease crying until she was murdered with a small
axe. I saw one of the party chopping at her chest and learned
later that they had taken her heart.'

He calls it 'one of the most dreadful murders ever known
in this land'; and although (since such events were not
uncommon) this is an overstatement, Jean-Anne and Hugh
agree it is not only understandable; it is a measure of his
distress.

Why then, they ask one another, when Flatt gave his
evidence to the House of Lords a year or so later, did he
describe the attack, the escape of his natives, and the theft
of goods, but say not one word about Tarore's death?

They go back to eating, silenced by a question to which
they have been unable to think of a convincing answer.

Did he feel he was responsible? Jean-Anne asks. That he
ought to have saved her? That he had been cowardly?

But they have discussed this before. If that had been the
case, why would he have written a letter immediately after
the event, in which he recounted it in detail — distressed but
clearly without any feeling of failure on his part, or that he
could have done anything to save her?

Defeated by that puzzle they turn their minds to another
— one Jean-Anne has come upon only in the past few days.
It is something added to one of Thomas Chapman's letters
to the Church Missionary Society in London — a postscript
dated 15 March 1837.

'These despatches having been unavoidably delayed —
beg to observe that independent of the resolution affecting
Mr Flatt in common with the other single young men, there

are other reasons which induce the Committee to think Mr F's removal from the Mission a desirable step. From your letter of June 12 1834 Par. 7 we conceive that he was sent out to this land for the one specific object of forwarding the agricultural interests of the Mission, but you will find by a Resolution of the Northern District Committee that his services for the above object are not required. The Committee feels it their duty to state that while there is nothing that could lead them to doubt Mr Flatt's piety or the purity of his intentions in offering his services, they cannot recommend his return, not thinking him fitted for Catechetical duties —'

There, without a full-stop, with only a dash, the statement cuts off abruptly. The rest of the page has been removed from the record.

Hugh stares at the photocopy Jean-Anne has smoothed out in sunlight in front of them. Her elbow and upper arm touch his. He can see the slight curve of her pregnancy.

It gives him a strange sense of satisfaction that he, a direct descendant of the man who could never himself have seen these sentences or known that they had been written about him, should now be reading them — as if, so long afterwards, a wrong has been exposed.

But why should it be a wrong? Perhaps Flatt *was* unsuited. Yet if he was, neither Hugh nor Jean-Anne can detect where in him the failing lay. His letters are fluent. The evidence he gave later before the House of Lords was balanced, factual, sensible, reliable . . . .

They are silent again. Jean-Anne pours herself another cup of tea, and waves away a sparrow that is hopping across the table towards her plate.

Why, Hugh begins to ask, did Brown send Flatt to cool his heels alone for five weeks in Tauranga?

But Jean-Anne cuts across him with another thought. She is sure Flatt's difficulties with the Society, or the Society's with him, all go back to that question of the post he was sent out to fill and was then denied by the local Committee.

'He never gave up on it. He resented it — felt it as a wrong and a slight. Remember the letter where he points out that

Christ chose fishermen for disciples, not Oxford graduates? And there's something I didn't mention, Hugh. It's the letter written to London while he was alone in Tauranga. He tells them he preached to the natives using Luke 12 as his text. If he was there five weeks he must have used five texts, ten — probably more. Maybe one every day. Thirty-five texts. But he mentions just one — the chapter that begins "Beware ye the leaven of the Pharisees, which is hypocrisy", and goes on about there being "nothing covered that shall not be revealed; nothing hid that shall not be known." When we looked at what Chapman wrote about him just now — it was there on the table in the sun, and I thought of the third verse: "Whatsoever ye have spoken in darkness shall be heard in the light; and that which ye have spoken in the ear in closets shall be proclaimed upon the housetops." Maybe he knew they were whispering against him, and he was telling Jowett he knew it. And there's another point: Luke 12 is also the chapter with the parable about the man whose ground brought forth so plentifully he couldn't store all his harvest, and instead of serving the Lord he said he'd pull down his barns and build bigger ones to make himself richer. I just don't believe Flatt could have read that and not thought of Davis sitting up there in Waimate treating the mission farm as his own . . .'

She looks up to see how all this is being received. 'D'you think I'm being fanciful?'

Hugh shakes his head. 'While you were talking it occurred to me — he had to deliver in Maori. He chose Luke. D'you think he might have borrowed Tarore's Gospel?'

Jean-Anne smiles. 'It was her most prized possession. I think when he was sent away for five weeks she gave it to him to remember her by.'

BAREBACK ASTRIDE THE MISSION HACK, bruised, distressed, bewildered, weeping sometimes, jolted as the animal made its way down the track that zig-zagged through the forest trees, John Flatt found in his head and spoke aloud the Psalm he had never consciously memorised, and did not know he knew by heart.

> Hear my prayer, O Lord, and let my cry come unto thee.
> Hide not thy face from me in the day when I am in trouble; incline thine ear unto me: in the day when I call, answer me speedily.
> For my days are consumed like smoke, and my bones are burned as an hearth.
> My heart is smitten, and withered like grass; so that I forget to eat my bread.
> By reason of the voice of my groaning my bones cleave to my skin.
> I am like a pelican of the wilderness: I am like an owl of the desert.
> I watch, and am as a sparrow on the house top.
> Mine enemies reproach me all the day; and they that are mad against me are sworn against me.
> For I have eaten ashes like bread, and mingled my drink with weeping.
> Because of thine indignation and thy wrath: for thou hast lifted me up, and cast me down.
> My days are like a shadow that declineth; and I am withered like grass . . .

Again and again he said the verses over, speaking them sometimes into his horse's ear, holding the animal round the neck as it found its way down a steep incline; other times, as they ambled over a flat, sitting upright and speaking them up into the trees.

Then, perhaps by association, came a memory of the hymn he had learned in childhood during his years in Durham. With a fervour possible only because he was alone in a forest in a wild land, John Flatt, riding bareback, wearing nothing but the two shirts that were all the taua had left him, far from home and far from happy, lifted his voice and sang, 'My soul repeat His praise.'

PART
TWO

To James Grady and Ethel née Christianson, a son, Hugo Wolf. Did the notice in the *New Zealand Herald* say also 'A little brother for Aida'? Hugh doubts it. That wasn't the style of the early 1930s.

That had been just a year or two short of a century after his great-great-grandfather, becalmed off the Bay of Islands aboard the *Blackbird* with Colenso and the Wades, was brought ashore in a whaleboat by Frank Mangold's forebear Gilbert Mair and (as James Grady, Irishly surveying his wife's family saga liked to say) 'the whole grisly business got under way'.

To James and Ethel a son. Ten years later a war was raging across Europe and down through the Pacific, while the son's two selves rode Hugo up Wolf down, down Hugo up Wolf, with Linny on the old buggy along the clay road to Kaiwaka. Just half a century after that (and it didn't take long) he was back, driving with Hat over that same road to see Frank Mangold in his box lowered away to the taped strains of a Last Post in sight of the remembered-as-boy-climbable macrocarpa which now, broad and tall and lightning-blasted, was surely retiree-resistant, but would serve as shelter against the passing shower that put an end to his and Hilly's graveside conversation.

Hugo-and-Wolf had long since resolved into Hugh and reconstituted themselves as Hugh-and-Hat; and though the road to the churchyard, now tarsealed, was no wider and scarcely less winding than it had been when it bore the brunt of the buggy, the District Court judge's and her retired-librarian-husband's well-sprung vehicle rolled not at all, and their heads and bodies maintained, as they had done through so many years, a constant relation.

It had all (and all meant no less than the best part of a lifetime) happened too fast for Hugh, with too little opportunity for memory and reflection. What was it that had crowded out the detail, caused so much of the ink of memory to fade? Sixty was a terrible number — only ten (and ten was insignificant at this accelerating pace) short of the biblical allotment, the due span which, at depleted evening after a day of more concentrated work than he had ever done when in paid employment, his mood compelled him to see as a cruelly lovely bridge between Nothing and Nothing.

But there was for Hugh, had always been, the solace of history, the shapeliness of narrative, the comfort of retrospect, of the long look back. And why, this time, should the story not be his own, his family's, their singing whakapapa, the history of their blood —

> here in this far-pitched perilous hostile place
> this solitary hard-assaulted spot
> fixed at the friendless outer edge of space?

All those years ago it had been Frank Mangold who had directed him to the history of his own land at a time when all academic eyes seemed turned elsewhere, outward. Why now should he not narrow the local focus, bring it closer, so that it would include Frank himself, their common ancestors, their forebears' crossing paths, their dogs, their horses, their binder twine moustaches, the bees that had swarmed in their hair?

Early retirement from his post as librarian had not seemed retirement at all; not a sinking into inaction, but on the contrary a breaking of bonds, the transmogrifying of Zarathustra's Camel, bearer of burdens, into Zarathustra's Lion, who defeats 'Thou Shalt' and sets up in its place 'I will'. It had been an exercise in recovery, in self-discovery. That he should have had, unsolicited, the young Jean-Anne's offer of help, and her enthusiasm and energy as the task went forward, had been more than a lucky chance or a bonus; it had been a blessing.

These late-in-the-day thoughts are Hugh's. He is at his desk again. Again at his elbow, or still, there is the photograph of the grave of Tarore, 'whose Gospel according to St Luke brought Peace to the Tribes of Aotearoa'. Under it, or to one side, there is a long-ago love letter in green ink (and we will come to that). The sun is doing another of its abstracts, going down again behind the Waitakeres. Every day the same canvas. Every day a different picture. Every day at this time Hugh's recognition of a particular mode of beauty, like Strauss's Four Last Songs — the mode that gives pain; and with it this consequent threat of gloom and despondency, this sense of puzzlement, of a life, his own, leaking away. Orderly, yes; but shapeless, not grasped, not understood. If not unfulfilled then at least under-used — Mansfield's moth-clerk again, crying 'The shortness of life! . . . and that whole vast garden out there, undiscovered, unexplored.'

Only Hat, boundless Hattie with the gin bottle in one hand and the tonic in the other, her bench-face set aside at the door with umbrella, baguette, butterhead lettuce and bagful of legal documents, can help him over this early evening stile, and does. He is glad of her now. But when, except for that brief mad breakout in his late thirties, has he ever not been?

WHEN HE WAS A YOUNG MAN Hugh sometimes thought of himself as a radical. Or rather, he was given sometimes to radical thought, which occasionally, less often than such thoughts came to him, he spoke aloud. It was the residue of the Wolf-boy, carried into manhood, and it began, or his memory of its earliest instances begins, in 1951 with the waterfront dispute which racked, and very nearly wrecked, the country. Hugh was, or believed he was, on the side of the workers. Told of this, and of other and similar eructations of radicalism, his mother never argued; but he could see at once that she was not interested in the issue ('Five and tuppence an hour, Mother, that's all, but everyone knows they'd settle for four and tenpence') — only believed that it was his role as a young student to entertain such ideas, her notion of what it was to be 'a student' coming almost entirely from Russian novels. The example of Wagner, she believed, also sanctioned such behaviour, the Master having been in all kinds of political trouble when young, even to the extent of being driven into exile. And then there was Nietzsche, Wagner's friend, who had said 'one must have Chaos in one to give birth to a Dancing Star'. As for the strike (or lockout, as Hugh taught her to call it) — she refused to consider either its mundane details or the issue of democratic rights and freedoms which he told her was raised by the Government's response to it, but saw it only as an occasion for the release in her son of a special kind of energy that went with talent — something she welcomed as a sign that though he was surely not destined to give birth to a Dancing Star, he did at least possess a little of what she liked to call the Divine Spark.

Frustrated by his mother's lack of political seriousness, Hugh turned to his father (for whom business was booming) and received as always such a flood of words and ironies it was impossible to guess which side, workers or Government, James Grady favoured. The Prime Minister's passion and anxiety about communism made him smile. The anxiety and passion of the union leaders about the Prime Minister made him laugh. Best of all, because it made him laugh louder and longer, was the Leader of the Opposition's statement that on the matter of the waterfront dispute he was 'neither for nor against'.

'Spoken like a true Irishman,' James Grady said, pouring himself a whisky. And to his son's objection that the Leader of the Opposition was not Irish any more than New Zealand was Ireland he offered, not an answer, but the reply, 'When a man can't afford to speak his mind, a nation's politics has come of age' — followed by a playful punch on the arm and another burst of laughter.

On another occasion when Hugh, feeling an eruption of

his old Wolf-self, accused his father of political evasion and cowardice, James Grady replied, 'Boy, it wasn't opinion that taught me to tie my shoelaces one-handed. It was necessity. But if you took time to look you'd notice it's the left hand I use, the better one having been shot into paralysis.'

Hat was not on the scene during that crucial year. And when she did come into Hugh's life, though she didn't encourage him in radicalism, she was careful in the way she contended with it, seeing his arguments always as deserving of the respect due to the case for the prosecution, but by no means the end of the matter. Hattie had been a lawyer at heart even before her mind was trained to it — a lawyer, James Grady liked to say when he got to know her, in her mother's womb and her father's pay packet. More than that, as a lawyer she was temperamentally neither prosecutor nor defence counsel, but always judge, always summing up, always weighing this against that, recognising that there were two sides to the question, heads and tails, pros and cons, on the one hand and on the other. She was a judge long before she became one, before it seemed possible for a woman to occupy that exalted place; and on every passionate issue which Hugh, or the pale and ill-fed Wolf-self who managed to persist in him, put before her, she would weigh up and sum up, but never give the verdict. That was not her task. The verdict lay with the jury of history, and it was always out.

Among friends and colleagues Hugh was known as a mild man, guessed to be (although he didn't often declare himself) as moderate in thought as in dress and manner, who nevertheless could sometimes, usually when heading for the tea room door, or as a way of ending a desultory tutorial, say surprisingly sharp and challenging things.

It was Vietnam which changed all that. By now Hugh and Hat had two children, schoolboys Richard and John, and Hat, who had never given up the law but had practised part-time, was taking more and more work more and more successfully, for the firm in which at the time of her marriage her father had bought her a share. Hugh was finding his work as librarian at the Teachers' College pleasant but untaxing, and his best energies were going into late-afternoon tutorials he was employed to do in the university's History Department. If appearances told the whole story (and Hugh sometimes asked the mirror whether they did) Wolf was dead.

But this was the late 1960s, and there was something in the air as tangible and unspecific as one of those shifts in the weather that you feel before you bring them to consciousness. Everywhere you looked there was hair, more and more of it. There were flowers, and feet, and sweat-bands, and peace badges, and sandals, and smoke clouds with the peculiar and soon-to-be-familiar aroma of marijuana. Student girls (they were still 'girls' then, only later 'women') scrabbling in their little woven bags for dog-eared scrappy notes and pencil stubs, spilled, not lipsticks but plastic packets with little nobbles and a system of arrows following the days of the month. Hugh, whose wife's contraceptive was still the diaphragm, once picked one up, not knowing what it was, and looked at it. Handing it to the student who had dropped it he received such an odd questioning smile, the incident stuck in his mind.

One day a letter appeared in the *Herald*. It was about the American action in Vietnam and the prospect of a further contribution of New Zealand troops. It hit hard, in short sharp sentences. It was signed H. W. Grady. That evening a young woman lingered behind after his tutorial, ostensibly to sort out her notes, but in fact to ask whether he had written the letter, and to tell him that she had read it, that it had taken her by surprise, and that . . .

'So you agree?' Hugh asked when she fell silent.

'Fuck yes,' came the reply.

Hugh was more surprised by that than she had been by his letter. He didn't recall ever having heard that word in the mouth of a young woman, certainly not one who was almost unknown to him. But more memorable than Hugo's mild shock was the instant certainty which came with it, that Wolf had risen from the dead — an eruption so sudden, so rough, it was as if a larger, bolder person had tried to elbow him out of the way.

Was it then or earlier that Hugh recognised something about himself that had happened unawares? 'The times they are a-changin', Bob Dylan sang, illustrating the audile aspect of this social revolution by the tuneless gravel in which he celebrated it. Visually they were also 'a-changin'. University lecturers, all but a few determined old professors, had stopped wearing gowns. There were mini-skirts. There were also those big overblown dresses that went all the way to the floor. Bras, if they weren't all being burned, were becoming less common, or somehow less effective in concealing nipples. Ties no longer seemed compulsory, or even desirable. Barbers were going out of business. One morning, naked in the bathroom, Hugh put his head back and for the first time in his life felt his own hair touch his spine between his shoulder-blades. New, shocking, unexpected, lovely even — to a man who had grown up in a sporting and warrior nation where Shortbackandsides was the official Church, it felt like the kiss of History.

HER NAME WAS LYDIA LAWRENCE. Lid, he called her, so there were now Hat and Lid, names which the peculiar and irrepressible joke part of his mind could tell itself were interchangeable. She called him Wolf often, and Cub sometimes, and Whistle; and sometimes Hugs, and just occasionally Huge. She told him also now and then, and just to put him in his place when the pleasure she took in his mind and body threatened to make him overweening, that theirs was the affair of the Lid and the Super Ego.

She came first to ask him about a mark he had given an essay she had written on the subject of the causes of what were still in those days called the Maori Wars. He was not the lecturer, only her tutor, and so had not set the essay; and what she suggested was that his comments were not so much a criticism of what she had written as of the topic. She was right, of course — he recognised that at once, acknowledged that he had never been happy with historical studies that talked of causes, admitted that she was not to blame for that, spoke of Wittgenstein and 'contingency' by way of excuse, and offered to read the essay again. The conversation was reasonable, the tone level, the statements on either side lucid, unhurried. She didn't attack, neither did he defend. Why this perfect detachment, when he found her at once so peculiarly attractive?

It was, he knew, (or knew for himself and believed he knew for her) because neither of them cared at all about the essay or the mark he had given it. That was only an occasion, an excuse for them to be in the same room together, talking. It was the ball with which they were playing a kind of sexual tennis, and almost any ball would have served as well.

It was Wolf who knew this, but Hugo refused to believe it, or anyway to act on it.

While they talked she seemed in some curious way to float before him, her head tilted up, her eyes seldom meeting his but fixed somewhere above and away to the right, her mouth smiling slightly, her voice playing tunes that bore no exact relation to the words being said. It was her voice he fell in love with first.

She left the essay and departed. At least he knew she would be back.

So began a long slow pregnant emptiness, in which she demonstrated her interest in him, her more-than-interest, and he, encouraging it, reciprocating, did nothing. She visited him often at the office he used as university tutor, and once or twice at the Teachers' College library; and when she found her invention of reasons for these visits becoming less and less plausible, told him frankly, coming very close now to declaring herself, that she was 'running out of pretexts'. He was grateful for that. It gave him the opportunity to say that he hoped she would come just to talk, because he always enjoyed seeing her and liked to think they were not just student and tutor, but friends.

All of this was true, but it was a truth that concealed the truth. He felt her impatience, and shared it, yet remained unwilling or unable to act, and unable to credit himself either with fidelity or self-denial. It was, he knew, neither concern at the pain he might give Hat, nor at the harm he might do to Lid, that held him back, but simply timidity.

Lydia had a little basement flat at the back of one of the houses on Princes Street looking over Albert Park, and she invited him to visit her there. He went, often. She made him Chinese tea, did the tarot cards for him, read his palm, showed him the poems she was writing, told him about her not entirely satisfactory family and her unsatisfactory boy-friends, one of them, a law student called Bernie, so much in love with her, so insistent, she said sometimes she thought of 'just letting go and being swept along on the flood'.

She showed him where the key to the flat was hidden, and invited him to come in if he called and she wasn't there, make himself tea, make himself at home.

All this time Hugh Grady was getting more and more deeply involved in the protest against the war in Vietnam. His feeling of political outrage was not new — he had felt it first in 1951, and often since; but he had never before felt he was free to express it, and he now gave vent to it in letters to newspapers, articles in journals, speeches at teach-ins and demonstrations. The feel of hair against his spine grew more familiar, though not less surprising nor less pleasurable. He grew a bushy beard. Hat didn't disapprove, acknowledged that he had a case and that he made it well, was glad only that she had decided, when they married, that she would practise as Harriet Enverson, a name which had sounded then more professional, nicer than Grady, and which meant now that she was not too closely or automatically associated with the radical views her husband was putting about.

One day when Hugh called on his little student friend he found her in bed. She said she wasn't ill, just sad. He sat beside the bed and they talked. Beside a reading lamp on the bedside table he could see the small framed photograph which out of the corner of his eye he noticed she always turned faced down when he came into this room, but which he knew was of Bernie, the student who wanted to marry her.

It gave him feelings of longing and of self-reproach. Soon she would 'just let go' and he would lose her by default. Wolf could rail on for ever; it would be always Hugo who made the rules.

When he looked at his watch, feeling defeated within himself, thinking perhaps he ought to go, she said, in that floating voice, her eyes looking away over his shoulder, 'Hughie, aren't you ever going to want to fuck me?'

It was another shock, and it brought a swift response. He was animated, lyrical. He wanted, had wanted, would want. She was cheerful now, eager, making room for him in the big bed. And then, seeing him hesitate, recognising shyness, she said she would go to the bathroom and that he should get into bed. While she was gone he took off his clothes and climbed in under the sheet. When she returned she was naked — pale, pink-nippled, golden-pubed, and beautiful.

Every dog must have his day, and this day, this year, was to be the Wolf dog's.

TO FUCK IS TO BE IN TIME. To keep time. To beat time, meaning to defeat it. It is to be in the world, the now-and-for-ever. To be in the all-there-has-ever-been, that brought you to being, and the all-there-ever-will-be, on towards the end-of-the-ever, if there is to be an end. It is to be in the only eternity, the one of here and now, the touch and taste of it, the action. It is to be at one with the world.

Out there are the green stalks, the insect wings catching light, the rain falling, rivers flowing. Out there are the desert winds, rock-breaking suns; the rats and the reptiles. The birds, fish, mammals. The airs breathed and dispelled. Out there is our true face in the mirror, a blue and white planet, magic, alive, our god-creating world-self which no god can correctly pronounce or convincingly lay claim to. And in here are the two bodies keeping it alive, catching its common tune, its syntax and rhythm, repeating the one long wordless and sacred text doubly hidden in the helix.

Hugh had known, still knew, would go on knowing this

with Hat. Why should he need to know it in another place? There was no answer to that, none, anyway, that didn't sound like sports-talk or special pleading. No why. No causes. He could only find it in himself, by way of a helpless stumble towards an explanation which failed to explain, to say that Middle Age had been coming upon him, coming early, and that the little pale student with the two-tone voice in the big bed not only set it back. She killed it dead. His body would grow old, if good luck should permit him enough of life, before it died. But in himself he would never again be Middle Aged. He would never be Elderly. Never grow Old. That was her inexplicable gift. (A gift, Hat would ask, or a curse? Would he never grow *up*?)

What gift if any he made to Lid in return he didn't know. He could not even have faith that there was one; only hope that there was, because for all Hat's scorn, and his acceptance that he deserved it, still he felt the debt as real, one he would like to think had been paid, but which could not be paid by any purchase, any gift, any act of will.

ON HIS DESK IN THE FADING LIGHT beside the photograph of Tarore's grave lies Lid's long-ago letter in green ink. He reads some of its sentences, only glancing at it, knowing it almost by heart.

'Yesterday I talked about Mind and Soul, but there are also a few things like VANITY and CHILDHOOD and VAGINA and MEMORIES and RUSHINGHUGS and TREE-LOVE. You touched them all. So next time I breeze into your office and talk about the first thing that comes to mind and all but ignore the controlled pain your face fails to hide, just remember that on a Thursday in September in a room scented with freesias a girl would have made love to you until she died. Someone told me I should read Proust. Would that help? Somewhere there has to be compensation for fighting continuous losing battles against ubiquitous invisible irony.'

Ubiquitous invisible irony? Where had she learned such talk? In what chamber of her twenty-year self had such knowledge been uncovered? And if he, Wolf or Cub or Whistle, he Hugs or Huge, had been the key, the means of access to such instinctive knowledge so instantly translated (almost, it seemed, before it was understood) into fluent phrase and sequent sentence, how then could she ever be expected to let go? How could he let go himself, when she was the one who had taught him the power he possessed? It was as if, a blind man, he had discovered he was also magician, water diviner, midwife to the birth of Soul.

And under her letter in green ink, because Hugh has been digging through his files lately, recovering his past, there is the one written from her parents' home (with the name of the house, 'Berescourt', printed at the top) in which she tells of watching a television programme about Scott and Zelda Fitzgerald's 'Love of the Century' which ended in disaster. 'And I think we have a Love of the Century,' she writes, 'but it wouldn't end in disaster because we'd work as hard at being boring as at being interesting.'

And under the 'Berescourt' letter lies the note on yellow paper, the brave one (but how long could bravery be made to last?) that must have come later, after Hat had blacked his eye and the game seemed to be up, the end in sight, the writing on the wall: 'I want to want nothing more than we have. I want you to want nothing more. I want us to be true — but to something else, not each other. To anything — *for* each other. Sometimes I see clearly that it is not what you do for me that counts, nor what you do for your wife and children, but what you do for IT — the Fat Lady. And I respect your Fat Lady, whoever she may be, as you so beautifully respect mine.'

I *want* to want nothing more. Yes, but . . .

HOW LONG DID IT LAST? A quarter of a century later Hugh Grady is unsure. It lasted for the blink of an eye of course, and of course for eternity. But not to be lyrical, he thinks certainly more than six months, probably less than a year. By which time Hat had made the unwelcome discovery.

But it was not quite a discovery — more like a confession, though not that either. Since his second student year Hugh had shared everything with Hat. Not to share something so momentous as his affair with Lid, though clearly necessary and prudent, flouted everything in his life up to that moment. He was not aware of it, it was not by any act of will or policy, but he recognised later that he had done all he could to make Hat know what was happening. There must have been some mad unrealistic hope, or dream, that he and she would talk about it, accept it, even be glad of it. What he must have been looking for was permission.

But Hat remained blind to every piece of evidence, deaf to every hint. Was she, too, unconsciously shutting out what she half-guessed he wanted to tell her? He didn't, and doesn't, know. Only that when she did discover, when something was said or seen which was so blatant she could not ignore it, and when he confirmed that he was having a love affair with a student, Hat's response was quite different from any he, or anyone who knew her, might have expected. There was no weighing up, no reasonableness, no on the one hand but on the other, no heads and tails, pros and cons, two sides to every argument. It was not the judge who dealt with this information, nor the skilled lawyer, but another, deeper, more primitive and passionate Hat, one he had never met before.

He no longer remembers what led up to the revelation, only that they were in the car, backing down the drive, having left the boys with a babysitter. Hat was driving. It was dark. Hugh still remembers the lights shining on the trees that lined the quiet suburban street. The revealing exchange continued as they began to pull away from the house. At the moment when there was no doubt about what Hugh was confessing, Hat put her foot down. The big car accelerated away, and then as suddenly she hit the brakes. Hugh can't have been wearing a seat-belt, because he was thrown against the windscreen. While he was recovering Hat reached across, opened the door on his side, told him to get out, and when he turned to protest, punched him in the eye, hard. He reeled sideways from this second blow to his face. When he turned again towards her she was bent forward, her brow resting against the wheel. 'Get out of the car,' she repeated, without looking at him. He got out, tripped and fell to the road, while she drove away, the off-side door swinging. The car slowed while she pulled it shut, then accelerated away.

He scrambled to his feet. One knee was twisted. He was at the corner of an alley that came to a dead end at the slopes of Mt Eden. He limped along it, clambered over a fence and then, as if his long-lapsed Catholic Grady genes were demanding an act of contrition, painfully crawl-climbed the steep four or five hundred feet to the summit.

Up there he sat looking at the stars and at the lights of the city, feeling sorry for Hat, for Lid, for himself. It was the bees again. He had reached for something blindly, and out had come the swarm, pursuing him across the landscape of his dream. Logically the next step would be that he should go to Lid, tell her what had happened, have her soothe him and bathe his wounds, and move in with her. Ahead would lie a new life, glittering, clever, sexy, artistic, romantic. What he discovered, consulting himself under those cold heaven-lights, was that such a future was impossible. Imaginable, yes. Conceivable. But simply denied by fate. There was not even a dispute over it between Hugo and Wolf, both of whom had been battered into silence. Sitting at the top of Mt Eden he seemed to discover that he was now truly and indelibly Hugh, one and only, and married to Hat. That was how it had been, was, and would remain.

It was two or three in the morning when Hugh, one eye half-closed and shadowy, his twisted knee wearing a surgical bandage, sat with his wife over mugs of strong tea in their kitchen and talked about Europe.

HAT'S PLAN WAS SIMPLE. A year ago Charlotte Christianson, Hugh's grandmother, had died. Her money and shares had been left to her daughter, her house to Hugh and his sister Aida. The property had been put on the market and he had just received his half-share of the sale. Now he and Hat would use the money to finance a trip to the northern hemisphere. It would be their first. It would be fun to plan, educative for the boys, better taken now than after they began secondary school. It would give Lydia time to get over the affair, and get the Hugh Gradys together again, as a couple and as a family.

He would take unpaid leave — six months, nine months, a year even — from the library; and if his employers baulked at that, he would resign (these were still the affluent years) and find himself a new post when they returned. Meanwhile Hat's interest in the law firm together, perhaps, with rent from their house, would continue to return them a modest income.

Hugh's eye ached and his head throbbed. He agreed, but sadly, half-heartedly. He was too tired to think, too sore to feel pleasure at the prospect of foreign travel, too pained by the image of a pale girl with strong cheekbones, beautiful eyes, a Roman nose, and an upper lip . . .

It was the memory of that lip which brought tears — the sensation of it, still vividly remembered, when he had first kissed her; and the slyly charming way it could smile, the witty things it could be made to say when it joined forces not only with lower lip, tongue and larynx, but with eyes, with brain, with heart.

He pretended the tears came only from the smarting of his wounds, and from the upset and violence of their quarrel. Next day, he assured Hat, he would visit Lydia Lawrence and tell her their affair was at an end.

THERE WAS A CARD Hat played which helped her win Hugh over more nearly wholeheartedly to the idea of travel in Europe. He called it, or anyway thought of it as, her Swedish card, and it was a strong one.

In her widowhood Charlotte Christianson had acknowledged that her late husband Carl had been strangely silent about his family in Sweden. To Ethel Elena it seemed there could only be one secret, one cloud hanging over her father's past to explain the fact that there was no person in his home

113

country he wrote to, and only one, the woman he called his foster-mother, he ever spoke of. She believed he had been 'illegitimate', 'born out of wedlock', a 'bastard' (already, in the late 1960s, the old terms had begun to seem unserviceable) — that Carl Christianson had been the child of unmarried parents. Why else should there be, among the papers sent back to New Zealand from Noumea where he had died, a passport, his New Zealand naturalisation papers, his certificate as a Master Mariner, his death certificate, but no certificate of birth?

There was a story her father had told her which remained with her like a scene from a movie. Carl had been born in Helsingborg in 1871, and his foster-mother, Amalia Becker, had been a poor widow with three children, living somewhere close to that town on the southern coast of Sweden. In his earliest years Carl had been visited at intervals by a woman who came in a carriage wearing furs and bearing presents. She would take him with her for a drive in the carriage or to visit shops. When he was five or six years old he decided, perhaps because his foster brothers and sister suggested it, that this woman was his mother, and he began to feel something other than pleasure at her visits — a mixture of loyalty to the widow Becker, resentment that she to whom he was emotionally attached was not his real mother, and at the same time a kind of puzzlement that this rich woman, if he was her child, should leave him in poverty. He began to notice too that she spoke differently, in what he would later know to be an educated middle-class accent, while his was the accent of the herring fishers.

So he became sullen, uncooperative, went with her protesting that he did not want to go, and refused to speak to her. He saw that this made her sad and was half glad of it, though it also made him unhappy. So many years later Carl had not been able to say how long those visits had continued. He knew only that in the end the woman must have begun to dislike the stubborn boy who would not speak. She stopped coming. He regretted that, but too late, and never saw her again.

At eighteen he ran away to sea to avoid service in the Swedish army, and perhaps to leave behind him the pains of his growing up. He never returned nor wanted to, but as he grew older and more forgiving, spoke of Sweden with nostalgia and even with pride.

It was after her mother's death that Ethel Grady began writing to Sweden in an attempt to discover the truth. After a long delay had come a letter to say that there was a sealed envelope in the Maria parish of the city of Helsingborg, and that if she should send documents establishing that she was the late Carl Christianson's daughter, and sign the enclosed letter applying to the Crown for permission to have it opened, the information would be duly conveyed to her.

All this had been done, the letter signed and returned, and Ethel Elena was every day expecting a reply.

All of which, Hat noticed, had engaged Hugh's interest and imagination, even at a time when, she now knew, he had found a new and absorbing horizontal hobby in a student flat looking over Albert Park.

So Hat talked not just of England but of Europe; not just of Europe but of Sweden; not just of Sweden but of Helsingborg. Why should their stay not include a northern pilgrimage that would give it focus?

THE DAY AFTER THE CONFESSION of his infidelity Hugh told Lid what had happened and what the consequences were to be. He rang first, to warn her, and then called at her flat. She kissed him at the door, sat him down, touched his blackened eye, listened, conceded, understood, agreed. They must not . . . It was all . . . They could never . . . It could only . . . They would always . . . It was not . . . It would never . . .

This was signing-off time, renunciation time, time for self-abnegation and self-denial. Words like Marriage, and Children, and Wife, and Family, were spoken, understood and accepted. There was so much beauty in this moment of saying goodbye for ever — goodbye not to love, but to the one loved — it felt, and therefore it was, all of it, every word and gesture, every tear and sigh, perfectly true and honest and genuine, on his part and on hers.

'Never' was the operative word — a dangerous one, because there is always the question, 'Never, yes — but after what point in time?' 'Never, never, never, never, never,' howls King Lear; and then, 'Pray you, undo this button.'

Hugh's were not buttons. This was the late 1960s and trouser flies were already zippered. But the place of entry was the same, and denial was an aphrodisiac. Not that any such help was needed; but no Puritans breaking the cast-iron bonds of their code ever fucked with more fervour than Liddy and Wolf that day — that day and the day after, and on towards the time when a ship would carry him away from her into northern waters.

None of this was disclosed. It was all secret. Every visit was only to say goodbye; every fuck was their last.

And all this time maps and timetables were being studied, plans became more precise, dates were chosen, bookings made. Somewhere across the world a white ship, once American, now, in its second incarnation, Greek, renamed *Ellenis*, was cruising south and east towards Auckland. As it passed through the Suez Canal, Lid was sitting with Hugh in his car looking out into the night from the Mission Bay waterfront, seeing North Head and Rangitoto through tears. As it swished across the Indian Ocean they were admiring what their bodies were doing to one another in a mirror. As it heaved and shuddered eastward through the Great Australian Bight, she was writing in her diary that she knew the end would not be the End, though what lay beyond the end was obscure to her. While it shone white at Piermont Wharf in the Sydney sun he was driving her north to Orewa where they walked along the beach, hand in hand, and talked about Time and Circumstance, Cause and Contingency. And in the terrible last seventy-two hours while it crossed the Tasman Sea, Hugh managed to have need to go to town two and three times each day, to the travel agent, the bank, the passport office, the packing firm, the bank again, the post office — the occasions were never-ending, and each meant another call at her flat, another wild flurry of tears and sex and sex and tears — until the time came when, as if out of a complete blackout of sense and memory, Hugh Grady found himself at the rail of the white ocean liner, Hat beside him, Richard and John on either side, the hooters going, the tugs working, the coloured streamers stretching and breaking, friends and relations waving and calling in the crowd down there on the wharf. And as his eye roamed over the crowd, there she was, his hidden Lydia looking out from under a big straw hat, seeing his eyes light on her, laughing at his surprise. Her presence was a secret, a promise — though of what, or whether it was something he should want, he no longer knew.

How could they bear to be parted? There was something his mother told him around that time which not only in substance but in the tone of floating innuendo with which it was delivered seemed so like a piece of secret helpful advice it was difficult for him to disbelieve what in fact he found unbelievable — that she knew precisely his predicament and was offering surreptitious assistance. The random fact so casually let go into the light airs of their conversation was that Hugo Wolf's great love affair with the married Melanie Kochert had had to be conducted by letter, sometimes for quite long periods, while he was travelling, as he so often did, away from Vienna; and that this was achieved by the use of poste restante addresses.

Why, Hugh had asked himself, should Hat's great efficiency in mapping out every stage of their journey, leaving nothing to chance, not be used to advantage? Accordingly, on a wall over Lid's bed they had pinned a map of the British Isles and Europe, and on it inked in beside major stopping places the dates when the Grady family would be there. In each place, Lid promised, a letter would be waiting for him poste restante at the central post office. He in his turn would write to her as he found time and freedom to do it. That way their communication would continue.

As for the future — well, of course, there was none, they

knew and accepted that. The break would have to come —
but not yet.

Not yet. Not quite. Not ever?

SIX

C APES OF GOOD HOPE AND HORN. Passage. Circumnaviga-
tion. Antipodes. The World. 'The great Globe itself, yea
all which it . . .'

Encompass. Compass and sextant. The Trades. The Spice
Islands. The Pacific. The Roaring Forties.

Passage.

Hugh Grady and Jean-Anne Devantier have been turning
over world maps and atlases. She is visiting. He has taken out
a metal box marked EXPORT which as a child he liked to look
through when he visited his grandmother's house, and
which, years later when his mother died, he found among
her things. There is a postcard with soft grey velvety leaves
fixed to it, one of the leaves painted with a picture of ships
— five sailing ships and one steamer with red funnel. Along
the bottom of the card in fine clear lettering Carl
Christianson has written 'Handpainted Silverleaf from Table
Mountain, Capetown, March 1891'. He would have been just
twenty that year; the New Zealand woman he was to marry,
Charlotte Flatt, only ten. Already using English; and not
heading for New Zealand, or not directly (in which case the
route would have been Suez) — so probably sailing on an
English ship, trading down the African coast.

Hugh and Jean-Anne look at it together. Her pale fingers
touch the soft grain of the leaf on its unpainted side.

Now Hugh looks again at the world map, thinking not
of grandfather Carl but of great-great-grandfather John.
Before Suez and Panama there were two barriers across
Europe's ocean path to Australasia — Africa one way, South

America the other. The Trades were no use because they blew you south and west into the blind alley of the Caribbean, like fish into a net. So you sailed south down the coast of Africa and caught the ocean equivalent of an express-train — the Roaring Forties that drove eastward along the southernmost reaches of the Indian Ocean, blasted you along the south coast of Australia and on, all the way to New Zealand, if that was what you should want.

Returning home you caught it again, the same racketing wind-express, ever eastward and tacking still further south until, as John Flatt said in his letter of regret at having to leave New Zealand, you were 'treading the frozen decks' somewhere between a north-pointing finger of the Antarctic continent and the south-pointing finger of southernmost South America that was Cape Horn.

They are trying, Hugh and Jean-Anne, to keep their minds on matters of shipping, rites of passage, but they are distracted for a moment by more personal things in Master Mariner Carl Christianson's metal box. Among faded and torn photographs of ships and wrecks, islands and palm trees and lagoons, white men in their white suits and white topees with black men in their black skins, there are two stiff-backed portraits, both taken in Helsingborg, one at the studio of Frans E. Arvidsson, the other at the Fotografisk Atelier of Hanna Forthmeiir. One shows a woman seated, wearing what looks like a peasant's best clothes, entirely plain, and with a white mob-cap. She might be any age from thirty to fifty. She is one of those for whom poverty determines that beauty and youth are gone with their twenties. On the back Hugh's mother has written, 'Amalia Becker, my father Carl Christianson's foster-mother'. The other photograph is of a woman standing with one delicate hand resting on the back of an elaborately carved chair. Her dress is elegant, high on the neck where there is a velvet bow and silver brooch, and tight at the waist. Her hair is done in two soft curls over the brow. She too might be anything from thirty to fifty, but for the opposite reason that she belongs to a class able to preserve youth and beauty all the way to the brink of old age. There is nothing to indicate who this woman is, but Hugh believes it must be a portrait of Carl Christianson's mother given him by his foster-mother when he left Sweden for ever.

Their minds return to shipping, prevailing winds, trade routes; in particular to one ship which left New Zealand in May 1837, rounded the Horn, stopped for a time at Rio de Janeiro, and reached London in early October, bearing a still-young man of humble, or at best modest, antecedents who had sailed (they are trying once again to take a grip on him) to those southern oceans to take up an appointment at Waimate as Missionary Agriculturalist and who, having suffered the disappointment of finding himself denied that post, had travelled through strange and sometimes hostile territory on foot, on horseback, by canoe, by small sailboat; had learned to survive in forests and among cannibals whose language he had taught himself to understand and to speak; and who had been witness to war and death, and to one death the memory of which he carried home with him like a throbbing wound. A young man who, it seems, through all of that adventure had not relinquished for a moment his sense that those at whose behest he laboured had done him an injustice. It was something that must have been in his mind often in the long weary months of the homeward beat.

But in Hugh's mind, while they look at maps and discuss winds and currents, there is also a white ship which sailed out of Auckland towards the end of the 1960s, heaved and shuddered north through rough weather accompanied for a time by great gliders almost too big to be thought of as birds, anchored off Pitcairn, sailed into the calm of the middle latitudes, passed by means of lift-locks through the Panamanian jungle, threaded its way (with comfort stops) through the islands of the Caribbean and then north to New York, and sailed finally five mostly turbulent days across the Atlantic to London, taking for the whole journey four and a half weeks — a week for each month John Flatt's sailing ship, the *Pyramus*, had taken 130 years before to arrive at the same place.

He and Jean-Anne speak of that too. He points out on

their maps the route he took with Hat and the boys. He says nothing of his student-friend left behind on the streamer-strewn wharf, nor of the letters she sent winging ahead of him to wait post-restante in England and Europe.

Jean-Anne is interested. She has travelled to Europe, but only once, and by air — just twenty-four hours flying time. Hugh's journey seems remote to her — almost as old-fashioned as those of Carl Christianson or of John Flatt. It happened, after all, before she was born, and to her that seems a very long time ago.

BUT THEY MUST TRY TO FOCUS more closely on their task — or so they say to one another, and then laugh and ask why. They enjoy this work for its own sake, in its own time. There is no particular aim or object, no deadline. Is there? They can think of none. Nevertheless . . .

Jean-Anne has managed to transcribe some parts of Flatt's diary of his voyage home. Much is water-damaged, illegible. Some, it seems, may have been deliberately erased — scored over, pages torn out. She doesn't guarantee every word of her transcription but believes most of it is correct.

She has established that after the closure of the Matamata mission station and the murder of Tarore, Flatt remained at Tauranga until 8 February 1837 when he boarded the *Columbine*, sailed to Puriri, then to Fairburn's station at Maraetai, leaving there on 23 February and arriving two days later at the Bay of Islands, where he found that the Rev Samuel Marsden was making what would prove to be his last visit to New Zealand.

The legible fragments of the diary continue:
'7 May: At sea out of Hokianga Harbour. Goodbye New Zealand! Or rather (in spite of all, it is my fervent hope) au revoir! The beautiful coast, like most things, alas, more beautiful, better appreciated, in loss. Some tears at the rail when the others had gone below. It has all been more — both better and worse — than I could have imagined when I set forth. My cabin is the one occupied by the Rev Marsden when this ship, the *Pyramus*, brought him from Sydney.

'10 May: Well pleased with my companions, the Rev Wilkinson and Mrs Wilkinson from New South Wales, and two children. Little Agnes shy and a sweet child. Young Freddie reminds me of the Fairburn boy I liked so well at Puriri — keen, excitable, eager to talk and to learn. Also of little Marsh Brown. Our Captain, Mr Livesay, a bluff forthright even-tempered man.

'11 May: Porpoises in the bow wave. I am half-reminded of a biblical text. Spend most of a morning hunting for it without success.

'21 May: The albatrosses which sailed with us for many days, never seeming even once to beat their wings but only to glide in our wake, have left us. Two days ago two were caught by the sailors on long lines. They use the skin from their webbed feet for tobacco pouches, and the meat for excellent pies.

'22 May: The birds are gone but my sadness is not, or not entirely, though I combat it to good purpose with prayer and inner conversation.

'25 May: On deck at night. Never forget the stars in these regions, their brightness, how the Southern Cross seems to lean forward out of the heavens, and how the Milky Way streams back into infinity.

'28 May: Service in the saloon with Mr Wilkinson. 16 Chapter of St Mark.

'29 May: One bird blown far from land, exhausted, recovering on the deck. A text from Nature.

'30 May: Learning Greek of Mr W as weather permits.

'2 June: Greek verbs in cabin and saloon with Mr W abandoned as ship heaves and groans in rising gale. Captain Livesay warns of storm. Mrs W ill.

'3 June: Morning Lat 51 S Long 150 W. Most serious gale. Prayer for salvation. Despise my own fear and go with trembling knees to walk on deck. Sails dropped. Ship tossing as if nothing can save it. Wind screaming in the rigging. I am ordered below.

'4 June: Afternoon. After 24 hours the wind at last abating. Capt Livesay says the worst is over. The huge waves still lift as if each is commissioned to overwhelm us. We sink into the trough and then miraculously rise to the crest. One crashed on the deck yesterday throwing Third Officer George Johnson bodily into the scuppers, severely injuring him. Dr Prior bled him but it was of no avail and he died two hours later.

'5 June: Rev Wilkinson read the burial service for Mr Johnson and we consigned him to the deep. A dark and terrible loneliness, to sink into this waste of waters, so far from home. Faith comes hardest sometimes when we are most in need of it.

'14 June: Sailing east but edging ever south into colder darker waters. Very short days. Snow on the decks this morning, and frozen in the rigging.

'18 June: Remember Mr Wilkinson's sermon of today. 1 Epistle of St Peter, iii, verse 13: "Who is he that shall harm you, if ye be followers of that which is good." I thought in response "I could name some", and then reproached myself inwardly for this self-obsession which cuts me off from the healing Word.

'21 June: Mid-winter day. No escape from the cold. Decks permanently frozen. Much snow. Lat 60 S. Sun now only 7 degrees above the horizon at noon. We take dinner at 4 of the afternoon, by candlelight.

'25 June: Rounded the Horn in seas Capt Livesay assures us are quiet for this region and time of year. Fortunately we have our sea-legs. The ship is lifted, as by a giant hand, and lowered, on the huge swell, but not tossed about, twisted and made to grind and groan as it did in the worst of the storm.

.   .   .

'24–25 July: For a month I have not kept this journal, some of my deeper thoughts being better argued out with myself in the darkness of the deck at night than committed to paper. I think I begin to win some kind of battle over my sense of disappointment and loss; but forgiveness comes not easily. It being a Divine thing, why should it? We have been sailing north into brighter days and calmer weather. My public life has been Greek and the Gospels; and playing with the Wilkinson children, whom I have taught many words and phrases of the native language of New Zealand. Early morning yesterday I heard the sweet words "Land! Land-ahoy!" Captain Livesay declared it to be Cape Fris and Cape St Thomas. The whole day very fine and the land becoming more clearly visible, a fine bold coast. As we approach the Harbour of Rio Janeiro the country behind rises to an immense mountain.

'26 July: Rio Janeiro. Anchored in a fine spacious harbour.

'1 August: Grieved to see the ill treatment of the African slaves. I have seen the earth's dark places, and how justly they are called the habitations of cruelty. Lord God, why hast Thou forsaken the Innocent?

'3 August: I have found the only Protestant church. Attended service. The Rev Arthur Maister. Congregation of just 24 brave souls.

'8 August: To sea again.

'10 August: Vivid dream of T's death. Horror — and my own fear. The shot, the axe blows falling. Blood on the grasses and on those small white flowers. My thought that the flowers were spoiled, as if I could not believe the worse truth. But my dreaming mind could not accept that end, and the dream was repeated. This time my voice was listened to, she was saved by my intervention, the blows did not fall. I took her hand and we ran together into the forest. I woke with such sweet relief, and then to the disappointment of bitter truth.

'12 August: Conversation with Mrs Wilkinson — commit to memory the quality of her pity for the convicts at Sydney.

'15 August: Greek verbs. I sleep many hours and grow lazy in the warmer weather. Long for hard work.

'18 August: Sailors teaching knots to me and young Freddie. Rev W disapproves I think, that I should join in, but is tolerant. Freddie wishes he could climb into the crow's nest. So do I.

'23 August: Reading under an awning close to the bow. Constantly distracted by the beauty of the flying fish sprinting out of the bow-wave and skimming away over the glittering ocean-surface. At night the sailors set a light so the fish sometimes fly towards it and are trapped on the deck. They make excellent eating.

'2 September: We cross the equator in the 27th degree of West longitude, I think not many degrees W of where I crossed it on the way to New Zealand, though heading then down the coast of Africa.

'(Footnote: I see from my old journal that on the way out we crossed the line at 26° 50′ W longitude, on August 9 1834, 52 days out from Gravesend. That was on board the *Prince Regent*. So it is four years and one month I have been in the Southern Hemisphere, and feel I have lived there at least a decade. I look back upon that setting forth, our enthusiasm, mine, Colenso's, and the Wades'; and our fears. On June 18, the day of our departure, I wrote, "We have left our native land! We form a small knot in the saloon and go down on our knees while Colenso prays for us together: God of Truth keep us. To Thy care we commit ourselves, now and evermore!")

'7 September: Under a vertical sun with a fine N.E. trade wind sailing 7 knots.

'8 September: Dream again — and of Henry Williams and Richard Davis, gloating. My dreams now seem to mix England and New Zealand, passing from one to the other.'
[damaged pages — illegible, but for a few disconnected words]

'9 October: Arrived at Plymouth. My heart leapt to see upon waking that dear familiar coast. We have sailed out of such a turbulent world into this peaceful haven, with lights burning out of the half darkness. Home, yet not quite so; not, at least, in the sense that it can any longer be said to be the place where the whole of one's heart resides. "Half of my heart I consecrate." A confusion of emotions. I look forward with pleasure and something like apprehension, a kind of shyness, to meeting with my dear parents again, and my sisters and brother. And there will be sad farewells to the Wilkinsons, especially the children whom I have grown to love.'

IT WAS THE SEASON OF MISTS and mellow fruitfulness, as John Flatt's near contemporary and almost namesake had written.

John Keats was already dead, and John Flatt had never heard of him. But as the coach took him along the highway to London, between hedgerows bright with berries, under huge trees some already yellowing and sending down early scatters of leaf, through a landscape sometimes of yellow stubble, sometimes of black fields turned over to lie fallow, sometimes of apple orchards whose boughs, red and green, were pulled down like arms by the weight of the crop, Flatt remembered a brown-bound poetry book, *The Seasons* by James Thomson, with elegant steel engravings, which had been among those possessions of the Rev Brown taken by the taua that killed Tarore. He had looked at the book often in Mrs Brown's parlour, and remembered the lines,

> When the bright Virgin gives the beauteous days,
> And Libra weighs in equal scales the year;
> From heaven's high cope the fierce effulgence shook
> Of parting Summer, a serener blue,
> With golden light enliven'd . . .

The natives would have used those pages for the making of cartridges. England's spring summer autumn and winter as described in the lovely words of Mr Thomson, which had a feel about them that made him think of clotted cream, would by now, one way or another, have gone up in smoke.

John Flatt was back where the seasons came as they should, spring in April, autumn in October. But it meant he had sailed out of winter and into autumn. There was a summer his life would not have; just as on the voyage out he had missed a winter by leaving England before the end of summer and sailing into the southern spring.

These facts were not mysterious, but they teased the mind. The returning traveller could say that he had walked on the globe's underside without falling off; that he had bathed in a river in January in order to cool himself at the end of a day's labour; that he had seen and spoken with the anthropophagi. These were truths that might entertain his nieces and nephews. They would also conceal a sense of puzzlement which he brought back with him, and which in all his pacing the decks at night through the tranquil middle latitudes he had not been able to come to terms with — a sense that his mind had been stretched beyond anything his education and his religion had prepared it for, and so beyond his ability to understand.

The 'savage heathens', for example, had proved more savage and heathen than he had ever imagined possible; but they had also been more human, closer, more like kin. The gap between the clergyman Brown and the chief Waharoa had been absolute and unbridgeable, and at the same time narrow, so that for Flatt it had constituted not so much a practical problem (his duty had been to serve Brown) as a puzzle to the mind.

Because these were things he could not explain to himself, they were not subjects for discussion with friends and family. Better to tell picturesque stories and keep one's own counsel.

But the sense that there was something large still to be grasped and understood must explain why even during the first days of his return, and the pleasures of his coach ride up to London in good weather and through the countryside in harvest time, he retained the feeling that he was merely on a visit home, that there was work for him to do in New Zealand — work which could be given the appearance of being for the good of the world beyond self, and no doubt would be so, but which would also and more importantly be an inner process.

It was a recognition he feared to speak aloud or even, except at very rare moments, to commit to paper; because although the only means to get back to New Zealand (or so it seemed to him during those autumn days of 1837) lay with the Church Missionary Society, and required, therefore, due protestations of pious intent, Flatt knew there was a painful conviction growing within himself that God's world was larger, richer and more mysterious than could be accounted for by the Book and the rituals which as a missionary he must declare contained all the answers needful to the human mind and soul.

London came in due course and brought with it a change in the weather, partly a real change, and partly something that would have been felt in any case, because the great city had a climate of its own. Now the 'mists' that went with the 'mellow fruitfulness' of the countryside at this season became fogs rising off the river. Streets closed in. Smoke came down from chimney pots, and above them the sky seemed a near and almost tangible gauze through which the light struggled, and out of which from time to time an unclean drizzle fell, mixed with flakes of soot. The coach wheels scraped and rumbled on paved streets and clattered on cobbles. There were crowds and much shouting, jostling, laughter and anger. Small boys ran alongside the coach in ragged clothes, asking for money or offering to sell things. Old women coughed in doorways. There were smells of food and sometimes of urine and excrement. Everywhere there was mud — wet on the roadways and pavements, dry on the horses' flanks and on women's skirts. It had not occurred to John Flatt that there could be clean mud and dirty mud. But the mud he had tramped through on the swampy edge of the plain of Waikato seemed, by comparison with this black grime of London, pure — wholesome and uncontaminated.

London had never been home; and now it seemed to the returning traveller a kind of hell on earth, exciting, but not a place to give ease and comfort. But there was an inn he knew, the Swan, close to Holborn Bridge. He remembered with pleasure its cheerful landlord, Mr Broughton, its coffee-room and tap-room, its fireplaces and cabin-like bed-chambers, because it was there he had stayed on his first visit to London when he had been interviewed and accepted by the Church Missionary Society. In those rooms he and Colenso had tried to imagine New Zealand and their work there. Colenso, whose intensity and deep sincerity of purpose had now and then made Flatt doubt his own, had told of battles fought with the great Adversary who came sometimes as Doubt, sometimes as Lustful Thoughts. Feeling himself called upon to match this confession, Flatt had admitted that what lay ahead of them presented itself as an adventure and an opportunity for advancement, and that he needed to remind himself constantly that their journey was not to serve or gratify themselves, but for God's larger purpose. Together the two young men had prayed for strengths that would make them equal to the task of bringing Truth into one of the world's dark corners.

At the Swan John Flatt now lodged, staying on through October and November. On 21 October he wrote to the Rev Jowett of the Church Missionary Society a letter of a single page saying that his one wish was to return to New Zealand and to take up once again his work as a missionary; and he named Matamata as the place he would like to be sent, where he would, if permitted, 'stay until the end of my days'.

NO MENTION OF WAIMATE, Jean-Anne points out. No mention of the job as agriculturist denied him by Davis and Henry Williams — not forgotten, of course, but set aside. 'No complaints. Almost, you might say, the submissive posture. And he asks to be sent back into the area of danger. The Matamata mission was closed, but he knew Brown hoped to see it reopened one day. He was offering himself.'

It is getting dark. Hugh turns on the lamp. He acknowledges that this letter surprised him when he first read it. Does Jean-Anne have an idea . . .

She points to its date — 21 October. Now she shows Hugh Flatt's journal. Very few entries at this period. But there is one two days before the letter to Jowett — 19 October — just two words: 'One year!!'

Does Hugh see the point? It was one year since the murder of Tarore. It had been a period of slow transition for Flatt, almost of retreat — from the plains across to the coast, from Tauranga north to the Bay of Islands, from there around the world, back to where he began. The date had crept up on him, taken him by surprise. It had made him reflect on his position for two days, and brought this decision to write to Jowett making his wishes for the future clear. The letter, Jean-Anne believes, showed a new certainty of purpose.

Matamata — *'until the end of my days.'* The thought of the plains was now perhaps even more important, in some ways more real to him, than the appointment denied him at Waimate. It had taken hold of his imagination and he wanted desperately to get back there.

WITHIN A DAY OR SO Flatt received a reply from Jowett asking him to call at the Society's headquarters at Salisbury Square. There was something about this summons which gave him anxiety. The city seemed dark and threatening as he made his way there. Rain was falling. He slipped in the street. He muddied his best boots in 'a puddle of uncommmon size and depth'. He arrived early for his appointment and was called late. While he waited he was struck by a sense of aridity ('a tomb of a place', he called Missionary House, 'which it made my throat dusty just to enter'). When he was called at last it seemed to him the Rev Jowett's speech was choked by his clerical collar. His coat, Flatt noticed, was in need of a brushing, and the watch chain across his ample front looked 'big enough for a convict's leg'.

Jowett was civil but not cordial. The Society, he said, was appreciative of the work Mr Flatt had done. It had had good reports of his skills as a gardener, his ingenuity in practical matters, his physical fortitude, and his ability to speak the language of the natives and to treat with them civilly and diplomatically. But as matters stood at present in New Zealand the Society, on the recommendation of those whose responsibility it was to determine how best the Word of God could be carried into the heathen heart, had resolved that it would have no further use for his services. In consideration, however, of his labours in New Zealand, the Committee had decided that the debt of £15 incurred by Mr Flatt when outfitting himself before setting out in 1834 should be deemed cancelled. It had also prepared a testimonial which would serve to show that he left with the Society's good will.

The document was handed to John Flatt and it read (though in his shock he was not able to make sense of it):

Mr John Flatt

Dear Sir,
On the occasion of parting with you, the Committee
desire me to state that they are well-assured of your
Piety and good Conduct, having received satisfactory
Testimonials to that Effect from their Friends in New
Zealand, of the Missionary Body.

We earnestly hope that it will please God to guide
you by his Grace in whatever Situation His Providence
may allot to you.

I remain, very truly, yours,

Wm Jowett
Clerical Secretary
Church Missionary Society

Flatt did not trust himself to speak. They had sent him
to the end of the earth to take up an appointment that was
then denied him. They had sent him back again so that he
could be married, the better to meet their requirements, only
to tell him now, and without explanation, that they had no
further need of him. But any show of anger would only
confirm, in Jowett's eyes, that he was an unsatisfactory
person. And pride was not so undermined as to allow him
to beg.

Flatt took his testimonial and left. He walked without
knowing where he was heading. The rain drifted down out
of a dirty sky. He found himself on the steps of St Paul's, went
as far as the doors, listened for a moment to the strange echo-
effect of voices that seemed to fly up and then come down
again out of the dome, then turned away. That sound of
sepulchral voices, which had once stirred his sense of the
mystery of the Creation, now affected him as something cold
and enclosed, having more to do with death than with life.
He longed for the vastness of southern oceans, the brightness
of southern light, the infinity of the southern skies.

He walked on past business houses, banks, on, east and south, through narrowing streets lined with brick-walled warehouses until he came to the Thames. The tide had turned and was sweeping seaward with the backed-up river-flow. Barges edged this way and that, straining at their moorings. Overhead winches and pulleys lowered cargo on ropes to and from sailboats tied up at small riverside wharves. The stench of sewage and other waste came up from the water. Had his nostrils grown more delicate in New Zealand? Or had the smell grown worse in the years of his absence?

He stared out across the water, up-river to Tower Bridge, down-river to London Bridge, up into the clogged sky beyond which it seemed to him at this moment (and to permit the thought was an act of rebellion) there was nothing but emptiness and silence. He tried to think of something positive, something random that would make him happy. What came into his mind was the memory of teaching the native children to sing English songs at William Fairburn's school at Puriri on that New Zealand river, the Waihou, so inappropriately renamed the Thames, and how the little coffee-coloured singers had been able to distinguish the half note from the natural as readily as he could himself. Sheltering from the rain under the heavy dark timbers of a wharf shed, the sound of those voices came back to him as clearly as if they were there around him.

He did not know what he would do next. 'One thing at a time' was the phrase that came to him, as it had come to steady him on the morning of the murder of Tarore; and the first was simply to trudge back to his lodgings, dry himself before a fire, and change his clothes.

It was, Jean-Anne points out, while Flatt was in this state of shock and bewilderment that he came to the notice of the rather grand yet somewhat tarnished Whig gentleman whose name every latterday New Zealand schoolchild learns belongs to one of the colony's founding fathers — Edward Gibbon Wakefield.

IT WAS JUST FOUR DAYS after his meeting with the Rev Jowett that John Flatt was called to the inn parlour to receive a footman who was asking for him. What took place there is not recorded, except that as a result of their conversation Flatt agreed to go at once with his visitor in a carriage to a house in Hans Place where he was shown by a servant into a well-furnished high-ceilinged room, its walls lined with pictures, in which a good fire burned in the grate.

The gentleman who came to meet him there had keen eyes, a broad brow, and an air of command. He introduced himself as Edward Wakefield, and asked what Flatt knew of him. Had Flatt heard of his interest in colonisation, his role in the formation of the New Zealand Association, and the arguments that had blown up around his name? In particular he wished to know what ill reports Flatt had heard of him which would incline his visitor to treat any dealings they might have with caution, or even suspicion.

Flatt replied as best he could. He knew of Wakefield from his fellow missionaries. He knew that the New Zealand Association and the Church Missionary Society were antagonists over the question of whether or not New Zealand should become a British colony, the Society believing that such a development would not be in the interests of the natives, the Association holding, on the other hand, that colonisation was inevitable, and that it was better it should be planned than left to chance and the French. He had noticed, too, that *The Times* newspaper had taken sides with the Society against Mr Wakefield and the Association. As one of the missionary body he had been, he acknowledged when pressed, predisposed not to think well of Mr Wakefield.

Edward Wakefield seemed satisfied with these replies; but he urged Flatt further on what ill he had heard of him. And to Flatt's uneasy reply that he could think of nothing, Wakefield asked had he not heard of the abduction of an heiress — and that he, Wakefield, had spent three years in Newgate for the offence?

Flatt admitted now that he had indeed heard something to that effect, to which Wakefield replied that if they were to be of use to one another there should be no pretence between them. His misdemeanour had been, he freely acknowledged, almost as extreme as the penalty had been severe. Nonetheless, he believed that every man of spirit was likely to commit errors and follies in his younger days. The greater the error, the stronger the challenge to rebuild one's life and make it useful, and — wasn't it so? — the greater the difficulty in doing this, because the world never let the wrongdoer forget his mistake, particularly if he later sought a life which put him before the public. 'So let it be acknowledged,' he suggested, 'but let it not stand between us as an obstacle.'

As for his guest, Wakefield went on before there was time for the glow this frankness had produced to dissipate: he knew that Flatt had displeased his employers, the Church Missionary Society, and how he had done so. He knew also that Flatt was now dismissed. How he had come by this knowledge was immaterial. He would be frank and admit that he had little sympathy for the senior men in that sanctimonious body, whom he considered, with some few honourable exceptions, canting hypocrites wanting to keep colonists away so they could make New Zealand a theocracy in which they might live as petty overlords, divinely sanctioned by God, yet mundanely protected by the aura of the Crown and by the guns of the British Navy. Their arguments, which they persuaded some in powerful places — and perhaps even persuaded themselves — were for the benefit of the natives, were in fact self-serving.

He asked John Flatt to forgive his ardour. He was, he explained, just now engaged in a public controversy with Mr Dandeson Coates of the Society, who had replied to his own recently published book on the subject of the New Zealand Association's plan for colonisation by addressing a pamphlet to the Secretary of State for the Colonies, Lord Glenelg, attacking the book, its author, and the Association. It was essential that this pamphlet be replied to, and he was doing that — writing a similar open letter to Lord Glenelg.

It was a tiresome business, this pamphleteering, but

necessary if the Association's plans for colonisation were to have any chance of success. His problem, however, was this. Coates had argued, citing evidence of the missionaries — who were, it could be argued, those best placed to report on what was and was not possible in New Zealand — that land for settlement could not be obtained of the natives. Wakefield knew this was not true. How could it be? The natives, it was said, numbered scarcely more than one hundred thousand in a country the size of Great Britain. The southern island was almost uninhabited. In the northern island were vast tracts unoccupied and unused. Further, he had it on good authority that the missionaries, while assuring those at home that land could not be obtained, were buying up blocks for their own use and for their children. But these reports, though he was convinced of their truth, were not such as would do in evidence. They came at second or third hand, or from people who could not afford to be seen publicly to stand by them. What he needed was the voice of one who had been that long journey around the world, had lived there for some years, had worked as a missionary and seen for himself what was happening. A person, in short, such as Mr Flatt.

'I am not asking for lies or deception,' Wakefield told him. 'I am asking only that the truth be told.'

When Flatt left Hans Square, having declined a return by carriage in favour of a walk through city streets which would help him to weigh up and reflect, he had agreed only to give serious thought to Wakefield's request, and to return within a few days. But the outcome of his deliberations with himself was hardly in doubt; and if he had not immediately assented it was perhaps not only because he had learned that when there was no need for haste it was best not to make it, but more, because there was a pleasure to be had in savouring the opportunity that had so unexpectedly come his way.

However he thought about Wakefield's proposal, what came always to the forefront of his mind was the recollection of that hot almost windless January day as they had drifted south towards Puriri on board the *Columbine*, and how he had resolved that he would store in memory the suspiciously circuitous procedure by which Henry Williams had put a huge tract of land into William Fairburn's possession while himself seeming to retain a hold on it; and that if the means of using what he had seen against those who had denied him his rights should ever come, he would not hesitate. Then he had reproached himself for thinking vengefully. Finally, he had decided there was no occasion for self-reproach. The thought of revenge had been meaningless — no more than an empty dream to relieve his feelings. Only God, he had told himself, could put into his hands the means to hit back at the men who had misused him.

Was Providence now putting such means in his way? And if so, was the opportunity one which the strong and righteous man would seize, or a temptation to be resisted? ' "Vengeance is mine", saith the Lord.' As a missionary in New Zealand Flatt had so often heard that quoted in vain attempts to persuade Waharoa and his warrior subordinates that utu was the pathway only to repetitious violence and, in the end, to a darkness of the soul.

But could it be vengeful to tell the plain truth? Wakefield had asked for nothing more, and if Flatt should be asked for more, or other, he would refuse. No one had ever suggested that he should conceal anything the missionaries were doing in New Zealand, so he would be breaking no trust. Yet he knew that the truth would be an embarrassment. The missionaries were acquiring land while reporting none was available; and they were not telling even their superiors in London the extent to which this was happening. In not protecting his brethren who had not protected him would lie, if not revenge, at least satisfaction. Let them sweat a little, he thought, striding faster through the London streets. Let them be the ones made to walk barefoot over the hot sands of disappointment. Let them at least be made to remember the eager agriculturalist they had treated so cavalierly, and had cast off so lightly.

So Flatt's response to Wakefield was to be in the affirmative. But before giving it he wrote a brief letter to the

Rev Jowett. Whether he felt, despite the termination of his service, that he owed the Society at least a warning of what he was about to do, or whether he was meaning to convey the message 'You will have reason to regret dismissing me,' is uncertain. What he wrote to Jowett was hardly more than a single cool sentence, though he spun it out to the length of a small page of notepaper. He considered it his duty, he said, to inform the Society and its Clerical Secretary of his next step, and that would very likely be, when certain matters of fact were cleared up and certain minor obstacles removed, a step in the direction of the New Zealand Association.

That written and despatched, he arranged his second meeting with Wakefield.

SO IT CAME ABOUT — and now Jean-Anne has secured through inter-library request a copy of the document — the pamphlet by Edward Gibbon Wakefield Esq, with the title *Mr Dandeson Coates and the New Zealand Association, A Letter to the Right Hon Lord Glenelg*, issued from Hans Place, dated 12 December 1837, and published by Henry Hooper, 13 Pall Mall East, London. In it Wakefield rehearsed yet again all the arguments for a planned colonisation of New Zealand with which he had sought to persuade the British Government that the New Zealand Association's views were right and the Church Missionary Society's opposition to it wrong. His writing was well-turned and trenchant. But this time there was something he had lacked before. Now he had hard evidence, facts about land acquisition, acreages, even names; and all this was reserved for the closing pages. It represented the sting in his pamphlet's tail.

Quoting Coates to the effect that the missionary experience had proved it would not be possible to purchase from the natives land of any extent suitable for settlement, Wakefield offered 'the following naked statement of facts' which had been 'taken down from the lips of Mr Flatt, quite recently a Catechist of the Church Missionary Society in New

Zealand', and which would 'suffice to convince your Lordship that Mr Coates is not so well acquainted with secular matters in New Zealand as he imagines himself to be.'

There followed Flatt's list of senior missionary names and the extent of their land holdings, including:

'The Rev Henry Williams, not less than 4000 acres at Titrianga near Waimate. Mr Williams has commenced farming there; has sheep, cattle and horses, farm buildings built by the natives, and an American superintendent. He employs about 30 natives. He visits the establishment two or three times a week. He sells produce to the Mission.

'Mr James Kemp, Catechist, has purchased at least 5000 acres at Kirikidi and Wangaroa.

'Mr James Davis, Catechist, has purchased at least 4000 acres at Waimate. Mr Davis has a farming establishment, buildings, sheep, cattle and horses. He employs about 20 natives. He superintends the farm himself. His father is the superintendent of the Society's farm at Waimate.

'Mr James Shepperd, Catechist, is supposed to be (apart from Mr Fairburn) the largest English land-owner in New Zealand. His property extends from Kirikidi nearly to the Hokianga forest, a distance of more than fifteen miles. He has no farming establishment but is about to commence one under the superintendence of his eldest son.

'Mr Charles Baker, Catechist, has a large landed property at Wangaroa.

'Mr George Clerk, Catechist, has purchased a large tract of land at Waimate, adjoining the Society's land on the west side. He has a farming establishment, with buildings, including a large barn; and cattle, sheep and horses. He employs about 20 natives. He lives at the Mission station, and attends to the private property himself.

'Mr William Fairburn, Catechist, owns small tracts of land at the Bay of Islands, adjoining the Mission station at Paihia. He has recently bought a very extensive tract, supposed to extend for thirty miles in its greatest length, at Tamaka in the Frith of Thames. This purchase took place in January 1836. The contract was drawn up in Native and

English by the Rev Mr Williams, Chairman of the Committee, and was signed by him and myself as witnesses. Mr Fairburn has obtained leave from the Committee to commence farming establishments on this purchase with the assistance of his eldest son.

'Several other members of the Mission have purchased smaller tracts.

'In November 1836 a Petition to the King of England, praying for *the protection of British property in New Zealand*, was signed by *all* the Church Missionaries, clergymen and catechists, myself included. This petition was brought home by the *Pyramus*, and is now before the Government.'

'TIME FOR A DRINK?' They are shuffling together their papers, journal extracts, letters, the precious xerox copy of the Wakefield pamphlet.

Jean-Anne glances at her watch, nods, smiling. They are both smiling. They have made a breakthrough.

'And Wakefield's meeting with the Prime Minister, have you noticed the date?' (this is Hugh). 'Thirteenth of December. That's the day after he completed his pamphlet. Glenelg was there, of course; and eighteen members of the New Zealand Association. Flatt's information was their strongest card. He'd been a member of the Missionary Society that had been saying land couldn't be bought. Wakefield argued that the Society had been exploiting distance to keep the public and the Government in ignorance.'

Jean-Anne accepts the drink he has poured her. 'Which wasn't quite true, was it? Or not of the Society in London. They didn't know what their missionaries in New Zealand had been doing.'

Hugh shrugs. 'Probably not. Or maybe they'd preferred not to know.'

'But now there was to be an enquiry.'

'A House of Lords Select Committee. We're going to have to look again at Flatt's evidence.'

W HAT IS VICTORY? What is defeat? What were the causes of the war-or-whatever which led to this victory/this defeat?

It was Frank Mangold who first put Hugo Wolf Grady on to the idea that New Zealand history was waiting like a vast garden undiscovered, unexplored, and that he should be the moth to fly out into it. Frank had explained to the boy in the big kitchen at the long scrubbed table who had noticed an r missing in the spelling of Mediterranean that the word meant middle earth, and that for the early European civilisation that is what the Mediterranean had been, the middle of the whole world. Wasn't that more or less where it remained for the European mind? But should it be so for us? Frank had pointed to New Zealand on the same wall-map, so peripheral it occurred twice, tucked away, far down, once at the extreme left, a second time at the extreme right. Yet today's kauri had fallen, hadn't it? bang in the middle of their world, his and Hugo's. Shouldn't someone in New Zealand's schools and universities begin to teach and write as if that were the case?

Sixty years old, Hugh Grady looks back with pleasure and regret on the ironies of the half century that has accelerated by since that last late day of cross-cut, ten-team, log-race and pit-saw. He has long since fought his way past — around and through — his inability quite to conceive of historical events as having 'causes'. He has made a life for himself, a profession, even a name as a minor historian. The old world view has gone, as he was persuaded it should. New Zealand history has become respectable, has been studied, written, taught and read.

But for Hugh there is a feeling, looking back, that a door opened and then closed again. There were a few years, decades even, when it all lay before him, the unexplored garden waiting to be mapped, the stories waiting to be retold. Here were the documents. Here were the letters and journals, the newspapers, the records public and private. Forget the obstacles put up by elderly English-born Oxbridge-trained professors who would never believe that this was a subject to engage a mature mind, and get on with it. So he did, and not, of course, alone. Even before he began, others were at work. Soon the garden was full of reporters and photographers. He was one, and a minor one, among many. 'Bliss was it in that dawn to be alive . . .' — or if not bliss, at least it was exciting.

Who blew the whistle? Who shouted 'All change!'? Who said, 'The facts are not enough. We must have morals!'? Who demanded that the past must become a club with which to beat the present over the head, knock it into shape, make it behave 'correctly'? It was no one person who made these demands, no committee, no identifiable group. The order came, not from Wellington, not from New Zealand at all; it came from 'overseas', as such things (Hugh knew it well) always do in regions which have ceased to be colonies but remain client cultures. It was the big world that spoke. It was the international fashion-houses of the academic intellect. It was the Zeitgeist. It whispered in the ears of sleeping young scholars who woke, as from a vision of Paradise, determined to be Good and to prove in their work that they were. 'Show us the sins of your forefathers,' the voice demanded. 'Show us how they wronged Women and the Native race.' And in a space of time so short it took the wind out of Hugh's and History's sails, that garden, so fresh, so various, so inviting, so incompletely explored, had become the stage set of a conventional musical melodrama where cardboard-clad figures sang over and over the same three or four songs to the tune of 'I am white and male and I wrong those who are brown and female'; or 'I am female/brown/femaleandbrown and I am wronged/wronged/doublywronged by those who are white and male.'

But the change had come too late to affect Hugh Grady. He had been born, all pale, male and unsuspecting, descendant of the descendants of patriarchal colonisers, in the Garden of Mt Eden in the shadow of a hill still terraced as for war, on which, it was said, a slaughter so terrible had once taken place, so many Maori Abels struck down by their brothers Cain, that the consequent tapu had lasted two hundred years. If Hugh carried from birth the sins of the fathers, so did everyone else, brown and white, female and male. So universal a guilt belonged to the realms of theology and ideology, and to the preacher's art. Hugh had no wish to earn the interest an investment in it might ensure, and felt distaste for its peculiar psychology. In his old-fashioned way, learned first from Frank Mangold, he was interested in knowledge. Every new fact was a precious stone. Opinion was only the bad breath of the ideologues clouding the mirror; moralising was a fog in the garden of his dream.

What is victory, and what defeat? So often the passage of time proved those words ambiguous and interchangeable. For Hugh the defeat of the study of history as he had known it had coincided with his liberation. In retirement he had no one to please but himself. He woke every morning a free man, feeling that a day of discoveries and excitements lay before him. In his intellectual garden the morning webs glittered and the flowers arranged themselves in patterns. Like the lilies of the field, they wove not, neither did they spin. No one gave them B+, or asked them to speak a moral. Their function was to be.

WHAT IS DEFEAT? What is victory? In those last days of the decade of the 60s, while the white ship steamed north and east towards Panama, and Lydia Lawrence in Auckland wept and filled her emptied life and empty lecture pads with letters only some of which (there were so many) could be sent to wait at their appointed poste restante address, Harriet's was the victory. She had repossessed the body of her matrimonial partner. Only his imagination floated free, glided over the ship's stern, followed its wake back south and west to a little downstairs flat looking out on a park full of birds, lovers and summer flowers.

But nothing is simple. There were the splendours and boredoms, the storms and calms, of the world's greatest ocean to fill his mind. There were the deck chairs and deck games, the swimming pool, the books, the food and the drink. There were bars and movies and cabin parties. There were the small boys to be entertained, and Hat to talk to. There was the Panama Canal and the islands of the Caribbean. There were the American east coast radio stations, picked up by poking one's radio aerial through the porthole, broadcasting the songs of Joan Baez and Bob Dylan, the news of war in Vietnam and of protest in Washington and San Francisco. There was the New York skyline on a fine cold morning, and Fifth Avenue, the Museum of Modern Art, the Guggenheim, Washington Square, Greenwich Village. There was the cold five-day heaving, inner and outer, of the Atlantic swell.

Finally and definitively there was England, which went right through all those 'post colonial' intellectual flak jackets, past all those determinations that this was no longer 'the Old Country', no longer 'Home', straight to the heart. For the few magic days until it became familiar, and in brief flashes for a long time after, England offered itself as Through the Looking Glass land, a world that belonged to reading not to reality, full of book-looking pubs, palaces, parks, policemen, full of red letterboxes and rolled umbrellas, copses and country lanes. It was the pakeha Hawaiki, ultimate setting-out point of the singing whakapapa. It was as if, Hugh confessed to Hat in a sentence that felt so like self-betrayal, or self-denial, it had at once to be called home and rephrased — as if they had been holding their breath for more than a century and now at last could let it out.

London was also the first of the post restante addresses for letters from Lydia . . .

Hugh is at his desk again in the afternoon light. It is so long since he has read the secret letters that waited for him in London and beyond, he brings them out with feelings of excitement and apprehension. He flicks through a sheaf of them, seeing himself addressed as Wolf-one, Wolfie, Woof-woof, Whippet, as Hughie, Hugely, Hugs, Hungry, as Loup, and Loop-the-Loop. Sometimes they are signed Lid, sometimes Liddy or LL, sometimes Lawrence or Elle. He lets his eye slide over the first one addressed to him in London.

'We are so close. Do you feel that? Ever since I saw you from the wharf I haven't worried for a minute. I'm even happy. Do you hear the smile in my sentences? The departure was beautiful — the streamers, the sun, the huge white ship shining as we all waved and waved and waved. I only felt desperate when you began to go out of sight, but once gone I didn't feel empty or hopeless as I feared. Not at all. The whole thing was like a promise. I can still see your expression . . .

'I have painted my kitchen wall — Tonka-toy yellow. Will you like it when you come to visit me? (Always the same question — everything addressed to my absent Wolf-one.) And yes, you will like it . . .

'Sweetheart we've never *danced* together. I'd love to dance with you. One is supposed to know if someone is a good lover by the way they dance, so I know you must do it beautifully.'

He turns over a few pages.

'Your *absence*, Wolf-man, is HUGE. At times like these I'd rather write nothing if it weren't for the weeds of misinterpretation that would surely grow up in the cracks. Do you remember that I once shook you and strangled you and told you how much I missed being with you in advance? — anticipating what I do feel now: the hopelessness of molecules strung together and coloured blue.'

He doesn't want to read these letters but now he has one in his hand he finds it difficult to resist. Shuffling the pages he allows himself to read the final paragraph, a postscript.

'It's Saturday. Couldn't sleep. Need to hear from you but it's too soon. Feel miserable. Miss you. Can't keep up this cheerfulness. I hoped I would at least dream of you. In the end I got up, put on my duffle coat and went for a walk. I look at the stars and ask God to fucking lay off me.'

There is a ring at the doorbell and he goes down. It is Jean-Anne. She has been to the clinic for tests necessary (she explains) before the end of the second trimester. Everything, it seems, is in order. Now she has an hour or so to spare before she must go into town and pick up Philip. She has brought Hugh some books he asked for, and some xeroxes.

They go up to his study and she sees the sheaf of letters. He explains that it has nothing to do with their work; and then, before he has had time to think about whether the confession is wise or called for, he has begun to tell her about his affair of long ago. The letters are gathered up as he talks.

Jean-Anne sits very still. When there is a pause in his monologue she says nothing, just reaches forward and pats his knee. He apologises — says he hadn't meant to tell her this story. She says she's glad he did. She can imagine how they both must have felt. Hat too, of course. It must have been hard for her. But especially hard for Lydia Lawrence.

She reaches down and picks up a blue aerogramme that has fallen from the bunch, and hands it to him.

He glances at it, and hands it back to her. 'Read it if you like, J-A. It will give you the flavour.'

He goes downstairs to put the kettle on and leaves her reading.

LONDON WAS ALSO A SNOWFALL. And Wagner. They wintered there, living in a flat that looked out on Regents Park, where Richard and John, who for a short time went to a school in Primrose Hill, played in the afternoons, observed and made notes on the wolves in their zoo cages and the birds in their huge aviary, and dropped twigs and matches from a small stone bridge on to the decks of barges on the canal.

In the evenings Hugh took the boys for walks around the streets north of the Park, inventing a second city called London Two which existed underneath, exactly matching

London One, and which could be glimpsed sometimes in the reflections on the canals, and through drain-grills and basement windows.

In the daytime Hugh looked at libraries and Hat at the law courts. She had introductions to legal persons, he a letter which gained him admission to the Reading Room of the British Museum. There he read for the first time his great-great-grandfather's evidence to the 1838 Committee of the House of Lords. Not studying it as 'history' but merely for family reasons, knowing as yet nothing of what came before or after, Hugh recognised nothing contentious in John Flatt's evidence, which seemed mild in tone, factual in content.

Lydia's letters came regularly to the poste restante address — it was an office close to Trafalgar Square — and he replied as and when he could. She described how she had become depressed, gone to a doctor who had given her some pills to help her sleep, and that these seemed to make her sick and even caused her to lose her memory. She had thrown them away, and now she was better again, eating and sleeping.

In another letter she wrote, 'I've been worried about myself. I'm very happy — too happy, and I fear a reaction. It's alarming how instinctive one can be. But my senses are so alive I feel if I don't do something soon I'll have done away with my brain.'

And a few pages on in the same letter: 'I have another special place where I always love you — in the middle of Grafton Bridge. When I'm walking across it I'm not quite tall enough to have a clear view of the sea — I catch glimpses of it as my stride sends me up on my toes. As I get near the middle of the bridge I'm not sure I haven't seen your ship in the harbour, and when I get there and stand on tip-toe I really do see it, shining white — so *real*!'

At the end of another letter, when she had gone to stay first with one group of friends, then with another, hoping to make herself 'more real', she wrote: 'This morning I woke up and realised that life actually is a hardship. It is a difficult thing to get up and endure the day. This can't be wrong because I feel it in every cell. I find it intolerable that there always have been and always will be people fucking in the next room.'

These ups and downs worried Hugh, but what could he do? After the snowfall, and Wagner (the first he had ever seen of either) he sat through most of one afternoon under the murmuring dome of the British Museum Reading Room and wrote her a long letter about *Götterdämmerung* and the death of God, about Nietzsche and history, about history and causality, about causality and snowflakes and randomness and love.

Not long after that her letters stopped. This silence as it went on made him anxious. He worried about her state of mind, and then suffered pangs of jealousy when he thought that she might be over her infatuation, enjoying herself now with Bernie, her persistent suitor, or worse, with someone new and unknown. He knew that this was how it should be — that he should welcome her silence, not try to hold on to her. But as the days went by his anxiety increased. Now he was the one who couldn't sleep and found it difficult to concentrate.

He and Hat were preparing for the continental part of their tour when Lid's next letter came. She had been sick — vomiting, and hadn't felt like writing. And his long letter, 'full of snow-flakes and Rhinemaidens', hadn't helped. She knew it had been meant as a gift. She could see that London was turning out to be a high point in his life, and that she ought to be grateful that he was sharing it with her, even if it was only on paper ('like fish and chips' she had added, then crossed it out, but so it could be seen). But hadn't he realised that it was a letter he might have written to just about *anyone*? Full of observation and intelligence — but she would have been happier with something much less wonderful if only she had felt it could have been written to her and no one else. Did she have to tell him that she wasn't a shelf of books, or his history tutorial? She was Lid, Lydia Lawrence, LL, Elle — remember? Real. Particular. With eyes nose mouth breasts voice; with hands feet legs cunt . . .

So it had gone on. But then, on the fourth and final page there had been a sudden change in her weather:

'*Look*. It was this morning when I wrote all that radish and now it's this evening. The cats are rushing around Albert Park while the birds are settling down in its trees. When I've posted this I'm going for a walk in it. I will wear my NEW shiny black coat (with little shiny white lollies for buttons) with the detective's collar UP. I will stride — aloof and enigmatic — so that everyone scurrying home to cook spuds will sense I am somebody's mistress. And if somebody doesn't feel like writing until he gets to Paris (where my next will await him) that's alright with me because in spite of all my grumblings I trust him to love me in the middle of the night/ road/occasional sandwich.

'Lid loves you always, and all ways, and a lot.'

LID LOVES YOU. So that was alright. Always. That was better — and yet it was also worse. Could he be responsible for . . . Did he want . . . What would she . . . How could he . . . Every victory for his ego and his lust and his romanticism and his deeply lodged ever-abiding affection, was also a defeat for his conscience. But the more painful anxiety — that she should have fallen in love with someone else — was gone for the moment. Once again he slept well and woke refreshed by daisy dreams. He began to look again at the 'Unreal City' that was becoming real to him, of which someone important had said 'he who is tired of it is tired of life'. London was the power source of old empire and new fashion. These were the very streets and squares and buildings where long-ago decisions had determined that he and his blood should be born, and live, and feel that they belonged and must be buried, under southern stars. Britain might no longer be — indeed was not — 'Home', but that was what it once had been; and to historian Hugh, old enough to remember school maps draped over blackboards with the Empire-on-which-the-sun-never-set (including New Zealand, the farthest finger of its longest arm) coloured red; old enough to recall teachers who liked to quote with pride Kipling's 'Recessional', in which Auckland was described as

'Last loneliest loveliest — exquisite, apart' — to him such acknowledgements of London's place in his past were not retrogression, but reclamation. By them identity was not compromised or diminished. It was enlarged.

So all the four Gradys were smiling as they set off by train and ferry and train again for Paris. There, as Hat's plan unfolded, they stayed in a hotel on the Place St Sulpice, took their breakfast of coffee and croissants on the square, visited the Louvre, photographed one another among the trees and statuary and fountains and walks of the Luxembourg Gardens and the Tuileries, took rides on the Métro, crossed and recrossed bridges and walked under them over cobbles along the Seine, looked into Notre Dame with its forests of candles, strolled along boulevards and sat in cafés, Hugh and Hat doing, as far as the constraints put upon them by two small boys permitted, those things which first-time visitors to Paris do. And before they were off again south in their hire car, Hugh had managed (with difficulty, since they moved always together) to pick up the letter and the aerogramme that were waiting for him poste restante, and even to write briefly in reply.

Now it was Dijon and the vinyards of Côte d'Or; after which came Nîmes, Arles, Aix-en-Provence, and then east along the Mediterranean coast, which if it wasn't any longer the earth's centre even for Europeans, was so for Hugh and Hat for just as long as they could go on sitting outdoors at a waterfront restaurant under the velvet night sky, looking at reflections on a tranquil bay, watching bats flitting among the heads of palm trees, eating moules marinières and bouillabaisse and drinking whatever the patron chose to offer by the carafe as his vin de la maison, while down on the beach the boys who had eaten their meal and grown restless, amused themselves throwing pebbles out towards the rich men's yachts at their moorings.

They kept to their schedule, Lid's letters matched it, and Hugh did his best to reply, careful now to remember that it was not enough to tell her of his travels, indeed that these excitements might seem to shut her out of his life, and that consequently it was better not to write at all if he could not give his mind and heart to her before putting pen to paper. She was never far from his thoughts; there was a sense in which he took her with him wherever they went. But it was also true that, despite the poste restante letters, Hat's plan to distract him from his love affair was succeeding. Lid was becoming more fantasy than reality, merging with the unreality of these beautiful places, or of a parallel life, like the parallel city called London Two, that might be pushed to the limit because it was never to be lived in fact.

He wrote as he could, and Lid replied as she felt. The blue aerogramme picked up by Jean-Anne and now read by her, for example, had reached him on the Ligurian coast after they had left the French Mediterranean behind and were making their way towards Pisa and Florence:

'I'm being a real sneak writing you this, Wolfie, because I've come back to Auckland to finish *four* essays (all overdue, of course) and I've made a vow not to read anything that will sweep me off with you to illusion-land until I've damn well done them. I've screeds of unfinished notes to you written before your last beautiful letter, and screeds of unfinished silence after that, and a few explanations waiting to be cast off but I've hidden my knitting needles until Free Day. I'm quite surprised that I'm actually doing it and I thought I'd better let you and your passport know just in case there isn't a naked little woman curled up in your post restante box next time you enquire. I strongly suspect that you're now flitting across Italy like a cad and a bounder and won't be sending me so much as a postcard. However your apologies are accepted because you're my secret Huge and I love you even (or should that be especially?) with my back to the wall. My mother asked me whether I was having an affair with a married man, and if I were, would I tell her anyway! She wants to give me money to buy new shoes and a jacket — but I *can't*. How I loathe conscience! Guess wot, darling, I have a new girlfriend (something you're not allowed to have) — a French girl. She has a degree from a select school in Paris and is truly intelligent. She is so beauteefool, with olive skin and rings in her ears and has travelled everywhere and is very mature and has rings in her ears. Tonight I had a macrobiotic supper at her place (chopsticks) and we went to the Celonese ballet — delightful, colourful, graceful, humorous. I wish I was the *type* to have rings in my ears but I'm not — they look so violent on fair skin. I'm not even going to ask you what you think because I've been sitting here imagining it for a minute and I just feel it's wrong for me. And now I am going to write four essays at once — it should be easy compared to the things I've done with you in my mind, and in my bed, and in my mind-bed since you left me (why did you?) to go travelling with an old hat. When they're done, the essays, you will get all of me that will go into one envelope.

'Yours (oh yes!)

'Lid.

'PS: Please don't say at the end of your letter "I'll write again", or "Write again." It plunges me into deep (unreasonable) depression.'

SO WHAT HAPPENED? That is Jean-Anne's question when he returns with the pot of tea and cups on a tray. Even now he finds it hard to answer, it is all such a jumble of fact and circumstance and emotion.

They were reluctant to leave the pines and sand and blue sea and painted wooden fishing boats of the Marina di Massa, and for the first time Hat, who liked plans to be made and adhered to, suggested they might linger. For Hugh, wanting his next message from Lid and therefore reversing roles with Hat, not to stick to their schedule was unthinkable. So they left the coast and drove on to Pisa, where Hugh remembers only that Hat climbed the Leaning Tower with the boys and photographed them crouching under the bells looking unsafe and uneasy, while he on some long-forgotten (except that it was flimsy) pretext made his way to the post office. There was nothing. Nothing at Florence either, reached a day or so later; and though he still remembers the yellow waters of the Arno flowing under the Ponte Vecchio, and Botticelli's

Venus whose face reminded him painfully of Lid, those memories are mixed with the sense of foreboding which increased as they made their way through Bologna and Ferrara (where again there was nothing) to Venice.

There is a photograph he shows Jean-Anne of himself with Richard and John at a café table in the Piazza San' Marco. It was Mayday. You can see the square jammed with people, crowds flowing in and out of the Basilica, its golden spires and painted facings glittering in the spring sun. Three enormous flags, two tricolors flanking the Venetian lion gold on red, lift in the breeze. The family has been for a ride along the canals in a gondola (which cost more than they could afford) and the boys look happy, excited. Hugh is trying to smile at Hat's camera but not succeeding, and the effect is one of extreme anxiety.

'You look desperate,' Jean-Anne says, and he laughs that she should choose that word. In the pocket of that new jacket of Florentine suede, he tells her, he was concealing a reply-paid telegram the words of which he is still able to quote:

TRULY DESPERATE STOP FEEL AS IF DROWNING STOP WILL
YOU MARRY ME STOP MUST HAVE ANSWER LOVE LID

He had telegraphed a reply at once, urging her not to panic, to expect a letter, and to be assured that he loved her; but his expression, caught in Hat's photograph, shows that he knew this would not do. To the question Lid had put to him, anything other than yes had to be read as a negative.

There was now a long silence, and Hugh's memories of where they went during the next three or four weeks are vague. He knows they travelled north again, into Switzerland and Germany, and then across to Holland. He remembers looking at Van Gogh paintings in Amsterdam, and looking at himself in a hotel mirror in that city, feeling unable to recognise his own face. At every stopping place he found a way to call alone at the post office. There were no letters from Lid.

All went according to Hat's plan, and he believes that in some mechanical way he managed to keep up appearances.

153

The weather was growing warmer now and they were moving north where the second part of their programme, the enquiry into the origins of grandfather Carl Christianson, were to be carried forward.

It was in Copenhagen, before they crossed into Sweden, that Lydia Lawrence's final letter reached him. It read:

'Darling Hugh,

'This is only to explain my silence and tell you that you must not look for any more letters from me; there won't be any. And you must not write to me. I'm leaving this flat; and my new French friend, Danielle, who is taking it over and whom I love and trust, has instructions that any letters which come for me from Europe must be destroyed unopened. I know how unhappy this decision will make you, and I can hardly bear the thought of that. It kills me to think of you being hurt, especially by me. And I don't know where I have found the strength to resolve to forego your letters. But I know too, darling, that you are the most intelligent being ever to have crossed my path, or ever likely to, and that however much it pains my Wolf and makes him want to howl at the moon, he will understand.

'I want us to remember one another, but not so it hurts too much and crowds out LIFE. Let's each be a secret cupboard in the other's mind — a breathing space, a dew-drop of morning consciousness, a spring wind in the apple blossom, a red herring that is also a holy mackerel, some corner of a foreign field that is for ever Us-land . . .

'You are a good man, my wonderful lover, and I am a good woman; and in another life, but not in the lives we are obliged by our karma to lead, we will love one another for ever.

'Goodbye, Wolf-one, and promise me Hugh will be as happy as Lydia intends to be. (Why should *that* not be our project?)

'Your Elle.'

EVEN AFTER SO LONG Hat sometimes remarks on what she calls the curious effect Sweden had on Hugh. He had always romanticised that part of his inheritance, telling his friends and family, not once but often, that Carl Christianson's genes were the strongest rungs on the ladder of his double helix; that they were the ones that had predominated in the alphabet soup of his engendering; that Hugo might have inherited Scottish bones and Irish eyes, but Wolf's were Swedish brains and Swedish balls; that consequently it was his northern European orderliness rather than anything reprehensible which put him sometimes out of step with New Zealand's Anglo-Celtic muddle . . . And so on, in what Hat liked to call his mode of Nordic genetic euphoria.

Yet when they set foot there, Hat goes on (telling the story to friends at dinner parties, or to Richard and John and their wives) he seemed to go dead. As they crossed by car-ferry from Copenhagen to Malmo, she remembers, the man who had so looked foward to seeing the homeland of his Master Mariner grandfather didn't even want to get out of the car. He looked at the city, and the countryside along the road to Helsingborg, and at Helsingborg itself, as if he was seeing nothing. He never got excited, or interested, or even, so far as she could tell, bored. Sweden, she decided, must have meant to him something more profound than she had imagined. It tapped something so deep the effect was like a tranquilliser. During those weeks he seemed to be taking in his surroundings and the people they met, but silently. Everything was internalised. Hugh had nothing to declare.

But by now Hat was herself enthusiastic about their plan to learn all they could of Carl Christianson's family and antecedents. Already the sealed envelope from the Maria Parish had been opened and the name of Carl's mother revealed. Other descendants of this woman, Cecilia Haakansson, had been discovered. Contacts had been made, shocks delivered from a distance. With one or two of the older survivors of the family the revelation that great aunt or grandmother Cecilia had had a child out of wedlock had come as an unwelcome surprise. The younger ones, however, had responded warmly to this voice from the world's remotest islands, and had promised welcome, hospitality, and more information if the Gradys should visit them.

So in the early summer of southern Sweden Hugh met his relatives — descendants, as he was, of Carl Christianson's mother. They were good people, with keen blue intelligent eyes, open faces, lean healthy bodies, and good English, spoken with a mournful Nordic intonation. There was at first perhaps a slight feeling of embarrassment that their forebears should have cast out a child in order to conceal his mother's fault, but that was something which soon passed.

As for Hugh's lack of animation — since the family (Haakanssons, Lofqvists, Rosenstroms) had no particular expectations of him, they were not to know it was unusual. In fact, Hat said later, it seemed to pass unnoticed, merging into the slight formality and reserve of Swedish middle-class occasions.

CECILIA HAAKANSSON (so they discovered) was born in 1850, daughter of a rich landowner and farmer residing not far from Helsingborg. As a child she was educated at home; but her skills in music suggested that she would benefit from special tuition, and a tutor was brought every week to the house. Later, when she was in her teens, she and a brother and sister moved to a house in town owned by their father. There was an elderly housekeeper, Minna, a strict and trusted family servant, authorised to watch over them; and their mother came and went, dividing her time between the farm, where the younger children of the family remained, and the town-house. They too, of course, returned from time to time to the farm.

Cecilia began to offer piano lessons to schoolchildren. This occupied her spare time and meant she did not always have to ask her father for spending money. She also sang at social gatherings and her voice attracted notice. Her singing teacher, Christian Svensson, was a Swede who wore velvet jackets and loose cravats, smoked cigarettes rather than cheroots, and talked nostalgically of Paris where he had been a student and where he intended to return just as soon as he could get his affairs sufficiently in order to persuade his wife that they and their two children would be well provided for there. He was Cecilia's teacher for more than three years, and though she learned singing from him, she learned much else as well. He admired her intelligence and soon treated her as an intellectual equal, encouraging her to read Turgenev and the new Russian novelists, telling her about new movements in the arts of France and Germany, and new ideas in philosophy, describing poetic dramas by the Norwegian Henrik Ibsen whom Christian had met two years previously in Stockholm, and playing and singing for her extracts from the new operas of Richard Wagner. These international movements, he believed, would soon sweep away the moralising gloom of the arts in Scandinavia. But to profit by them in the meantime one needed to live abroad, as Ibsen had chosen to do.

Christian Svensson opened for her a small window on a big world making her feel her home town was provincial, intellectually unsatisfying, stultifying especially for a woman with taste and intelligence. He was said to be anti-clerical and politically radical, and to have aroused in her an appetite for things which were considered inappropriate, even dangerous.

She must have been twenty or twenty-one when her father discovered a little of the influence her teacher had been having, and told her that this liberation had gone far enough and that her lessons were to come to an end. But by now she was in love with Christian and he with her.

The discovery, or anyway the suspicion, of their love affair persuaded Christian's wife to accept the return to Paris which he had wanted. He half resisted now, reluctant to leave his new young love behind; and then agreed, persuading himself that she would soon break away from her family and follow him there, where she would find it possible to live a bold free bohemian life.

The plans for his and his family's removal were quickly completed. Underneath all his brave talk about their future in Paris he must have recognised that Cecilia's following him was unlikely — that she would lack the means, and perhaps also the courage. But he let the illusion of it tide them over. What neither of them could have known was that in the passionate and careless love-making that accompanied their final farewells, Cecilia had been made pregnant.

It was Minna, the trusted old servant, who was first told of the pregnancy and who helped Cecilia's mother decide what should be done. It was to be kept secret from all the family, including Cecilia's father. Around the sixth month of the pregnancy she was to be sent away with Minna — it would be said to a health resort, on doctor's orders — and kept out of sight. As soon as the baby was born it would be given to a poor widow, Amalia Becker, a distant cousin of Minna's who was struggling against odds to provide for her three children, and who would be paid a small regular allowance to bring the child up as an orphan. The allowance would rescue the widow and her family from destitution, and see the new child provided for. Cecilia herself did not know where the money came from, how it was paid, nor whether the child's father in Paris contributed. All contact between her and Christian Svensson was broken; and though she probably never loved either of her two husbands as she had loved him, her affair had had such painful consequences there was a long period of her life when she was unable to think of him except with bitterness.

All this time there had been a suitor, Johan Rosenstrom, a respectable young man considered quite suitable by the Haakansson family but not favoured by Cecilia. Returned from the 'health resort', she was once again courted, and no longer discouraged him. She seemed now to have lost all her intellectual pretensions, all interest in the new music and literature, wanting only marriage and children. She was perhaps secretly grieving for the child she had had to give up and whom she was not permitted to visit. After her marriage and the birth of her first child to Rosenstrom, however, Minna yielded to her pleas and arranged for secret visits to Amalia Becker's cottage, where Cecilia was able to see her son, known as the orphan Carl Christianson, and to assure herself that he was well looked after.

It was only when she was a very old woman that Cecilia told her eldest daughter the facts about her first child, born out of wedlock. He had long since left Sweden, she thought for America, and would never return. His father had died in Paris and Christian Svensson's children had grown up as French. There was no longer any reason to tell the story except, Cecilia said, to release it from inside herself, something she felt she needed to do in preparation for her death.

She told her daughter of the visits she had made to the little boy growing up in poverty in a two-roomed white-washed cottage on the coast just out of Helsingborg; and how she had been forbidden to make him expensive gifts which might call attention to their relationship — though even the small things she was permitted to take him seemed to attract notice. She said that at first he had seemed to her the liveliest, brightest, cleverest child in the world; and that later he had seemed no less intelligent, but reserved, and finally with-drawn — resistant to her overtures. She felt that although he said nothing reproachful, and probably would not have dared to, since she must have appeared to him very grand, a 'rich' woman, he had a way of looking at her which seemed to signal that he had guessed their secret, knew she had abandoned him, and blamed her for it.

His accusing eye distressed her; but there was something worse. As he grew old enough to learn mannerly behaviour he always bowed to her on her arrival and at her departure, as a person of low birth in the Sweden of those years bowed to a person of quality. He did it without thought; but at those moments the sight of his neatly trimmed ginger-blonde head, his white neck and small shoulders, caused her more pain than she could bear.

He must have been six or seven when she made her last visit. After that she was absorbed with her own growing family, her three children to Johan Rosenstrom, and after his early death, her hasty marriage to Per Lofqvist, owner of a small shoe-making factory, to whom she had two further children. But the child Carl Christianson remained present to her. The thought of him was like an oppression which

159

seemed sometimes to squeeze out the spontaneity and naturalness that had once been hers. It made her seem to her children a strict and unrelenting mother, suspicious of any interest they took in anything unconventional; and while she recognised this in herself and regretted it, it came from an anxiety she could not properly control. Yet at the same time there was a secret compartment in her life they could never have guessed was there, which led her sometimes to make her way to the poorer parts of the town, and to the docks, believing that one day she would come face to face with her abandoned son.

It was twenty years after his birth, thirteen or fourteen since she had last visited him, that she believed she saw him down on the docks. She found herself caught in a narrow passage between a pile of rope coils on one side and a box of fish in a crane sling on the other. Looking up, her eyes met those of a young sailor who looked at her with an expression which she thought mixed appreciation, enquiry, and faintly impertinent humour. She was disconcerted by the instant conviction that this was her abandoned son, and moved back as if to make way for him. This was quite inappropriate; both her sex and her station gave her the right of way — and the young man, smiling his surprise, stepped back and waved her past him, bowing slightly. She felt faint, held herself steady against the box of fish, and moved forward murmuring thanks. She walked on down the dock, and when at last she found the courage to turn and look, the sailor had gone.

For months afterwards she carried the image of this young man with her, and found herself returning to the waterfront in the hope of seeing him. It must have been a year later that she decided she would visit Amalia Becker and ask what had become of Carl. The cramped rooms of the cottage, their poor furnishings, the signs of extreme poverty and the humbleness of the aging woman in her peasant clothes, renewed Cecilia's sense of guilt, and even before she spoke she was regretting her visit.

In response to her enquiry she was told that Carl

Christianson had left Sweden just before his eighteenth birthday when he would have been due for military service. He had simply vanished; and then written from Kiel to say that he had crossed to Copenhagen where he had signed on as cabin boy on a German freighter. He sent his best and abiding love to his foster mother and to his foster brothers and sister, asking them to remember him always, as he would remember them; but he said Sweden held no promise for his future and he would not be returning. That was almost four years ago, and there had been no word since. Amalia Becker believed he would by now be in America and that they would probably not hear from him again.

She said he was a fine boy, intelligent, sensitive, orderly and reserved, and that he deserved more of life than he had had thus far. She prayed that he would find it in the New World; and she believed he would.

Cecilia felt herself reproached, felt she deserved it, and could find nothing to say. She offered money, which was accepted, and left. That the young man she had met on the wharf could not have been her son disturbed her unreasonably. She felt confused and lost, and once again tried to put the past behind her, only breaking her silence in the year before her death to tell her daughter the story of the abandoned child. The daughter in her turn had written down what she had been told, and this account had been found by Cecilia's grandson after the death of his mother.

WHAT IS VICTORY? What is defeat? What is strength/ weakness? Success/failure? When Lydia Lawrence, in a despairing and briefly quarrelsome moment a few days before Hugh's departure had told him that he lacked the strength to leave Hat he had replied that one might choose to say so, or one might prefer to say he had the strength *not* to leave her.

Might not Christian Svensson have offered the same reply if there had ever been a chance for him to argue it out with Cecilia Haakansson? Was his defeat also a victory? And would the terms of such an argument have been changed if they had known there was to be a child?

In tracking down the facts about Carl Christianson's parentage and relatives — facts of which Carl himself had remained ignorant all his life — had Hugh and Hat achieved a notable success? That which had been hidden was now made known. A darkness had been rolled back — too late to cast a light for the abandoned child either in his infancy or later, but not too late to cast one back upon his memory. Yet the details of the story, so entrancing to Hat, were received by Hugh with increasing despondency. They seemed to make him anxious. The very success of Hat's plan — her Swedish card as he had called it — had the feel of failure about it, and they left Sweden without regret.

AND WHEN JOHN FLATT, whose blood-line was to meet and mix with that of Cecilia Haakansson, returned to Hans Place late in the year of 1837 to give his response to Edward Wakefield's request, was he laying the ground for a victory or a defeat?

Victory, any detached historian would have to say — a 'revenge' beyond anything Flatt could have believed possible when that word had first come into his thoughts one mild still January day on board the *Columbine*. Yet (as Hugh's and everyone's mother was in the habit of saying) nothing is ever simple.

Flatt had sometimes set his imagination free to play, far beyond all likelihood, upon that thought of a revenge. Had he not given a warning in his quotation from Luke 12, where it was said there was 'nothing covered that shall not be revealed; nothing hid that shall not be known'? Had the same passage not warned the missionary body that 'Whatsoever ye have spoken in darkness shall be heard in the light; and that which ye have spoken in the ear shall be proclaimed upon the housetops'? It was from Tarore's gospel he had delivered these messages to the Tauranga natives in their own language. To his principals he must have believed (were they not clergymen?) it had been enough to deliver them by text-reference and innuendo. How could they have received pointed mention of Luke 12 without remembering the verse which says, 'Beware ye the leaven of the Pharisees which is hypocrisy'? How could they not have remembered the story of the rich man who built barns to increase his wealth instead of doing service to the Lord?

But if Flatt had consoled himself with the thought that these dark undertones of warning were hidden in his communications with London, he must also have known that even if they did not go unnoticed, they could not have been properly understood, since the London missionary body remained ignorant of those land purchases and profitable dealings in New Zealand which might embarrass it if made known.

This is something Hugh and Jean-Anne have discussed more than once, puzzling over what seem to be warnings delivered to men who were not in a position to understand them. And it is Hugh who has come upon what they agree seems the most likely explanation. Hugh has discovered that all letters to the Society's Headquarters in London had first to be submitted to Henry Williams's Committee in New Zealand — of which Richard Davis, who had rejected Flatt's services, was secretary. So it was for the members of that New Zealand committee that Flatt's warnings were intended.

Were they noticed, registered, understood? Were they sufficient reason for the recommendation that he should be dismissed? Jean-Anne doubts it. But whatever the reason, Jowett had acted with brutal promptness, never supposing that this was a young man possessing information which could cause the Missionary Society public embarrassment; possessing, furthermore, a motive, and the will, to make use of it.

For Flatt, then, was it to be a victory? Or was he, Samson-like, about to do as much harm to himself as to those who had wronged him? He was a man now with a driving ambition — to return to those plains where he felt he had, for the first and only time, lived life to the limit; and what path was there back other than the missionary one which he was about to render, for himself, impassable?

There can be no doubt that as he knocked at Wakefield's grand, heavy, black-painted door to be received and welcomed, Flatt was lighting a fuse that would burn over distance, twelve thousand miles, and through time, ten years and more. The immediate consequence of his compliance was Wakefield's pamphlet, followed quickly by the New Zealand Association's meeting with the Prime Minister, Lord Melbourne, and the Secretary for the Colonies, Lord Glenelg. At once the Missionary Society was thrown into confusion and uncertainty. Could it be true that their men in the field, clergymen and catechists who were lending strength to the argument against colonisation, were obtaining extensive tracts of land, themselves becoming colonists and making colonists of their children?

On 20 December 1837, one week after the publication of Wakefield's pamphlet, a letter went off from the Society on its long slow journey to New Zealand, requesting facts, answers, explanations — above all rebuttals to Flatt's assertions. These had 'occasioned the Society much Surprise, as we have no Reason to suppose that Purchases of Land have been made by the Missionaries to the Extent asserted. Mr Flatt's Statements operate at the present Moment very prejudicially; for though we disbelieve their Accuracy, we are not in a Situation to contradict them.'

On 9 February 1838 Flatt was called to a meeting of the Society that had dismissed him. It lasted a long time; he was closely questioned, and stuck to his guns.

Was it not true, he was asked, that the missionaries had the welfare of the Natives at heart? They did, he confirmed; but they had their own welfare and that of their families to consider as well. Sometimes the two became confused. In fact there was only one safe way to ensure that they did not — and he pointed out that some missionaries, the Rev Alfred Brown, for example, and Mr William Colenso, had chosen to trust in God as to the future, and had elected not to buy any land except, in Brown's case, a small parcel to be owned by the Society for the establishment of the Matamata mission.

That same day, 9 February, a further letter went out from the Society to its missionary committee in New Zealand. 'Mr Flatt,' it said, 'has asserted the general Accuracy of the Statements made on his Authority in Mr E. G. Wakefield's Letter to Lord Glenelg.' Though some of these statements, it went on, 'might rest on loose and dubious authority', nevertheless it could now 'scarcely be doubted that Tracts of Land of considerable Extent' had been acquired from the Natives. The Society had been caused 'much embarrassment'. The missionaries in New Zealand were therefore reminded of the terms of the Society's Resolution of 27 July 1830 governing acquisition of native lands, and requested to address their minds to Mr Flatt's assertions and give detailed information as to land purchases and holdings.

But before these letters had even reached New Zealand, a Select Committee of the House of Lords meeting to consider the State of the Islands of New Zealand, had called Mr Flatt before it to give evidence. That was in April. In June the House of Commons debated the matter; and on the evening of 20 June it heard Mr Barring, MP, make a speech 'of great length' in which he cited Mr John Flatt as witness to the extent of missionary purchases.

EIGHT

MONDAY EVENINGS bring sons and daughters-in-law, bring grandchildren, bring (this one does) Jean-Anne Devantier and her husband Philip and their evident impending progeny. It is all arranged, agreed to, organised. The grandchildren have been fed and are playing upstairs. There are eight places set at the glass-topped table, where Hugh sits at one end, Hat at the other, the three young couples interlocked and overlapped down the sides in the approved bourgeois manner. Yesterday they got it ready, Hat as cook and kitchen-commandant, Hugh as sous-chef — chopper, peeler, stirrer, mixer, grinder. The courses (minestrone, squid salad, chicken cacciatore, fruit and cheese, cake and coffee, with appropriate wines) come effortlessly now from the kitchen, with pauses for talk and more wine and even cigarettes, the three, Evie, Philip and Hugh, who have lately or long ago given up, taking cigarettes from the one, Richard, who has just relapsed, while the others-who-have-never warn and cajole but say they don't mind, not really — though in recognition of Jean-Anne's condition they smoke only a few and with a window wide open.

It is — this Jean-Anne and Philip addition to the family occasion — a once-only, by agreement; Hat has even welcomed it, but with an overtone of magnanimity and a consequent undertone of reserve. She has been, Hugh is sure of it, suspicious of his friendship and workship with this healthy young librarian-female, more when he doesn't talk about her than when he does. Better to have her here, on display, visibly pregnant and with her very presentable husband.

And now Hat is locked in conversation with Philip, a young medic, GP returned to Auckland Hospital where he is specialising in pathology. There has been in the past day or so a killing — several killings by one man — and Philip has seen all the bodies and done the post-mortem on one, a woman. Since the killer killed himself there will be no trial, no chance that the depositions and accompanying forensic evidence will come before District Court Judge Harriet Enverson, and they are able to talk about it freely. He is describing the wounds inflicted by shotgun — the first fired at close quarters, out of doors, and deflected by the victim's outstretched hand so that it sprayed along her right arm, across her upper body, and along the other arm, without inflicting a fatal wound. Leaving a trail of blood she ran in to call the police but in her panic and distress neglected to lock the door. Her call got through, but as she talked to the police operator she was shot in the body at close range. The third shot was point blank, straight into the middle of her face as she lay on the floor. Philip is explaining to Hat, who is accustomed to photographs and accounts of such matters, how with shotgun wounds at close quarters there is always, in addition to the pellets, a wad from the cartridge, and how he had to hunt for it inside the head, finding it at last buried deep in the back of the throat.

There is a curious excitement around the table, a mixture of horror and something bordering on hilarity, hands across mouths concealing perhaps nausea, perhaps nervously inappropriate smiles. Rising to it, Philip says he has hardened himself to dealing with human flesh and bone, but not to the smell of decomposition. In this case it was bad because the wound was to the liver and the body was left lying overnight where it fell. He tells them the young cops who bring bodies to the post-mortem room put Vicks in their nostrils.

Hugh observes that Philip's face is pale and slightly drawn, and that he is probably more loquacious than usual.

He thinks there may be a bravado which conceals shock. He thinks he notices Jean-Anne noticing him notice this. It's as though in the moment of eye contact they have had a brief concerned exchange, an aside *sotto voce*, agreeing that Philip is showing signs of the strain but that this is to be expected and no cause for alarm. Hugh is pleased and at the same time disconcerted by the sense of an intimacy — as if he has a more instant rapport with this young woman than with his own sons.

He has some idea of shotgun wounds. Silent, he is remembering the deep scars all down his father's emaciated right arm, and the paralysed hand which as a small child he used to try to prise open. He thinks of the Beaumont farm, and wonders why he never asked his father to show him where the accident happened. He thinks of James Grady wandering over those fields in later life, knowing exactly the place on some distant fenceline where he had pushed his gun ahead of him, where the trigger snagged in a bush and the safety-catch failed to operate. He imagines his father staggering across fields and over fences, through manuka and swamp, skirting the bush, desperate to get back to the house but not making it, collapsing from loss of blood, his wounded arm under him, his own weight checking the bloodflow.

It was a neighbour-farmer out looking for a sick cow who saw something in the twilight he mistook for the missing animal. Somehow James's relatives got him to the house, bound up the torn flesh and shattered bones, carried him on a trap through most of one long night to a hospital. There was to be an amputation, but before there was anyone to do it pneumonia had set in, and by the time he was strong enough for the operation it was decided that his arm could be kept. He was eighteen years old; spent more than a year in hospital, neglected by his turbulent, distracted and bibulous father, recovering slowly, learning meanwhile how to write with the left hand, how to tie shoelaces one-handed, how to use a knife and a fork alternately, not knowing that his mother was dying; until the day when a patient reading the *Herald* death notices in the next bed asked if he was related to Nellie Grady. He said that he was and was told that she was dead.

Hugh thinks of how one part of the line might have vanished that evening in Kaiwaka, leaked away in a swampy field in the fading light; and that what would have replaced it, in the form of some other husband for his mother, would also have displaced himself and these children and grandchildren — which in turn would have meant (since the man his mother would have married must in real life have married someone else) further displacement of other lines — on and on, how far? It is a dizzying thought, ripples spreading endlessly outward in space — in space-and-time — like the boy on the Bycroft's biscuit tin of Hugh's childhood, who ran, his scarf flying behind him, carrying under one arm a tin of Bycroft's biscuits with a picture of a boy carrying . . . On, like mirrors mirroring one another, a whole generation's first lesson in the horror of infinity.

He looks up and sees Jean-Anne looking at him. He smiles faintly; she returns his smile in a way that seems to ask a question. He lifts the cigarette Richard has given him and nods towards it by way of answer, thinking it is the unfamiliarity of the smoke, and the strength of the brand, that has given him this momentary feeling of faintness. In a voice that is too loud and sudden, so that he surprises himself, he sends a question down the table to Philip. Listening to the answer he hears at the same time, and is distracted by, the beginning of Jean-Anne's answer to a question from Richard about John Flatt. It is like changing queues and finding the one you left because it was stalled is now moving faster; or boarding one of two buses and seeing the other head off in the direction you meant to take. He hears her say, 'You become involved. There's a temptation to take sides. But that's no good. Only the truth's interesting. That's what we're after.'

THE TRUTH — YES INDEED. It was a commodity always said to be prized, but not always welcome, and when John Flatt made his way to Westminster on 3 April 1838, called there at the instigation of Edward Gibbon Wakefield, to give evidence before a Select Committee of the House of Lords, he knew that if he was to offer truths they must come from him without decoration, plain and unvarnished. He was of yeoman stock, a solid and simple man, yet not so simple as to be unaware of the danger of feeling oneself suddenly elevated beyond one's station. Pausing to look at the ruins of the old Palace of Westminster, which had burned down (he now knew) ten days before the *Prince Regent* had carried him and Colenso and the Wades into Sydney Harbour in 1834, he remembered what his father had told him, echoing his own thought, as he had set out from Deptford. 'Keep a cool head. Tell the truth, and don't babble. It's not you they're interested in, remember. It's what you know.'

He was called that afternoon to give evidence, and again three days later; and the panoply and comfort even of the Upper Chamber's temporary quarters, the hauteur of the noble Lords in committee and of their Chairman Lord Devon, the officiousness of their lackeys who directed him hither and yon, reminded him again that neither forelock-tugging, nor charm, nor piety, pride, boldness, would earn him attention or advance his credibility. There was one fact, and one only, which brought him here, and it was that he had travelled that vast distance to New Zealand, had crossed and recrossed its land and waterways, had worked among its missionaries, had seen its natives at peace and at war, had learned to speak their language and understood something of their ways. In that, and in that alone, lay his authority and his confidence.

His answers were level and factual. No person and no policy was attacked or defended. It was as if he were speaking without interest in what their Lordships might make of the intelligence he was able to put before them; and in that appearance there lay, not dishonesty, but forethought — even (Dandeson Coates Esq, who would have to follow him, might have considered) a degree of cunning.

He was not, however, able to resist saying at once that he had been sent out by the Society as agriculturist to assist on the mission farm at Waimate, 'in order that Mr Davis might be more at liberty to attend to his catechetical Duties and the Spiritual Concerns of the Natives'; but that 'Mr Davis refused to accept of my Assistance', and as a consequence he had been sent south to the new mission station at Matamata.

He described his work teaching the Native adults and children at the mission station. Asked about their intelligence he said he had found them 'very intelligent; not at all inferior in point of intellect to Europeans.'

On the subject of land, reverted to many times in the course of the questioning, he insisted that the chiefs were anxious to sell, knew what they were doing when they sold, and felt they stood to gain by it; and that there was much land available.

Asked to illustrate this point, John Flatt offered by way of example that place he hoped to return to: 'I have passed over fifty Miles of Country with not an Acre cultivated, fine rich soil from Puriri to Matamata by Land, crossing the River Thames twice.'

Asked whether he had been offered land himself, he said he had, 'but I had no Payment to give them, neither did I want any.'

On the subject of missionary purchases he needed to volunteer no names, their Lordships, it seemed, having been provided in advance with an alphabetical list; and in response to each question — about Baker, Clarke, Davis, Fairburn, Kemp, King, Williams — he was able to confirm that a purchase had been made and to describe its location and extent.

He had, he said, ridden over Henry Williams's land and considered it to be seven square miles in extent. He had been present at the Fairburn purchase — indeed had been a witness to the document of transfer. The extent of the land had been 'quite a County; an immense large Tract.' But he had been told by some of the Natives present (and he repeated this fact four times in the course of his two days of testimony) that it had been previously sold to another, or others, European.

Asked whether he was 'not of opinion that the Labours of the Missionaries have been successful as far as might be expected?' he replied that they had been successful, but that he thought 'greater Effect might be given to them if their Minds were relieved from those secular Things which press so heavily upon them.'

Questioned about Waharoa's war and the circumstances which had led to his being stripped at the foot of the Kaimais in October 1836 he gave a long and, for the first and only time, incoherent answer, which must have left their Lordships confused.

Asked why the Arawa natives who had taken everything had left him his horse, he replied that he thought possibly they had never seen a horse before.

His horse was discussed, but not his young friend Tarore. No mention was made of her, nor even that a death had occurred.

PHILIP IS STILL TALKING to Hat about forensic pathology. Hugh imagines for a moment Dr Devantier in the witness box, Judge Harriet Enverson on the bench, Richard Grady, QC (Hugh awards his son the 'QC' in advance of what he hopes will one day be the fact), counsel for the prosecution, asking the witness to describe Tarore's wounds — the axe blow to the head, the bullet wound, the opened ribcage, the tearing out of the heart. 'Ehara, ko te tamaiti o Ngakuku ka mate i Te Wairere,' shouts the accused defiantly from the dock.

But Hugh amends that. There is no accused. The dock is empty. This is the inquest of History. Tarore's murderers, according to one report, died a year or so later in an attack on Waharoa's pa. By that time her St Luke Gospel, which they had stolen along with everything else Flatt's party had been carrying over the mountains, was being read in Rotorua by those who would later say it influenced them towards Christianity and peace.

Hat's voice and Philip's recede, lose focus. Now Hugh is again listening to the conversation in which Richard is asking

172

Jean-Anne about their research. The keenness of Richard's questions surprises Hugh. He has sometimes wondered why his sons seldom enquire about their distant forebear, and then has reminded himself how little interest he took, as a young man, in his grandmother's and his parents' stories about their past, so that now he often has occasion to regret the questions it is too late to ask. Richard's present interest, he decides, is not in the subject but in Jean-Anne. Or rather, the subject has truly engaged his mind, but only because the vehicle of this information is an intelligent and very attractive young woman.

Hugh feels no resentment. It is as it should be. If anything he feels satisfaction at this demonstration to his sons and daughters-in-law that he is not occupied in some dusty and pointless rifling of the family vault, but in the piecing together of a story (which is many stories) sufficiently rich in puzzling questions, and adequately rewarded with significant answers, to engage the mind and emotions of a talented young woman. He knows now why he has wanted to overcome Hat's slight resistance and invite Jean-Anne to one of these family occasions. Since Frank Mangold's funeral and the intimations of elderliness that followed it, Jean-Anne has been for Hugh a kind of accreditation to the world of the young and still-viable. He is happy now to sit back and let her do the talking.

Richard is telling her that Hugh has been referring to John Flatt's disclosures in London as 'the gardener's revenge'. He says it sounds like the name of a British pub.

Jean-Anne says it's difficult to be quite sure of Flatt's social status. He was appointed as an 'agriculturalist', and described in the 1838 wedding register of St Andrews Parish, Holborn, as 'farmer'; but when those he had displeased wanted to minimise his importance they referred to him as a 'gardener'; or in the case of the Rev Maunsell, in his diatribe against Flatt ('How treacherously has he that did eat bread with us lifted up the heel against us') as a 'farm labourer'. Flatt's father, she says, was described as a farmer. Two of his forebears had stood for Parliament. He wrote well, decently and clearly, though with no sign of higher education. And when he pointed out in a letter to Jowett that Christ had chosen fishermen for disciples, not Oxbridge graduates, he was clearly meaning that his own modest status should be no disqualification for missionary work. Finally, his occupation on his death certificate was given as gardener.

So 'gardener', she says — yes, as long as the designation wasn't used to suggest an unlettered clodhopper.

As for 'the gardner's revenge'. Certainly — even if it was one that cost him dearly. But it took effect slowly, over a long period. 'He lit a slow fuse,' she says, 'and it needed other forces to bring about the consequent damage to his enemies. But the damage was real, much worse than he would have thought possible. If he'd imagined the outcome he might have held back, I suppose — but I doubt it.'

'What damage exactly?' Richard wants to know.

'The damage that followed on the gardener's revenge? Ah well . . .' And Jean-Anne enumerates.

WILLIAM FAIRBURN WAS THE FIRST TO FALL. The Tamaki purchase had been too large, too conspicuous, too near to what was now being called 'land-sharking' for the principals of the Church Missionary Society to stomach. Nor, when it became plain that Fairburn was determined to hold on to a large part of it, could they swallow the explanation that such a swathe of the Auckland isthmus had been bought only in order to make peace between warring tribes.

It took time for the questions and replies to go back and forth; but on 17 January 1840, and with the acquiescence of senior missionaries in New Zealand, it was resolved that William Fairburn should be asked to resign, on the understanding that he might remain honourably superannuated, with a small pension in recognition of his years of work for the mission.

Fairburn deeply resented this, and spent the remainder of his life arguing to ears wilfully deaf that the Society which had dismissed him for the purchase had been, through the agency of the Rev Henry Williams, a party to it.

Meanwhile all members of the Society in New Zealand were being asked to supply Salisbury Square with details of their land holdings, and to comment on the problem. Those who responded often protested at the imputation of particular wrong-doing, while at the same time admitting it in general. Recent, and therefore innocent, arrivals wrote more in sorrow than in anger of their brethren who had compromised the missionary cause. Those who had kept within the Society's strict limit on land purchase furnished the promptest and clearest replies.

Henry Williams and Richard Davis prevaricated, arguing, after the February 1840 signing of a Treaty with the Natives at Waitangi, that precise information about their holdings could not be supplied until the new land commissioners had ruled on them, as the Governor now required.

But the mills of God ground on in London, slow and fine. Even the largest space the world could put between employer and employee, and the obstacles of wild winds and unpredictable waters, could only delay, not prevent, the inevitable. And there were now a Bishop and a Governor in New Zealand, both eagle-eyed, the one wanting to expunge, the other to expose, missionary transgressions.

On 20 May 1843, Richard Davis, elevated since Flatt's departure from catechist to ordained priest — the man who had boasted of the heavy burden of his missionary work but had rejected the assistance of a young agriculturalist who might have observed precisely how, and with what profit to himself, his labours were apportioned — was writing to a friend in London that he had been appointed to serve at Kaikohe, and that in consequence he must leave the mission farm he had in effect made his own business, his private estate, his domain: 'This I HAVE FELT ACUTELY, yea, and DO FEEL IT. I could never have supposed the Church Missionary Society could have treated a faithful servant in such a way. To be rendered houseless after twenty years of faithful servitude, is calculated to make me FEEL. I HAVE SERVED THE SOCIETY FAITHFULLY . . . To live and die for the benefit of the heathen is the wish of my heart. But to treat me so uneeremoniously . . . I CANNOT THINK THE SOCIETY CAPABLE OF SUCH BEHAVIOUR TOWARDS ME. There is some mystery in the case.'

But there was no mystery. Salisbury Square had had enough of this long-running embarrassment, and was simply determined to be rid of it. Henry Williams — Archdeacon, as he had now become — was next.

Williams, who had served in the British Navy during the Napoleonic Wars, fought long and hard, with courage and resolution — against the Bishop and the Governor in New Zealand, and against the Society in London. After the signing of the Waitangi Treaty the land commissioners halved his 22,000-acre holding, and he had no choice but to accept their decision. When the Church required him to reduce it still further he pointed out that he had transferred the titles to his children, and consequently no longer had power to do so.

The complexities (Jean-Anne explains to the table, who are all now listening) would take too long to unravel. What it came down to in the end, she says, was that the Society's Parent Committee required him to reduce his family holdings to 2560 acres. He refused.

On 30 November 1849, eleven years after the gardener had put the London clerical cat among the New Zealand clerical pigeons, Archdeacon Henry Williams was dismissed.

THERE IS A SILENCE when Jean-Anne comes to the end of her recital; a collective in-drawing of breath. Hugh guesses it contains a certain family satisfaction, a willingness to believe, but also a grain or two of doubt. Could a man subsequently so anonymous, so buried in the public record and long-forgotten, have been responsible for so much? He answers the question before anyone puts it. It is, he tells them, not unlike the small action that sets off an avalanche in the mountains; or the single match that destroys a hundred acres of bush. And Jean-Anne agrees. If the missionaries had not been buying up tracts of land without letting their superiors in London know, Flatt could have done them no harm. His weapon, she says, was truth — he had only to tell it to

Wakefield, and Davis and Williams were in trouble. And by recommending Flatt's dismissal they had given him a motive.

But how good a motive was it? Had Flatt really been treated badly? What if he hadn't been good at his work? Lawyer Richard asks the question, and Judge Harriet nods from the bench. 'Surely it's not safe just to accept an employee's uncorroborated complaints against his bosses.'

Hugh and Jean-Anne exchange smiles. They've discussed this — often. The evidence seems to support Flatt's account. But in the past week they've discovered something further. Their new folder of notes is labelled 'The Case of William Wade'; and Hugh explains to the table how they stumbled on the story only when they found a letter of Flatt's written to Salisbury Square in 1840 after his return to New Zealand, referring once again to the actions of the Committee which had 'disengaged' him from the Missionary Society, and adding darkly, 'You will see it has come home to them in the case of Mr Wade.'

Hugh had lost sight of William Wade, who sailed with Flatt and Colenso in 1834. So in the past week he has borrowed microfilms of Wade's letters to London and worked his way through them.

What he has found is a 'case' exactly parallel to Flatt's. Wade was appointed by the London body as superintendent of the Mission Press, while Colenso was to be its printer. On arrival in the Bay of Islands Colenso was set to work at once, printing translations of the Gospels into Maori; but Wade was told that a superintendent would not be needed. Supervision of the Press would be in the hands of Mr Davis. Wade was to be sent south where he would work as a catechist in one of the new stations.

Like Flatt, Wade complained — direct to Henry Williams, and by letter to Salisbury Square, but to no effect. Sent south to work at the Tauranga station he became absorbed in his dealings with the tribes.

'His letters didn't allow Jowett to forget that he was still kept out of the post he'd been appointed to,' Hugh tells them; 'but he also made it clear how he was entering into the excitement of bringing the message of peace to tribes at war. He might even have let the matter of the Press lapse — it's possible; but after a time he was ordered back to the Bay of Islands.'

That would have been, Hugh thinks, around the time that Flatt was returning to London. Prevented in the Bay of Islands from doing the work he'd been appointed to do, and unable to return south where he had enjoyed himself, Wade now wrote more indignantly to London, and this time his complaints got a response. Instructions were sent that the printing press should be removed from Paihia to Waimate, and that Wade should take charge of it.

Williams and Davis, however, were adroit in working around instructions that didn't accord with their own views and plans — expert at (and Hugh quotes Wade's words to London) 'a politic appearance of carrying a measure into effect, with a positive intention of finally frustrating it.'

But at such a distance the London Committee had only limited powers to adjudicate. And by now there was a larger problem occupying their minds — the embarrassment of John Flatt's revelations about land purchases. Compared to this, the problem with the Press was minor.

'Wade continued underemployed and dissatisfied,' Hugh goes on. 'Late in 1838 he wrote asking to be called home, saying it was four years since he'd left England, and throughout that time he'd been kept out of the situation he was engaged to occupy. The reply from London made soothing noises. They were sorry for him. But it wasn't a recall — and that was it. He'd had enough. He resigned. He'd arranged a new job for himself in Australia. That was January 1840. It must have been the point of Flatt saying it had "come home to them in the case of Mr Wade". He and Wade had caught up with one another at last in the Bay of Islands just before the signing of the Treaty, and they'd found their situations were exactly parallel — both baulked by Davis, who was backed up by Williams. Davis had been determined to keep control of everything — the mission farm, the Press, everything.'

BUT ALL OF THAT LAY in the future. Having given his information to Wakefield in December 1837, and then, four months later, to the House of Lords, John Flatt fades for a time from the public record.

What happened to him between those dates and his reappearance back in New Zealand at the beginning of 1840? Hugh knows a little, but there are gaps. Here is the summary he has prepared for Jean-Anne:

'Flatt and Caroline Haslip met before he set out for New Zealand, and exchanged letters while he was away. Their engagement was announced early in 1838, after his return to London.

'They practised singing together (St Andrews' Church Choir), visited one another's parents, went for walks in parks and squares, etc. He records talking "incessantly" of New Zealand — plans are made not just for marriage but emigration, including Caroline's younger brother, Reuben Haslip, and sister Mary Anne. Their enthusiasm made Caroline less apprehensive but added to Flatt's anxiety, because responsibility for success fell entirely on him.

'E. G. Wakefield had promised help but was in Canada with Lord Durham during these months; but an Admiral Hawker (surely prompted by Wakefield?) suggested Flatt and his party might go to South Australia where a post could be arranged in the service of three Hawker sons establishing themselves there as farmers and market gardeners. This proposal, helpfully intended, became the cause of friction. Flatt's journal makes clear he has no other purpose than to get back to New Zealand. But for Caroline, South Australia would do as well — better, she decided, when she was told the Australian natives were not cannibals.

'While this difference continued she was urging Flatt to write some kind of begging letter to Dandeson Coates, asking the Missionary Society to help outfit them, he refusing on the grounds that he could never ask a favour of those who had wronged him. Caroline thought the Society owed him something and that his scruple was foolish. Told him so, and that she had already composed the letter in her head. His journal records her foot stamping and weeping when he refused to write it — engagement "at an end".

'Flatt doesn't appear to have taken this seriously, but it must have had its effect, because on 13 August 1838, exactly ten days before the date set for marriage, she dictated and he wrote a letter to Coates, liberally sprinkled with "Sirs", promises of gratitude, bizarre anticipations of happy meetings in the world beyond death, etc.

'No record of how it was received, whether it had its intended result, but when Flatt next writes they are in Adelaide.'

'OUR REVELS NOW ARE ENDED and these our actors, as I foretold you, are melted into air, into thin air, and like the baseless fabric of this vision . . .'

Awake and not wanting to be, suffering from having overeaten at the family table, and perhaps from climbing the hill too quickly on his walk before bed, Hugh is trying to put all thought of 'the case of Mr Wade', and all questions that flow from it, out of his head, lulling himself back towards sleep by running through irrelevant mindless remembered things — verses, lists, bank account numbers, the registration numbers of cars he has owned, names of schoolmates, poems, the words of songs.

'And like the baseless fabric of this vision — the cloud-capped towers, the gorgeous palaces, the solemn temples, Yea, the great Globe itself . . .'

'*Gorgeous* palaces?' Could that be right?

> So ist die Lieb'! So ist die Lieb'!
> Mit Küssen nicht zu stillen:
> wer ist der Tor und will ein Sieb
> mit eitel Wasser füllen?
> und schöpfst du an die tausend Jahr'
> und küssest ewig, ewig gar,
> du tust ihr nie zu Willen.

He sings it under his breath, and Hat stirs in the bed beside him.

Die Lieb', die Lieb' hat alle Stund . . .

But he can't remember what it is love always offers.

He brings up image and voice, Jean-Anne singing him Hugo Wolf lieder in the archives room on his birthday, while in some other room in his brain the whakapapa is repeated: John Flatt and Caroline Haslip were the parents of Robert Flatt, father of Charlotte Flatt who married Carl Christianson whose daughter Ethel Elena married James Grady whose twin-son Hugo-and-Wolf united with Harriet Jane Enverson to send through sons Richard and John, and grandchildren Louise and Daniella, Freddie and Carlo, those boundless post-Wagnerian possibilities of ear and throat and lung — on they go, forward, into that not-quite infinity which is what we now know, or think we know, the future to be.

Was that all? Were there no branch lines, no side tracks?

Die Lieb', die Lieb' hat alle Stund

Now he remembers — it brings new strange joys. Kissing, they bit one another's lips until it hurt:

> neu wunderlich Gelüsten;
> wir bissen uns die Lippen wund,
> da wir uns heute küsten.

Hat moves again and mutters something in her sleep, not wanting to be woken.

He tries to run through the heavyweight boxing champions of the world up to Joe Louis who was the champ when he was at school and knew such things, but finds some have slipped down through the cracks of recollection.

He asks himself questions: who held the world record for the pole vault in 1946? Answer: Cornelius Warmeradam (USA). Height? Forgotten. High jump? Lester Steers (USA). Height? Six feet 10 and a quarter inches, perhaps? Half mile? Sydney Wooderson, (GB). One minute 49.4 seconds. Definitely . . .

He repeats the first sentence in his third-form science textbook: 'The protozoan amoeba respires by simple diffusion through the cell walls.'

Now he runs through the names of those stations which together used to make up the sentence meaning 'The summer holiday is over and it's back to school for Hugo and Wolf': Kaiwaka, Topuni, Te Hana, Wellsford, Hoteo, Kaipara Flats, Woodcocks, Ahuroa, Tahakaroa, Kanoki, Kaukapakapa, Helensville, Wharepapa, Woodhill, Rewiti, Waimauku, Huapai, Kumeu, Taupaki, Waitakere, Swanson . . . Before he has quite reached the Auckland isthmus and the new school term he has fallen into a kind of sleep.

In his dream, which is not quite, or not entirely, a dream, but rather a deep recall suspended and controlled in the limbo half-light between sleep and waking, he is looking down into a pool shaped like a large deep saucer, its sides and floor loose scoria rocks. That is what is strange. Those rocks would not hold the water; it would seep through and around them. Underneath there must be something impermeable. The water is clean and clear. Nothing grows in it — no weeds or grasses. Tadpoles swim in it; the insects he knows as boatmen, with tiny oars on either side of their bodies, scull across the surface, and dragonflies hover above it. From the grasses around comes the croaking of frogs.

Now he is walking up Queen's Avenue, on the side where there are no houses, along a track under pepper trees. The track swerves a little to left and right according to the thickness of the trunks. You step over the larger roots which bulge across the track. When you walk there with a friend you go in single file, and you don't speak. It is bad luck to talk under pepper trees.

At Matipo Street he turns right, crosses Kensington Avenue, and goes into the alleyway that leads to Marsden Avenue and Centennial Park. There is a sign pointing to a public air-raid shelter. Not a shelter that has been constructed; just the surface broken in the back garden of a house, and steps down into one of the scoria caves that run with the old lava flows under houses and gardens. He walks through Centennial Park, turns left into Peary Road, climbs the hill to Landscape Road, turns into Whitworth Street and down a path to the tennis courts.

Beyond the clubhouse that looks like a concrete bunker he climbs the fence into unused land, full of gorse and blackberry and fennel among scoria outcrops, following a track until it brings him to a stone wall. He climbs the wall and looks into the garden. There are fish ponds and fruit trees and a girl with long red hair and freckles. Her father is a sailor. She has four sisters. Her name is Lois.

They walk together over the unoccupied land to the cave that opens like a mouth with broken teeth in the side of the hill — one of the lower slopes of Three Kings. She says she is afraid to go any further.

He goes deep into the cave and smells the dark damp earth smell, and listens to water dripping from the roof on to the stone floor. He looks back and sees that the sky has become a small jagged-edged cutout of bright blue paper, growing smaller as he goes further down into the darkness. There he . . .

He wakes right up — sits up, in fact. The image has come to him of Jean-Anne smiling at him enquiringly across the glass-topped table. All at once he has remembered who she is like, why she seems so familiar.

THERE IS VERY LITTLE RECORD of John Flatt's stay in South Australia. From time to time he wrote to the Rev Jowett in London, letters that were sometimes informative, sometimes angry, sometimes teasing, enclosing cuttings from an Adelaide newspaper with reports of land-sharking in New Zealand and of the alleged greed of the missionaries in buying property there.

There is the letter — surely a joke — in which he informs the Society that he may soon be sailing for New Zealand in a vessel called the *True Love*, there to act 'as agent for gentlemen who wish to purchase surplus land from the missionaries'.

In another, having adopted a jaunty tone, he suddenly veers off into bitterness, concluding, 'I believe the following questions should be put to Mr Richard Davis: *why* did he not accept of my assistance? And why does his elder son James receive pay from the Church Missionary Society and continue to farm for himself on land acquired by his father? I am very thankful, Sir, when I consider that my Lot *is not, and never was*, left in the hand of Davis.'

It is clear from what he later wrote that Adelaide was for him tantalisingly close, yet impossibly far, from what had become his dream. He felt baulked, defeated, and took out his frustration sometimes on the Missionary Society which had treated him unfairly, sometimes on the new colony. In what seemed to him the heat and dryness and harsh light of the place he remembered mild airs, abundant rain, soft light and flowing waters; in the grey and brown of its landscape he longed for greens and blues. Working among class-conscious English settlers determined to hold on to the social status which they had brought from home but which the circumstances of the colony threatened, he discovered a nostalgia for that freedom from his own past and class which New Zealand had given him, and for the tribes whose ways, though alien, barbaric and often incomprehensible, had shown him excitements, taught him independence, and opened his consciousness to another world, and even another language, than his own.

How he was employed in Adelaide, and by whom, is never explained. The only possible hint comes in the form of a Government House letter from George Hall, private secretary to the Governor of South Australia, 'consenting to offer no objection or impediment to Mr John Flatt's proceeding to New Zealand', and affirming that 'his Excellency the Governor has expressed the same disposition'.

Since no permission was required to travel it seems Flatt must have been in the service of the Governor, and at his own request he was being released. But of this Hugh can find no proof.

What is clear is that Caroline was pregnant, and that Flatt wanted their first child born in the country where he hoped they would live out the remainder of their lives. His last letter from Adelaide is dated 16 November 1839, and he says, with evident pleasure and excitement, that his next address will be the Bay of Islands. Seven weeks later he was to arrive in the Hokianga harbour — almost exactly five years after Gilbert Mair had taken him off the *Blackbird* and brought him ashore with Colenso and the Wades. A few days later their first child, Joseph, was born on a litter carried by natives, bringing Caroline from the Hokianga to Paihia — the first New Zealand baby, his twentieth century descendants might in due course claim, born in a taxi. After the birth it is said Caroline sang to her baby for the remainder of the journey.

The singing whakapapa was under way.

PART
THREE

NINE

LONG BEFORE JAMES GRADY DIED, business had stopped booming. He used to say that as a one-armed bandit he had had the luck of the Irish. His had been the good years for bad business. He'd had a licence to import certain things, and no competition. If the times had required him to be good at business he would have gone bust in a week. Oh for the days of bad business! he liked to croon tunelessly in his bath. Two cheers for Protectionism (on principle he never gave three cheers for anything), and none for the Free Market!

James Grady died quietly one evening in his chair in front of the television. His heart, he had said, had been 'playing the jumbo lately' (he may have meant the mambo), but he had relayed this information casually, almost inaudibly, so that no one would take fright, and no one did. 'It's boring me to death you are,' he said to the box, putting on his fake Irish accent — and closed his eyes.

It was, Frank Mangold had observed at James's funeral, 'the great Post-Colonial death'. The last sight those Irish eyes, which had never left New Zealand's shores, had smiled upon had been the chimney pots of Coronation Street.

Finding herself alone, Ethel Elena declared that she would waste no time in following him. But first, and as a way of coming to terms with her sense of loss, there was the small matter of her life story. Determined not to go out of the world without leaving a record of her otherwise unremarked sojourn in it, she bought herself a supply of school exercise books and began to write. It was her intention — possibly even her principal object — to include her husband in the

189

story and to do honour to his memory; but like many with the autobiographical itch, Ethel wrote fluently of her childhood, after which energy, or memory, or confidence — probably, indeed, all three — began to falter and fade.

She took to walking up to the Mt Eden shopping centre with her stick and sitting on a public bench, waiting like a spider for a fly. Hugh would see her there and wave as he drove by to the Training College. She would talk to whoever took the seat beside her and had time and the inclination to listen. 'If you're in a hurry, dear,' she would say, 'I won't trouble you by beginning.'

To tell the later parts of her story, she had discovered, was easier than to write them; and so they were issued in random instalments to residents who promptly forgot all, or all but some small fragment. A terrible waste, Ethel admitted; but there was a certain pleasure in it — like taking money out of the bank and giving it away to strangers. And it was important that it should be told here in Mt Eden, in sight of the hill. Stories, she believed, even the forgotten ones, were like a fragrance released. They remained in the air of the place.

When she died, three years after her husband, Hugh found among her papers the exercise books containing her abandoned autobiography. She had called it *Venus is Setting*. It told, or began to tell, the story of three lives — her parents' and her own; and she had incorporated into it the facts which Hugh and Hat had only a few years earlier uncovered during their visit to Sweden.

The title came from an anecdote about her birth. She had 'first looked upon the world', she explained in her opening sentence, at 5.30 a.m. in a house in Elgin Street, Ponsonby, Auckland, on 24 January 1905. Master Mariner Carl Christianson, her father, was somewhere on the high seas at the time; but the baby was delivered by a midwife and handed at once to its grandmother, Charlotte's mother Annie, who waited at the door. It was then that the midwife went to the window and observed that Venus was setting.

'I have often wondered,' Ethel had written, concluding

her opening paragraph, 'whether my life would have been less ordinary if Venus had been rising.' She had then crossed out 'ordinary' and written 'unsatisfactory'. Finally 'unsatisfactory' had been replaced by 'disappointed'.

Reading that sentence and its amendments, Hugh wondered whether, if *Venus is Setting* had ever been brought to completion, that would have been her final word, or whether another would have replaced it.

CARL CHRISTIANSON COULD NOT SAY at what age he understood that the Widow Becker was not his true mother, and that his brothers and sister were so only in name. It must have come to him very young, together with the realisation that the rich woman in the carriage who came to visit and to take him for drives in the countryside was the mother who had abandoned him.

There was one memory of this visitor — Madam, as he was instructed to call her — more vivid than any other. He was perhaps five years old. It was summer, the trees were in full leaf, the sun was on the water, and she took him in her carriole on a road out of town that wound along the coast. She had two or three small packets of food, some chocolates, and something sweet to drink in a flask. They came to a place where there was a ramp for small boats, and she must either have brought a fishing line, or persuaded Amalia Becker to let him bring one, because his next recollection was that he was standing at the edge of the ramp pulling in a small beaked fish, bright silver and with black markings.

He was very excited by the fish — it was perhaps the first he ever caught — but not so excited as Madam, who was running up and down the slippery ramp, shouting and laughing so wildly he was afraid she would fall into the water. He was surprised that a rich lady should behave in that way; and he was struck for the first time by the recognition that she was beautiful. Afterwards they sat in the grass and in a moment never to be repeated he rested his head in her lap while she stroked his hair with an ungloved hand. For a few minutes he allowed himself to think that after this it would not be possible for her to leave him — but the visit ended as usual. He was returned to Mother Amalia, and Madam drove away, as she always did, staring ahead with tears in her eyes.

His foster-mother was always kind to him, as were his brothers and sister. But there was an unspoken understanding that he was set apart from them. He was never beaten as the other children sometimes were. Special little cakes were sometimes made for him. He was kept warm, and any sign of illness in him seemed to cause them concern. His birthday presents, though few and small, were always more than the mere tokens received by the others.

It satisfied his childish ego to feel that he was in some way deserving of privilege; but it was also a source of unease. The more he was special the more he was alone; and he began to resent the visits by the rich woman in her furs and carriage.

Once when his sister Betty had been reading to him the nursery story about the goose that laid the golden egg, she ended it by ruffling his hair and saying, 'So there you see, Master Goose' — laughing in a way that made him remember it.

He found schoolwork easy, was acknowledged to be clever, and could soon read and write better than his older siblings; but school was not a place he enjoyed or would leave with regret. Sitting as still and as quiet as 'good' children were supposed to do on the hard benches was a torment; and although learning the catechism and the Books of the Bible was easy for him, merely a matter of listening and remembering, there was something so harsh and unlovely about the way religion and biblical history were delivered, it laid down in his mind, long before the wonderful and liberating possibility of unbelief had occurred to him, the recognition that talk about God-and-Heaven-and-Hell was loudest in people and in places a boy with good sense, or good taste, would want most to avoid.

But for young Carl Christianson school lasted only a short time. At the age of ten work was found for him. He was sent inland to a farm where his foster-brother Martin was already employed. From then until he left Sweden at the age of seventeen, Carl was a farmhand and shepherd.

The farmhouse was a large low rambling brick building with a tall, steep-pitched roof of thatch. The drive that approached it was of orange gravel lined with willows pollarded in autumn to huge stumpy knuckles, and in spring sending out long sprays of fine branches like green wigs that were soon casting shade. On either side of the drive, close to the farmhouse, were timber buildings, also thatched — barns, the granary, the housing for farm workers.

Each day he was woken early and given his breakfast of herrings and coffee — not the brew of potato cake burned black and ground to powder which Mother Amalia offered, but real coffee such as he had tasted previously only at Christmas and birthdays. After that he was given a good-sized parcel of bread and cheese, and sent out for the day into the upper fields where he herded and watched over the farmer's flock.

In summer he was able to add wild strawberries and whortleberries to the bread and cheese; and to sit sometimes by a stream or in the shade of junipers, reading books the farmer's wife allowed him to borrow. That landscape of pasture slopes fringed with thorny juniper became as much a part of himself as were the views from Helsingborg across the waters of the Oresund to the coast of Denmark.

He was sent with the flock to different places according to the season and the growth of pasture. As the days grew shorter they stayed on lower ground where there were water-meadows with clumps of birch trees and hazel thicket, and a small wood of fir trees. In the stream were pike, which Martin showed him how to catch using a running noose of fine wire.

In winter when snow covered the ground and word might come that the sea across to Denmark had frozen over, there was work for him in the barns and around the farmhouse, or in the granary.

Winter was black and white. Spring brought first the tops of crocuses above the snow, then anemones, with a pungent smell of wet earth and mould under the thaw. The time would come for him to return with his flock to the upper fields where the woods were soon bright with new leaf and loud with birds, and where sudden outbursts of flowers seemed to take the pasture by surprise.

His other foster-brother, Erik, was working in Helsingborg, and Carl and Martin returned there at intervals, sometimes for Sunday visits home, sometimes for longer holidays. In good weather they wandered about the town together, in the gardens of the Hamnpaviljongen, or around the grounds and terraces of the castle, or met other boys and young men in the square; or best of all they visited the quays, checking on ships coming and going from the port and talking to young sailors. Carl noticed that some of these whom he had known as shy and awkward boys now strode about in their high-collared monkey-jackets and seaman's boots, exchanging phrases in English and looking as if they were the lords of creation.

As he and his brothers grew older and found themselves with small amounts of money they made ferry visits across the Oresund — first to Helsingor, later to Copenhagen.

For Carl the port of Helsinborg represented the gateway to the world. Almost every week someone they knew, or some friend of a friend, was leaving for America. Already he was determined that he would leave Sweden; but to be a sailor, not an immigrant to the United States. There was something about the thought of that long hang-dog line of Swedes, Poles, Irish, Italians, Germans, all America-bound, all looking for better fortune and expected to be grateful, which made his pride rebel.

He thought, rather, of vaster distances and greater oceans; of wild places — jungles, deserts, islands in the South Seas. What he wanted was space, and the freedom to shake off not just poverty but 'everything'. One day he would find a place where he would be free to rub his own personal slate clean and start again.

'IT WAS NOT ONLY,' Ethel Elena wrote in her memoir, 'that my father Carl Christianson possessed no recollections of his father. That was a lack he shared with others, orphaned young, or the children of young widows. But for him it was as if there had been no male parent. Though it seemed probable that Christianson was a patronymic, and that the man who had fathered him had been christened Christian, even that was uncertain, and would remain so throughout his life. When he was a small boy he once or twice asked Mother Amalia about his father, and was told she could not answer his questions. As he grew older, and might have received answers, he chose out of pride not to ask.

'For my mother Charlotte Flatt, on the other hand, born ten years later and on the opposite side of the world, there were clear and fond memories of the father who had died before she reached the age of ten. There were portraits of him, and stories her mother told about him. There was a grave to be visited; a name remembered and honoured. Even in death, and more, not less, when she acquired a step-father, Robert Flatt existed for Charlotte as a benign presence, a ghostly mentor.

'Robert, son of the missionary John Flatt, had prospered as a builder in Auckland, and died young of septicemia after a gash from a rusty nail became infected. A mild man, it was said that he died swearing. His widow, Annie, inherited his two small houses in Burleigh Street, and for a time lived in one, renting the other. How her second husband, an older man known always as Mr Freeman, had entered Annie's life, and why she had married him, Charlotte could not say. It remained a puzzle — except perhaps that Robert Flatt's savings were soon gone, and the rent from one house could not sustain them.

'Mr Freeman was a farmer at Kamo, just out of Whangarei, and it was there that Charlotte and her two sisters Ethel and Elena (after whom I was to be named), together with the little brother Vincent, born after his father's death, spent what remained of their childhood. Mr Freeman was what was known in those times as "a God-fearing man";

or as my mother preferred to describe him, a "mean and bigoted old hypocrite". His big black Bible full of revenges and punishment, his homilies, his demands for attention and lip-service, and his loveless discipline, were the means by which Charlotte was (as she later saw it) released from the burden of the Christian faith which had brought her grandfather as a missionary to New Zealand.

'Charlotte's memories of Kamo were of the beauty of the countryside and the beaches where they picnicked and swam; and of the poverty and harshness of life in the depression years of the 1890s, during which Mr Freeman sold his new wife's two houses in Auckland in order to keep his farm solvent. He had by his first marriage a son named Plummer who was never able to learn his lessons at school. Mr Freeman's remedy for this deficiency was a heavy thick round black rod with which he beat the boy often, but to no effect other than pain, bruising, squeezed tears and helplessness.

'In my mother's lexicon the darkest word was diphtheria. When an epidemic of the disease passed over the land, children died; or they survived with the permanent mark of its passing, that deep scar at the throat representing the scalpel-cut into the trachea through which breathing was sustained. Or if they escaped it altogether, others close to them did not.

'Ethel and Elena both contracted the disease, and died in the space of a single afternoon. Charlotte used to tell me, and even my children, how she had seen first one sister, then an hour or so later the other, rush blue-faced from bed to window, throwing up the sash, frothing at the mouth, gasping for breath, and fall dead, asphyxiated. It seemed it was something she had from time to time to repeat, to make others share with her the burden of horror. When the story was told she would weep. That over, she would sing.

'Charlotte, my late husband James used to say, had three registers — laughing, singing, and weeping. Mostly she laughed and sang. When she wept, it was for the past. Her favourite poem (with the remnant of the accent her grandfather had brought to New Zealand she pronounced it "poim") was Wordsworth's "We Are Seven", in which the little girl tells a stranger that there are seven children in her family. Two live at Conway, two have gone to sea, and two are dead — she sings to them in the graveyard; but nevertheless the stranger cannot get her to alter her insistence that they are "seven in all".

'Charlotte would recite

> The first that died was little Jane;
> In bed she moaning lay,
> Till God released her from her pain
> And then she went away.

> So in the church-yard she was laid;
> And all the summer dry
> Together round her grave we played,
> My brother John and I.

> And when the ground was white with snow
> And I could run and slide
> My brother John was forced to go,
> And he lies by her side.

> 'How many are you then,' I said
> 'If they two are in Heaven?'
> The little Maiden did reply,
> 'O Master, we are seven.'

'My mother had by heart many such Victorian graveyard poems, and would bring tears to her own eyes reciting them, because to her they evoked, not a sentimental tradition but the memories of real graves, actual deaths. Yet she was not really a sentimental woman. She was loud, hearty, and sang far more often than she wept. It was from her that I acquired my strong sense of music, though our temperaments, and consequently our tastes in it, were different.'

IT WAS IN THE SPRING OF 1887, before he turned eighteen and would have become eligible for military service (to be sent, probably, far north into the Arctic region) that Carl Christianson left the farm and travelled to Helsinborg to say his goodbyes to Mother Amalia. He did not tell her where he was going or for how long, and somehow conveyed to her that she should not ask. Copenhagen across the water was mentioned, but whether that was to be the end of his journey or a stop along the way was not declared. She believed he was on his way to America; and though it grieved her, it seemed that it was for the best — that in the New World the shame of his birth would be left behind, and the opportunity to make use of his talents would be offered.

Later he wrote to her from Kiel, where he had signed as cabin boy on board a German freighter. He sent his enduring love to her and to Betty, Martin and Erik, and asked that they should always remember him as he would remember them; but he made it clear that they would not see him again.

Soon he had transferred to English ships and was sailing on a regular route out of British ports down the West African coast to Cape Town. English had become his language, and he spoke it fluently, with an accent often taken to be Scottish. He was considered by his mates to be reserved, serious, studious, ambitious.

Bristol was his home port, and there a room was kept for him, a spacious top-floor attic with sloping ceilings and wide windows looking out from Cotham Brow. His home trunk was kept there, and his most treasured possessions — books, photographs of his foster family and of Helsinborg, a Swedish flag, mementoes of places visited.

In Bristol he took his shore leaves between long voyages, prepared for his examinations in navigation and seamanship, and had his first serious love affair, with a woman about whom Ethel Elena in her memoir was able to record nothing but her name, Rebecca, and the probability that she had a husband, since there appeared to be no other reason why she and Carl should not have married.

For the remainder of his life Carl would remember the pleasure of returning to that home port, climbing the steep hill through the town up from the docks, bringing Becky a bolt of cloth or piece of jewellery from a foreign country, knowing with what eagerness he would be received, how her impatience would match his own. And among the personal papers returned to New Zealand from Noumea when he died was the photograph he had kept of her, wearing a satiny dress with sixteen lined buttons curving up over her bosom to a brooch at her throat between wide collars. Her hair was cut short and combed softly around brow and temples. She had fine intelligent eyes, a straight nose, a generous, faintly smiling mouth. On the back of the photograph, where the name of the photographer was printed ('Mr G. Bellisario, George Street, Bristol, Fotografia Italiano') she had written in a flowing hand, 'To mia caro Scandy-Carl — let these loving eyes haunt you as long as you may live — Becky.'

THERE IS NOW A GAP in the record, and when Master Mariner Carl Christianson next appears he is walking with Charlotte Flatt in Albert Park (*the* Albert Park, as Aucklanders then called it) just after the turn of the century. He has gone as far as it is possible to go from Sweden, and found in Auckland ('Last, loneliest, loveliest, exquisite, apart' — yes, he now knows his Kipling) a port that reminds him in some ways of Helsingborg, but with a milder climate. Helsingborg, but of the South Seas. On the advice of the British board which passed him, aged twenty-eight, as qualified to be master of sea-going vessels he has grown a full beard in order to look old enough for command.

He is now thirty or thirty-one, captain of a sailing ship trading out of Auckland to Australian and South Pacific ports. Auckland, he has decided, is to be his home port for life, and because he has at last written to Helsinborg to say so — a letter (the first since that long ago message from Kiel) intended for all his foster family and the friends of his youth — he is carrying in his pocket the reply that has come from Martin Becker. Martin's letter begins,

'Bästa Broder, hjertligt tack för det kärkomna bref som jag bekom i går hvari jag ser att dec lefver och har helsan och

inte har glömt mig, det har jag aldrig heller trott för jag
känner . . .

'Dear Brother, very many thanks for your welcome letter
which I received yesterday from which I see that you are still
alive and healthy and have not forgotten us, I never really
thought you had because I know you better but believe me
I was happy to hear from you — I cannot describe how
happy, and most of all because everything goes so well for
you. If best wishes can do anything to improve a dear friend's
fortune you will become a "Big Man" — excuse the phrase
but you can be sure it comes from the heart.

'First, dear friend and brother, I have sad news to convey
to you, which I think from what you wrote to me may not
be quite unexpected. It is that our dear Mother Amalia has
been dead for rather more than a year. We often talked of
you and sometimes in her illness she asked did I think you
were dead because you did not write but I assured her no
because I believe that when your wandering is over you as
well as I will come to rest in the bosom of mother Sweden.
She was happy at this assurance. She died without pain. Do
not blame yourself for not writing, dear brother — I assure
you she did not.

'You ask for news of the town. Betty is married to a cigar
maker, she has two children by him but the elder is dead.
Her two by Sven have hardly slept one night at home since
this second marriagé because he beats her and has even
knocked out one of her teeth. Erik asks why she should have
put herself in his hands and I agree with him I do not know.
There was no need, after Sven's death she was getting
between 28 and 35 kroner a week. Erik will write his own
news and greetings to you soon, but meantime sends his love
and asks me to tell you he is well and prospers.

'Fritjof Ekberg is married, badly, they say, because she
cannot boil a potato or darn a sock.

'Sander Rolf is due to leave in a three-master called
Kristian. Johan Tengvall was home a couple of years ago. Lars
Klämme is married, Peter Klämme has lost a hand in the
molasses factory, Bernard Rosenkvist is married — well. His

sister too, very well. Johan Stamp is married badly, Karl is dead. Ludvig was run over and killed by a tram, he had rather gone to the pack sad to say.

'I, as you will see by the enclosed in my dress uniform, have done better than I think you all expected of me. And how do you like my moustaches? I can tell you they make the recruits tremble and the girls melt.

'What else to write but only to send you warmest greetings. My dear Minister of Home Affairs sends her love, also our three strapping boys, they will welcome you home one day — they have heard so much about you.

'Farewell, and good fortune is my constant wish for you, the clever young companion of my youth. Farewell and write soon, I beg you. Your friend and brother,

'Martin B.

'I met Elof Eckberg today and he sends you his best regards, but first and last comes the love of your friend and brother who has not forgotten you.'

BUT MARTIN BECKER'S LETTER, though it was in Carl Christianson's pocket, was not at that moment on his mind. He had brought Charlotte Flatt to the park with the intention of proposing marriage. He had spent his last leave courting her, being charming to her widowed mother, meeting their friends, and introducing them to his. He had taken her for walks, ferry trips, rides in a hired trap, picnics, visits to the theatre. She was young, vigorous, handsome, redoubtable, with a sense of fun and a wonderful singing voice. She possessed little knowledge of the world beyond New Zealand, and a great appetite to see it and to learn.

Obeying a convention which she admitted to finding ridiculous, since her feelings for her stepfather had never been better and often worse than cool, Charlotte was dressed in mourning for Mr Freeman. In fact his death had meant her release, and her mother's, from the Kamo farm with its weight of griefs, mortgages and Christian constraint; it had meant something like independence, financial and moral, and the freedom to return to Auckland; and Carl observed, but would not say to her until much later when they would laugh about it together, that he had never seen mourning worn so cheerfully, with such dash, or so successfully made to look like high fashion. Her dark full-length woven skirt was encircled with four strips of satiny black; her black satin blouse with full sleeves was ridged and pleated, fastened with pearl buttons; her black gloves were of the finest leather; her hat was huge with ostrich plumes which even their blackness failed to render funereal; her black umbrella with its pearl handle was so thin and tightly rolled it looked more than anything like a fin de siècle cane.

The sun shone on them and on the statue of gull-stained Victoria on her pedestal. Captain Christianson hid his nervousness behind a Swedish formality which made the moment more solemn than he felt it ought to be. But he got the question out — that was what mattered. Would she be his wife?

Charlotte's first response was to laugh; and at the sight of him, his expression stiff now with pain and embarrassment, the laughter returned.

But now she jumped to her feet, kissing him so impulsively he was knocked off balance. Oh she was sorry (she told him) for the laughter. It was nerves; it was *excitement*. Didn't he understand? Yes she would marry him, if he was so foolish as to want her to. Of course she would. There was nothing she wanted so much. It had been her *dream* . . .

Her hat with its huge black feathers had been knocked askew; the fine umbrella with its pearl handle lay on the gravel. They were both laughing now.

Forgetting they were in a public place, he put his arms around her and drew her close.

'THE RELEASE OF A SAIL' (Ethel Elena wrote) 'may save a ship; the failure to release it might mean its end, and the end of a story. An unsafe safety catch may bring a life to an end which is also the end of a line. A sick cow looked for in a field may lead to that line's fortunate preservation.

'I am writing,' she continued, 'of things which have occurred, and which, if I am spared, this narrative will bring me to. Stories are like lives, and are lives. Which of them are permitted to run a full and shapely course is random. Whether they find tellers is also a matter of luck.

'It is five months since a waning Venus remained on station for my birth, and we are on board a four-masted barque in the South Pacific, sailing from Rarotonga (where we picked up a gang of native workers) north towards a dot on the map just south of the equator and named Malden Island. The ship is loaded with chains and buoys, rails and timber, stores and provisions, wire and seed, goats and domestic fowls — even a ginger spaniel brought along for company and named Laddie.

'Malden Island has been uninhabited except by the seabirds which, building on its volcanic and coral base, have made it what it is — paradise to the romantic, to the business-man a pile of guano to be mined for fertiliser. We are about to inhabit it — to colonise it; but not for ever. What the gulls have deposited will be carted away by the shipload. What is left will in the end be abandoned once again to the birds which it may be supposed will over centuries, or millennia, do it again.

'Already a small team of men has arrived ahead of us, including a Norwegian carpenter and a Danish cook. The carpenter has built houses and store-sheds at one end of the island, native workers' quarters at the other, and between, a lookout and flagpole. The cook has planted vegetables and is inventing new dishes to be made, for example, of the flying fish that deliver themselves almost daily upon the beach, and of turtles which, knowing themselves to be a delicacy, arrive less frequently. These men and one or two others are awaiting the Swedish sea-captain (my father) who is to be manager of the island. He is approaching, together with his wife (my mother), his baby daughter (myself), his mother-in-law

203

(Annie Freeman, my grandmother), and a gang of Cook Islanders.

'Also in the area at this moment is a storm and a waterspout. Some way south of Malden, the spout and the four-master are on a collision course. Like a huge funnel or snaking tube, the spout is making giant strides across the sea. My grandmother, my mother and I, the babe-in-arms, have been sent below. So have the native boys who for the first time since they left Raratonga have stopped laughing and singing. The hatches are battened.

'As the waterspout strikes and the ship heels over it takes three men to hold the wheel. On deck, but not in charge, my father feels the ship tilting so far he is sure it will go over. He feels (as he was to relate it to me many years later) helpless, defeated. Has he come so far, he asks himself, only to go down in a storm with everything he possesses and loves? At what seems their last moment a sailor, acting on a desperate impulse, manages to unfasten a sail. It flaps wildly, cracking like a whip and sending ropes snaking overhead. The ever-downward tilting slows, stops. For several very long seconds, while those on deck anchor themselves with whatever is to hand, they skim yacht-like, looking out at a huge shoulder of water racing by. And then slowly, slowly, the ship rights itself. The tail of the spout moves away to the south-west and they are upright again, pounded by a manageable Pacific storm. Below there are bruises and breakages. No lives are lost.

'Two or three evenings later the Swedish captain is sitting on a windless verandah with the Norwegian builder and the Danish cook. The Dane tells a story which begins, "There was a Swede, a Dane and a Norwegian . . ." The Norwegian is the butt.

'Now the Swede tells a story with the same beginning and a similar end — in his story too, the Norwegian is the fool.

'It is the Norwegian's turn. He begins, "There was a Swede, a Dane and a Norwegian . . ." He spins it out. Who will be the fool? It is the Norwegian.

'Their laughter is long and loud. It is the joke of the joke that amuses them, rather than the joke itself. The sun goes down into the ocean like a big gold coin into a slot. The hair's breadth commonly called Life is behaving as if nothing has happened.'

IT WAS A TINY KINGDOM — Prospero's island, but without Ariel, without Caliban. Then sometimes, as time passed, it would seem to Prospero-Christianson that there was after all one Ariel, his baby daughter Ethel, and fifty Calibans, those bronze, white-toothed workers with their songs and laughter, their secrecy and unpredictable moods.

Everything was to be done for the first time — houses to be decorated, gardens made and planted, paths laid, stores sorted and rationalised. Gangs had to be organised and work allotted. Across the island rails had to be laid for jiggers that would carry the bagged guano to where the lighters waited to take it out to ships that would come for it; on the reef a wharf was to be built for the lighters; and in deep water offshore, moorings laid for the ships.

There were explorations, observations, discoveries — of the beach, the reef, the upland; of the soldier-like sharks that patrolled the reef and the frigate birds that kept watch; of the changing faces of sea and sky, and what the changes might portend. After a storm swept over, pounding the island with huge seas, calm returned and a walk along the beach revealed new shells heaped underfoot like spilled treasure-horde — pale mauve snail-like shells, shells curled like pink trumpets, marble-white shells with grooved sides, creamy crab-backs with red and yellow spots, lacy egg-like shells, spotted cat's-eyes, huge shells like gothic ornaments, shells so tiny it was difficult to believe they once contained a life.

Evening, when the sun, growing larger as it declined, raced headlong for its coin-slot, was the time for walks on the beach, with baby Ethel, healthy and strong, and the spaniel Laddie whom the reef sharks were teaching to stay in shallow water. The sunset colours, never the same, always magnificent, were poetry, and inspired it. Carl's reading in English had been literary as well as nautical, and it was the

Pacific's great sky-coin going down among heaped clouds that prompted from him verses, grandly conventional, beginning

> Visions of Glory
> Mountains of Gold
> Wonders on Wonders of Wealth untold.

In the evenings by lamp-light there were card games, talk, reminiscence, nostalgia; there were stories, even life stories, to be told or exchanged. Above all there was music. The cook played a fiddle, the carpenter a flute. Up from their long-house came the voices of the native boys singing, always and effortlessly, it seemed, in four-part harmony. Early and late, there was the wonder of the voice of Charlotte. And there was a gramophone with a big curved horn and three hundred cylinder recordings — Caruso ('the Great Caruso'), Madam Melba ('the Australian Darling'), Jenny Lind ('the Swedish Nightingale') — opera in abundance; but also music hall, popular songs, the Scottish nonsense of Harry Lauder.

There was also — there had to be, even in paradise — boredom and loneliness, fear and hard work, broken equipment and wasted effort, heat and exhaustion, frustration and anxiety. Out there beyond the sun-slot the world was rattling on at its own new-century pace; or it might be coming to a stop — there was not even a radio to tell them, and for news they must await the first ship, which would arrive in three months time.

Charlotte and Carl were happy and fond. Locked in by a vast ocean on a few square miles of coral and guano, she still managed to shed tears at partings that would not last more than a few hours, he to write her loving and whimsical notes. Their nights together — moonlight on the verandah, bats whistling in the palms, birds squabbling on the reef, the singing of insects and scratching of land-crabs, lantern light through mosquito netting, their own shadows moving against curtain and wall — it seemed, all of it, dream-like, beautiful, unimaginable.

By day, day by day, still there was everything to be done,

everything to be made, for the first time. Everything? Did either of them think that a human habitation must have a graveyard? If so, the fear was always and only for the child, that precious and precarious vehicle by which what had somehow survived in them would carry forward.

In the first six months, and before the second supply ship, Annie Freeman sickened with tropical dysentery. There was no doctor. Carl Christianson, who had charge of the medicines and had taken a course in how to administer them, did what he could. Charlotte nursed her. The tiny community held its breath. Released by the death of Mr Freeman, Annie wanted to hold on to her own life, to live for her daughter and granddaughter, and for young Vincent who was at boarding school in Auckland. But slowly the fight went out of her. One day, through cracked lips, she said to her daughter, 'I'll just have a little sleep, Lotty,' and died.

Carl read the burial service. It was something a sea captain must do. The native boys, their bare brown torsoes gleaming in the early morning sun, sang a hymn in their own language. Annie was lowered into what must have been the island's first human grave. When it was filled and heaped over, the carpenter planted at its head the memorial he had made in wood, on which was carved:

Annie Freeman, formerly Annie Flatt (née McDermott),
dearly loved wife of the late Robert Flatt
and mother of Charlotte Christianson and Vincent Flatt,
grandmother of Ethel Elena . . .

with dates, and the verse

Sweetness, Truth, and every Grace
Which Time and Use are wont to teach
The eye did in a Moment reach
And read distinctly in her Face.

Charlotte's singing stopped. The gramophone was silent. The evening stories were subdued, the card games silent, respectful of grief. Even the noise from the long-house was subdued. One of the native workers — a man of perhaps thirty and the acknowledged foreman — visited Charlotte on her verandah to convey their sorrow at her loss. When there was a death among his people, he told her, grieving went on for many days, and then there had to be a feast. Until the feast, the spirit of the dead person, which longed for release, was not free to go to the far world where happiness waits. After the feast the tears had to be dried and all wailing cease.

She thanked him for his visit and told him she would try to let her mother's spirit go — but not yet.

The Norwegian carpenter came and sat with her. He told her she must live now for her daughter. He brought a gift he had made for her — a boat in a bottle, its rigging magically erect, anchored on a pale sea against a background representing the island, with small blue-roofed, white-walled houses.

Charlotte was now without any woman companion. Sometimes she stopped what she was doing and stood weeping silently. She let the native boy, Purry, bath and feed Ethel, put her to sleep, take her around the island on his back. She walked alone on the beach and along the headland. She stood on the farthest outcrop looking over the ocean. She tended her mother's grave and decorated it with shells.

One morning she was heard singing. The native boys turned a turtle over on the beach and left it to die in the sun. That night they made themselves a feast and sang with full voice.

TWO YEARS AND THEN, after a return to Auckland, a further two. 'The quiet gentle island stands clear in my memory,' Ethel Elena would write in her old age.

Prospero's island, its greatest excitements were unscheduled ships. There were few of those, and most passed in the distance, a stain of smoke or a wash-day of white sails. If they called, it was for a purpose. One, the *Salamis*, seeking shelter from a storm, went aground on the reef and for three days its captain walked the Christiansons' verandah, wringing his hands, watching it break up. On the fourth day the sea was calm, the reef bright in sunshine, the *Salamis* gone. Almost seventy years later Ethel would write *Venus is Setting* at a table brought ashore from that captain's cabin, with a broad drawer for charts, and brass bolt-holes to attach it to the floor so it would not slide about in rough weather.

Another vessel, Danish, that appeared one morning anchored off the reef, called because a young seaman was dangerously ill. Captain Christianson was pulled out to it, taking his medicine bag and his silent doubts about his ability to be of use. The eighteen-year-old, delirious with fever and begging them not to let him die, was brought up from the fo'c's'le and put to bed on the deck under a canvas awning doused with sea-water. A day later he died and was buried on the island. One grave had become two — the island's graveyard. Annie Freeman did not lie alone.

At the end of the fourth year Carl's work was complete, the island in good order and full production. Ethel could remember something of the farewells, the feasts and tears, the last visit to Annie Freeman's grave which none of them would ever see again, and the final leave-taking, with native boys singing on the shore while the ship's sails filled, decks creaked, ropes went taut, and the sea swished past bows and hull.

Even more distinctly she remembered the weeks spent becalmed between Malden Island and Rarotonga. It was as if the great and terrifying ocean had died. Day after day they woke to slack sails, a sea glassy in every direction all the way to the horizon, with sometimes little spirits and whiffs of air darting and dying over its surface. Day after day the sailors put a heavy line and baited hook overboard, telling one another that until a shark was caught there would be no wind. Ethel did not believe her own recollection — or rather, she could not believe that it represented cause and effect — but at last a shark was caught, and her memory was that even while the stench of its being cut up was still in her nostrils the cry of 'Wind ahoy' came down from the crow's nest, and far in the distance the perfect sea surface winked, rippled, crinkled, broke, advancing towards them on a wide front like a column with bayonets.

The ship rocked, shuddered, spoke again — its voice that of timbers and ropes creaking and stretching. Sails flapped and filled. They were moving, gathering speed — on their way to Auckland, where a handsome bonus waited for Carl Christianson, and for his daughter her first remembered sight of children with pink-white faces.

TEN

THREE YOUNG ENGLISHMEN (should we call them?) William and William and John — the Colenso William, the Wade William, and the Flatt who was John — perhaps no longer quite young, no longer even to be described quite as Englishmen, though the year, 1840, makes it too soon to call them New Zealanders (that term belongs still solely to the natives, just beginning to be called Maoris), and Wade is soon to leave for Australia. Here they sit together in summer grass, talking about the past, speculating about what lies ahead. We may hover over them, angel-like, with the knowledge only gods and angels possess of what for them, being the future, is unknowable. None of the three will ever again set foot in the land of his birth. Of the two who remain in New Zealand, Colenso will die in 1899, aged eighty-eight, Flatt in 1900, aged ninety-five. Long before their deaths they will be able to call themselves, and feel they are, New Zealanders. Wade will die before them, in his late seventies in Tasmania, by which time he will consider himself an Australian.

And what of that piety, that Christian purpose so delicately entwined with personal ambition, which united them as their ship, the *Prince Regent*, set sail from Gravesend on 18 June 1834, lending fervour to the prayer they made together, 'God of Truth keep us, we who this day have left, perhaps for ever, our native land. To Thy care we commit ourselves now and evermore'?

In frustration at the obstacles put in his path by Richard Davis and Henry Williams, Wade has already resigned from his employment with the Church Missionary Society and is preparing to leave for Australia to take up the position as Baptist minister which he will occupy for the rest of his life. Flatt, the damage he has done to Davis and Williams now beginning to be felt, and yet to take its full, slow effect, is never to regain a foothold even on the lowest rung of the missionary ladder, and will lose, as he grows older, those Christian absolutes and certitudes his calling required him to profess. Colenso alone will achieve the Anglican ordination all three once hoped for; but for him will come, in an unhappy later sequel, disgrace and dismissal for fathering a native servant's child.

Time, which brought Flatt and Colenso together and then separated them, will cause their paths and interests to recross, as they do now. Colenso will marry Elizabeth, daughter of William Fairburn. Flatt's sister-in-law, Mary Anne Haslip, will marry Fairburn's son Richard. In late middle age Colenso and Flatt will find a moment to meet on common ground and in sad reflection.

In death, Colenso's disgrace will be set aside, and he will be honoured as the nation's first printer and the recorder of its founding historical event. Flatt will die remembered, if at all, only as 'an early missionary', a hardy pioneer, a family man who still sang in his garden at 90 and read the newspaper without glasses, unrepentant for the trouble he once gave his clerical masters ('I made them *dance*!' he will tell his granddaughter Charlotte), uncomplaining that he has been forgotten by the nation and its historians because unaware that they might be thought to have reason to take note of him.

But now it is summer, the first day of February 1840. The sun strikes bright, almost too bright, off the water. The pohutukawas are shedding the last of their Christmas flowers, and the sand and rocks along the foreshore are tinged with red. Seen from the grassy slope below the lawn in front of the home of Her Majesty's Resident in New Zealand James Busby, the islands of the Bay seem to float — even, with that dream-like quality the scene will preserve unto the fourth and fifth generation, to drift unanchored. After seven years,

James Busby's days in the post are to be terminated. The Union Jack is flying in front of the Residency. HM frigate *Herald* is visible, standing clear of the humbler whalers and traders anchored off Kororareka, approached by the interested and the curious — settlers in small boats, natives in canoes — who are warned off from coming too close. Two days ago Busby, accompanied by Colenso and the Rev Baker representing the missionaries, has been summoned on board to meet Captain William Hobson, appointed Lieutenant Governor of what is soon to be the British Colony of New Zealand. Colenso has been busy since, printing proclamations in English and Maori informing residents of the Governor's presence and intentions, and notices calling the chiefs to meet at Waitangi.

This morning Colenso, Wade and Flatt are sitting in the grass looking out over the water, having come from a meeting with James Busby on his verandah. They have called on him because they feel sympathy for the 'Man o' War without Guns' who they think deserves better than to be bundled aside without thanks or ceremony by an incoming authority ignorant of, and indifferent to, the difficulties he has laboured under. Grateful for the visit, Busby has told again how he has been slighted by the Mission, slandered by Captain FitzRoy in his evidence before the House of Lords Committee, and consequently discounted by his masters in the Foreign Office. The Maori chiefs, on the other hand, seem alarmed that he is to be displaced, and have also called on him to express their concern.

This morning's visit has been fortunate for Wade, who finds he will have a congenial companion in Busby on board the *Eleanor* when he and his family leave for Sydney towards the end of March; even more fortunate for Flatt, since the ever-generous Busby, hearing that Flatt and his wife and new-born baby are occupying a raupo house — hardly more than a whare — at Paihia, has said that they may move into the back part of the Residency while he is away, if only they will undertake to feed his hens and keep them from damaging his grape vines.

The meetings these three have had in the days since Flatt's arrival from Adelaide have been their first, all three together, since they were sent to their several posts in January of 1835. Now Wade and Flatt have exchanged confidences and discovered what they ought to have known long before — how exactly parallel their cases are, how Richard Davis, always supported and abetted by Henry Williams, denied each of them the post he had been appointed in London to fill. Wade, who has at times spoken critically of Flatt for his evidence to the Lords, now acknowledges that he told the truth there, and that if the truth has harmed the Mission it can only be because there is a fault to be acknowledged. Colenso, more passionate and puritanical, has never blamed Flatt, but on the contrary has argued that Williams, Davis and others of the Mission have no business making themselves landlords and traders. He holds to this view, citing the Wesleyans whose creed and manner of conducting themselves appeal to him, and who have bought no land. Williams he admits he grudgingly respects, but thinks him sometimes wrong and always stubborn and intractable. None of them can find a good word for Richard Davis.

A single cloud sails over and they watch its shadow on the water. 'Remember . . .' Wade begins.

Relaxed, comfortable in the sun, they give in to the inexhaustible game of shared recollection. They are in London in 1834, watched by numerous admirers, receiving final instructions for their great adventure. They are singing in the coach on their way to Gravesend. They are going through rough seas, Colenso helplessly ill, the Wades moderately so, Flatt, with his iron stomach, not at all. They are taking turns to hold services for the ship's passengers and to criticise one another's performances — Colenso's too slow, Wade's too long and low, Flatt's too brief in text and long on song. Now they are in mid-Tasman, on board that evil little ship the *Blackbird*, going nowhere because the drunken mate is refusing to navigate and Captain Crook lacks the skill. And last, they have arrived in sight of New Zealand and are becalmed — out there at the entrance to the Bay. They can point to the place, argue about its exact location, where Gilbert Mair's whaleboat came alongside and took them on board to be pulled ashore.

Flatt tries to tell them what it is like to come in a second time — the inexpressible excitement of the exotic which has become familiar and then, while remaining familiar, has by dint of absence recovered its foreignness.

Wade gives Flatt and Colenso his wife's good wishes and tells them about each of his children — their names and ages. Flatt talks about his new baby son Joseph, who managed to be born in New Zealand, but only just, and dramatically, on a litter meant to bring Caroline from Hokianga to the safety of the Bay of Islands.

Colenso admits how much he would like to marry and have children, and tells them (his old stammer returning) something he has previously kept to himself. A year or more ago, staying with the Williams family at Waimate, he conceived a great fondness for Miss Marianne Williams and hoped she might accept him as a husband. He wrote her a letter proposing this and, wanting to do everything correctly, gave it first to the father to be approved and passed on. Henry Williams declined to give permission, saying that Colenso's health was not good.

His health, Colenso tells them, is excellent, though he had suffered a brief illness at the time. But the hardest part is that he does not know whether Miss Marianne was told of his proposal, and so he has never, since that time, been able to speak to her without extreme embarrassment.

Wade and Flatt shake their heads at the image of the man who used to be their employer, and whom they sometimes called Old Ironsides. Wade puts an arm around Colenso's shoulders. 'One day you will marry,' he says.

Colenso nods, smiles grimly. 'No doubt,' he says. 'No doubt. Meanwhile, I burn.'

A FEW DAYS AFTER THIS EXCHANGE between three old friends the Treaty of Waitangi was signed on the same lawn. William

Colenso took an important part. John Flatt watched from the margins, but with an interjection which Henry Williams ignored but would remember as another instance of Flatt's 'impudence'. William Wade, his mind already turning to thoughts of his new life, did not attend, but six weeks later, on board the *Eleanor* heading for Australia, read Colenso's account of it.

The navy had erected a marquee in front of the Residency which would be known henceforward as the Treaty House. In the intervening time the settlement had been full of excitement and activity. The new Governor, finding himself unable to compose a satisfactory text for a treaty by which the natives would cede sovereignty to the Crown, had passed the problem over to the retiring Resident. James Busby had prepared the document in English, to be translated into the Ngapuhi dialect by Henry Williams and his son — Busby checking and agreeing to their translation. Prior to this Captain Hobson had come ashore on the beach at Kororareka, accompanied by Captain Nias and officers of the *Herald*, and walked to the little Mission Church where he had read to the congregation proclamations asserting Her Majesty's imminent authority over New Zealand and the Crown's right to determine the validity of all claims to ownership of land.

There was excitement and there was alarm. Forty-five settlers had signed an Address of Welcome to the Governor as the representative of British law. Others had declined; and some of those who had signed now regretted it, or felt uncertain. Was the long arm of British law about to reach out and take away from those who had escaped from it the freedom of action, and above all the right to be land-holders, which they had achieved by their enterprise in coming so far?

Now the treaty was to be put to the natives. All through the previous day the northern chiefs and their supporters had been arriving, many (since the tribes did not all trust one another or feel safe together) bearing arms. This morning the Bay was crowded with canoes. Ships were decorated with flags and pennants. Smoke rose from camp fires along the foreshore. The settlers, mostly dressed as they would be for church, were assembling on the lawn around the marquee. John Flatt was there; so was Caroline, carrying baby Joseph wrapped in a shawl.

At this moment the Governor was in the Residency, its doors guarded by two members of the Sydney Mounted Police, past whom, unchallenged, strode Jean Baptiste Pompallier, French Catholic Bishop of Oceania in full canonicals and accompanied by an attendant priest. Watching, Flatt could see Colenso and the Anglican missionaries standing about on the verandah in their dull black, and already the chiefs who had observed the Bishop's purple, his large gold crucifix on a heavy gold chain, and his access to the representative of Queen Wikitoria when others appeared to be shut out, were calling to one another that he must be a very great rangatira. Since it was said that the French eminence had been advising them against signing the treaty, the missionaries, Flatt knew, would be feeling they should have been in there ahead of him.

But now it was announced that the Governor would receive any who wished to shake his hand. Settlers queued to go in. Flatt held baby Joseph while Caroline joined the line. It was not the Governor she wanted to see (though she thought he had a nice face), but the interior of the house — its furnishing and decorations. These would have interested her in any case; but now, since Mr Busby's kind offer, it seemed, she would soon be living there, and the prospect had lifted her spirits.

Half an hour later the whole assembly had moved into the marquee. The Governor took his place on a raised platform, Captain Nias beside him, both in full dress uniform. Resident James Busby, with Bishop Pompallier, sat to the Governor's left; the Rev Henry Williams on his right. Missionaries King, Kemp, Baker, Clarke and Colenso stood in attendance behind Williams.

In front of the platform the principal chiefs, carrying mere or taiaha and wearing feathers in their hair, stood or sat, ready for their part in the korero. They wore woven mats, cloaks of dog-skin or feathers, and one (the most striking) a cloak of perfect white fringed with curl designs of dark red and black. The women among them also wore fine mats, with white feathers or even a small bird's wing through the ear-lobe. Beyond these central figures tribespeople and settlers ranged themselves out to the edges of the canvas top and beyond, and prepared to listen.

Caroline found her way back through the crowd to her husband's side. Her face was flushed and she was smiling. She took Joseph and jiggled him, though he seemed still to be sleeping soundly.

'It's lovely,' she whispered. 'And there's a *piano*!'

THE CROWD HAS FALLEN SILENT. The Governor is saying that Queen Victoria wishes to do good to the chiefs and people of New Zealand but this is not possible while they remain outside her dominion. She cannot regulate the behaviour even of her own British subjects in New Zealand, nor see to the fairness of their land purchases, unless the New Zealanders themselves choose to give her that power. That is the purpose of the treaty now proposed.

Captain Hobson reads its clauses, and Henry Williams reads the translations and explains their meanings in the native language, urging all present to attend carefully. The chiefs and tribes are to cede full sovereignty to the Crown. They are to be confirmed in full possession of their lands, forests and fishing grounds; and if they wish to sell land they will do so only to the Crown. In consideration of accepting these terms they are to be accorded the protection, rights and privileges of full British subjects.

The matter is now open for discussion. In the silence that follows James Busby speaks, assuring the natives that the Governor has not come to dispossess them. While he is saying this a chief, Te Kemara, leaps up and interrupts him. Busby falls silent and resumes his seat. Henry Wiliams translates what Kemara is saying, for the Governor and for those who do not understand the language.

The chief's movements are violent, his voice loud, he jumps forward and back, eyes rolling, feet stamping, muscles flexing. The tribes, he says, have no need of a Governor. Captain Hobson should go home. Kemara has no wish to be an insect under his shoe.

Now he is pointing at Henry Williams. 'You, you, you,' he is saying with each stab of his finger. 'You, bald-headed one, you have got my lands. Return them to me.'

Another chief, Rewa, rises to speak. 'How d'ye do, Mr Governor,' he says in English. The crowd laughs. But at once he switches to his own language and, like Kemara, urges the Governor to go home. He wants his lands returned to him which he says 'have been taken by the Missionaries — by Davis and by Clarke and by who and by who besides.' He has no lands left — only a name, 'Mr Rewa' — and what use is that to him?

When the next chief, Moka, takes up the same theme, Captain Hobson interrupts to assure them all that any land not properly purchased will be returned to its former owners.

Good, Moka says. That is very good. But where is that fellow Baker? He seeks Baker out among the missionaries and confronts him, asking whether what the Governor has said is true. Will the lands bought from Moka be returned? Baker meets his stare. Quietly, coldly, he replies in the chief's own language, 'We shall see.'

Moka leaps again to the space in front of the Governor. There, he says, is the proof. All such promises are false. The land will not be returned.

While Moka's speech, full of gesture and repetition, goes on, Flatt has been talking to Gilbert Mair and some of the settlers from Kororareka. As Moka concludes, one of them goes forward to suggest that Williams is not offering a complete translation of what is being said, and that a trader called Johnson would do it better.

But Johnson declines. He tells Captain Hobson that the gentlemen from the Mission can do the job very well. 'Only let Mr Williams speak out so all may hear,' he says. 'And let everything the natives say be interpreted. They say a great deal about land and missionaries which Mr Williams does not translate to you.'

Now Williams is stung to speak on his own behalf. In English, he says that a great deal has been asserted in London about excesses of missionary land-holding, farming, trading and whatnot. But the land commissioners will look into all this, and he has no fear of their enquiry — indeed he welcomes it. Everyone should recollect that if it were not for the missionaries, settlers would have not so much as a toehold in New Zealand.

His voice rising now with indignation, he says if anyone has first claim on land in New Zealand it must be the missionaries who laboured for so many years alone, when no one else dared show his nose in the place. He himself has a large family — eleven children. More, probably, than anyone present. What is to become of them when he dies if they do not have land?

As this is being said Flatt is taking baby Joseph from Caroline. 'We have a child here, Mr Williams,' he calls. 'What is he worth? How many acres, Sir, and when may we have them?'

Williams pretends not to have heard. His face hard, he continues speaking. He hopes, he says, that those who have slandered him will prove to have title to their lands as good and sufficient as his will be found to be.

Now it is James Busby's turn to defend his land purchases. But the baby, snatched none-too-gently from his mother, has woken and is crying. Caroline says he must be fed. They make a path through the crowd.

Out in the sunshine, as they make their way down through cabbage trees towards the river-crossing, Caroline reproaches her husband for his attempted interruption. How will they ever get on in this place if he continues to make enemies of those in authority? But Flatt is impenitent. Williams's speech, he says, confirms everything he told the Lords Committee about the missionaries' attitude to land-holding — that they believe they have a special claim to it which others lack, and that the need to provide for their children justifies it. So why has he been punished for telling the truth?

Caroline shakes her head. She learned a long time ago, she tells him, that truth-telling can be an expensive luxury.

WHO CAN SAY NOW WHETHER the noble warrior chief Hone Heke supported the treaty or opposed it? This is a question Hugh and Jean-Anne have found themselves considering, because it was Heke's war which would drive John Flatt and his family from the north.

Colenso's account of the speeches in the marquee insisted that Heke spoke in support of the treaty — even gave an English translation of what he had said, beginning, Hamlet-like, 'To raise up, or to bring down? To raise up, or to bring down? Which? Who knows?' — and then urging the Governor to stay: 'If thou shouldst return we natives are gone, utterly gone, nothinged, extinct . . . Remain, Governor, a father for us.' Then, turning to his own people, Heke is supposed (still according to Colenso) to have urged that if they did not accept the treaty 'the French people or the rum sellers will have us natives.' The Governor and the missionaries should decide the matter, because 'we natives are children. Yes, it is not for us but for you, our fathers — you missionaries — it is for you to say, to decide what it shall be. It is for you to choose, for we are only natives . . . Children, yes, children solely. We do not know. Do you then choose for us.'

Henry Williams also recorded that Heke 'fully approved' of the treaty. And next day, the day of the signing, when James Busby called Heke's name first among the chiefs, he came forward at once and signed. So why, Jean-Anne asks, should there be any question?

Only, Hugh explains, because the record is contradictory. The recollection of the Rev Robert Burrows was that Heke 'had given considerable trouble' at the treaty gathering. A Wesleyan missionary, the Rev Samuel Ironside, recorded that Heke's speech was so violent against the Governor it moved the great Tamati Waka Nene to speak up at once in Hobson's support. And Mr William Baker who was later a translator to the Native Department, remembered Hone Heke's 'very violent language'. Finally, wasn't it Heke's discontent with the treaty that made him cut down the flagpole — not once, but four times — initiating the war of 1845?

This is ground Hugh has been over many times. Colenso would not lie; nor did he pretend that Kemara, for example, and others who opposed the treaty, spoke in support. So did those who said Heke opposed it simply read his later actions back into their recollection of the meeting? Possibly. But Hugh has another idea. It is that Heke may have spoken with heavy and bitter irony — accepting the inevitable, but intending to make his dislike of it plain. 'We natives are but children . . . It is for you to choose, for we are only natives . . . Children, yes, children solely.' Is it quite imaginable (Hugh puts it to Jean-Anne) that a proud warrior who wanted above all to confirm his mana in front of the assembly would say to his people, 'We are but children. We are only natives,' in a tone of aquiescence? But on the other hand wouldn't a bitter, angry, even violent tone, suggesting 'This is what *they* think of us', reconcile Colenso's transcript of the words spoken with the impression of aggression and insult his speech made on some who heard it?

BY THE TIME JOHN FLATT had helped Caroline back to their whare on the other side of the river, and returned to the marquee, both Heke's speech, and his great opponent Waka Nene's, were over, and the mood had swung entirely in favour of the treaty. Nene in particular, Flatt heard from Gilbert Mair, had won the day. Addressing the tribes he had asked, 'Whose potatoes do we eat? Whose blankets keep the wind from our shoulders? Whose guns have replaced the taiaha? Who are the fathers of these children?' (pointing to some of mixed race). It was too late to turn back the page. 'Let us all be friends together,' he had said. 'Let us sign the treaty.'

Flatt heard cheers coming from the marquee as he returned. Now tobacco was being brought out to be distributed among the chiefs, and the Governor, having said they should take a day to talk these matters over before deciding whether to sign, was about to return to his ship.

Flatt joined the group of settlers who followed the Governor and his officers down to the water where a rowboat waited. At the water's edge an elderly chief rushed up to the Governor, stared at him as if to make a petition, and then let out a wail of disappointment: 'Auee! he koroheke! Ekore e roa kua mate.'

Governor Hobson asked Colenso what he had said. Flatt and Mair, standing back from the main party, glanced at one another, feeling the embarrassment of the moment. Colenso attempted to pass it off as 'nothing of importance', but the Governor insisted on an exact translation.

'He said,' Colenso replied, '"Alas! an old man. He will soon be dead."'

AFTER THE CROWDS, brown and white, the flags and speechmaking of the first day, the day of the signing was an anticlimax.

First there was the Governor arriving late and flustered, in civilian clothes but, absurdly, wearing his ceremonial hat; then Colenso warning that he did not believe the natives understood the full import of what they were about to sign, and Hobson's irritation at this suggestion; then the chiefs, those who had opposed as readily as those who had spoken in favour, lining up to sign or make their mark, and to receive the two blankets Colenso was instructed to hand out to them; and finally, as the sky clouded over and rain threatened, the camps breaking up, canoes paddling away, groups of natives trudging off into the surrounding countryside.

Flatt was not there for the signing. Like the Governor himself, and many of the settlers present on the previous day, he had been confused about when it was to take place, unaware that it had been brought forward a day because the tribespeople, running out of food, were showing signs of returning to their villages.

So it was that the Colony of New Zealand, a day ahead of schedule, declared itself, was proclaimed, came into being, was born; and Governor Hobson, taking advice from that ubiquitous and indefatigable midwife of our history Henry Williams, soon announced that the capital would be built 150 miles to the south on the Waitemata.

IN RETROSPECT, Caroline and John Flatt would sometimes say that 1840, the year which began with the signing of the treaty, though it ended sadly for them was nonetheless the last of the good years — the last, anyway, for a very long time. There were also conversations in which he insisted, and she would not dispute it, that they had all been good years, even the bad ones.

Though it was late March it still felt like high summer when they moved into the Residence, which some were already beginning to refer to as the Treaty House. At first they occupied only the back quarters. But Caroline spent more and more time in the front reception room, playing the piano in the daytime while baby Joseph slept in his crib on the verandah, playing it sometimes in the evening by lamplight when her husband joined her in singing the songs of their youth. She also weeded and hoed James Busby's garden, planted new vegetables, fed the hens and kept them away from the grape vines, dug for cockles and pipi on the foreshore and gathered mussels and oysters from the rocks.

So the Flatts spread themselves, taking over the whole residence, and Mr Busby, they were sure, would not have objected but for the fact that, without thinking to tell them, he had also offered it to a Mr George Cooper, the new Colonial Treasurer, whose salary of £600 per annum (only half that of the Governor, but still very grand indeed) seemed to call for respectable accommodation, and who arrived in the middle of the year to find it occupied.

224

Busby's letters to Gilbert Mair, Jean-Anne has discovered, showed a certain irritation at this; and more particularly at the fact that Flatt had not written to give him news of the house. Later in the year, however, a letter to Mair reported he was now assured that all was well. Mr Flatt had sent him 'a very satisfactory letter' of explanation and news; and Mr Cooper had confirmed Mair's own report that he and the Flatts were sharing the space amicably, even sometimes singing together in the evenings.

The Governor had announced that the new capital of New Zealand would be on the Waitemata; and Flatt would later say they should have moved there at once rather than waiting to be driven out of the Bay by Heke's war, by which time the price of land in Auckland had soared. But for Caroline the comfort of the Treaty House, the blandness of summer in New Zealand's far north and the mildness of its winter, her pleasure in the growth of baby Joseph who took his first step on the lawn where the treaty had been signed, and the company of her sister Mary Anne, now married to young Richard Fairburn and expecting her first child, made any talk of moving to the south unwelcome.

John Flatt worked early and late. Using timber supplied by Gilbert Mair, he and Caroline's brother Reuben were building a cottage on the piece of land where the raupo whare stood — a simple structure, one large room at the front, two at the back, with a verandah and an outhouse — all of which he hoped to have ready when the end of the year brought James Busby's return. But with the help of Mair and a settler called Powditch he was also establishing himself as a trader. There was still a good number of ships in and out of the Bay, and Flatt, speaking the native language, was able to act as middle man between visitors and the tribes that could replenish their supplies — pigs and potatoes mainly, but also fresh fish, fresh water, timber and spars.

So now (to move forward) it is December, two days after Christmas. Busby has returned from Sydney. The Flatts are in their new cottage. It seems — it is — cramped and sparsely furnished after the Treaty House, but they feel a special affection for it because it is their own. Also the warm weather, which throughout what was supposed to be a winter never seemed quite to go away, has long since returned. The sun is hot but not merciless as in their Adelaide summer. The bay sparkles, the paths are at last dry and hard underfoot, the pohutukawas are blooming all along the Bay; and trade, though never better than hand to mouth, keeps promising to improve.

Most important, in a nearby house Mary Anne's baby has just been born. There has been the usual pacing about, not only by the father but by all the fathers, and the usual brisk competence of the women, taking over, coming into their own. It has not been an easy birth, but not, they say, unduly difficult, and the baby, a girl, is healthy and well. Now there is only a small difficulty, not exactly explained to the men, and which the women are sure will soon be overcome. But as the day goes on the men detect a wavering in the female voice, an uncertainty, a doubt, finally perhaps, though suppressed and denied, a fear.

There are towels — a great many towels, a great deal of cold water soaking, a great many pails of hot water, hot compresses, consultations under the breath and behind the hand. The stain of red, in the towels, in the water, cannot be concealed. There is blood — sometimes more, sometimes less, but continuing. The baby has been held to the breast but the mother is weak and pale.

On the second day there is no improvement. The women have taken turns to sit with Mary-Anne through the night. Her pallor alarms all who see her. Her husband, Richard, calm and controlled while at her bedside, becomes frantic when left alone on his verandah — pacing up and down, running his fingers through his hair, trying and failing to believe the assurances given him that all will be well.

Mrs Henry Williams is called in. She has had eleven children, all of them surviving. She is also said to be the best midwife in the Bay and to have saved the life of one of the Busby babies at birth. She has a method, learned from a visiting surgeon, sometimes successful in stopping bleeding after a birth. It involves massage. The pressure must be strongly and even painfully applied if it is have effect. Richard is taken away by the men. Mary Anne's cries are anguished, but very weak. For a time it seems Mrs Williams has been successful. Hopes are raised. But that evening the bleeding starts again.

Next morning Mary Anne is lapsing in and out of consciousness. 'Am I to die, then?' she asks in a waking moment; but there is no need to answer — her eyes close again. Her pulse is weak and rapid.

Richard is allowed at the bedside. He holds her hands in his. She opens her eyes, smiles, but is unable to speak.

Caroline weeps at the head of the bed. Brother Reuben holds one of her hands, his wife the other. John Flatt stands near the door, his back and head pressed against the wall. He has seen violence and murder, but this is something different. It takes hold in the pit of the stomach. The horror and helplessness of nothing-to-be-done, no-one-to-turn-to.

They pray silently, fervently, and it makes no difference. It never does, Flatt thinks. But it is a channel for our feelings.

He looks out. It must be midday, midsummer. Along the foreshore the pohutukawas, laced with blood and shedding it on the clean white sand, are crouched like predators over their own shadows. When he turns his eyes again into the dim room he sees that Mary Anne is dead.

MARY ANNE — JEAN-ANNE. A pregnancy. A birth — yes, but a birth and a death. Jean-Anne, who would have found this part of their discoveries disturbing, is more disturbed because she is herself to have a child — a girl, they have just this week been told, and she and Philip have been making lists of names.

She and Hugh are sitting on his balcony in the middle of the day, looking out towards the Waitakeres. She has seen her specialist this morning for the monthly mauling, poking, peering — the blood-suck, the audio, the amnio — the Hugh-is-not-sure-what and she is not at this moment inclined to talk about it.

They talk instead about Flatt's three years remaining in the Bay after the death of Mary Anne. Like the much larger fish who helped him make a start — Mair, Powditch, Busby himself — Flatt was swimming against an economic tide that was flowing away towards the new capital, to be called Auckland. Like those larger fish he borrowed, and like them made losses, increasing his debts. 'I am now worse in worldly goods than I was twelve years ago,' Powditch wrote to Mair in 1843; and in the same year Flatt was 'sold up', lost his house, and was compelled to begin again.

But the same change in the economic weather was affecting the tribes of the northern region. They too were losing the trade that had made them prosperous, and for that loss some blamed the treaty which the missionaries had encouraged them to sign. There were threats, there was fear. When Maketu, son of the chief Ruhe, murdered an English-woman, Mrs Roberton, her two children and another child, part-Maori, who was in the house at the time, anxious settlers clamoured for a show of strength. Maketu was handed over, tried, and hanged in Auckland; but everyone knew it was only because the visiting child murdered had been grandson of another chief, Rewa — otherwise the crime would have gone unpunished.

After the execution there were stirrings of discontent among the tribe. The body of the murderer was demanded, exhumed, and in its decomposing state reclaimed by a tohunga who dismembered it, stripping putrid flesh from the bones which were returned to the family for burial. Still the murderer's father, Ruhe, was unappeased, regretted his acquiescence in handing his son over to the new Pakeha law, and was said to have chanted a song in Heke's ear urging him to take revenge.

And it was Heke, after all — the one whose speech had been recorded by some as supporting the treaty and by others as opposing it — who was to be the focus of discontent. A warrior like Piripi Korongohi might go from village to village announcing that he would soon kill every Pakeha man and take their women for wives and their children for slaves. No one believed him. But everyone knew that when Heke said something his words, like God's, brought what they spoke into being — and Heke's word now was war.

JEAN-ANNE IS LEAVING. Philip will be expecting her. She has gathered her papers together but is hesitating still as if there's something on her mind. They reach the door. She turns to say goodbye, then says she must come in again — just for a minute. Hugh says of course and they go into the downstairs living room. She puts her folders, books, handbag on the glass-topped table and walks up and down. He waits. She goes up to him and puts a hand on his forearm. Her touch, as always, warms him right through.

There's something (she says) she should have told him. That letter — she shouldn't have read it . . .

Letter? He's thinking of John Flatt.

'When you told me about your love-affair . . .'

Of course. She means the letter from Lydia Lawrence. He is listening. Waiting.

Jean-Anne does a circuit of the room. She is saying again that she should have told him, but she doesn't say what it is she should have told. It's as if he is two people, one of whom, the instinctive, the intuitive one, knows what she means — has no need to be told — while the other is all ignorance and puzzlement and curiosity.

What she says — gets it out at last — is, 'Lydia — she's my mother.'

Ah yes.

'I knew you and Mummy had been — friends. More than friends. I suppose it's why I'm here . . .'

He holds her. He wants to say to her that this explains so much — so many feelings which have drawn him close to her; so many which have made him hold her at a distance (yet nearer than arm's length).

He says none of this — only gives her a brief hug, then releases her, patting her shoulder. 'I'm glad you told me.'

It's only after she has gone that he thinks about Lydia.

Where is she now? Should they meet?
Would she want that?
Would he?

ELEVEN

BEES IN THE WEATHERBOARDS. Bees in his hair. Son John's bees — the trays, masks, meshed headgear; the stings. Hugh's own swollen long-ago boy's face in the dusty cracked Kaiwaka mirror, eyes like a snowman lost in fattened flesh. Bos'n's mad romantic dash, boy onboard, bees behind, the plume of them, the hum of it, a sky-high tuning fork struck and ringing above the brown dam — middle C (was it?), middle day, middle summer, and in the steady middle of the note.

They are driving north again, Hugh and his passenger Jean-Anne, and Jean-Anne's passenger Baby Devantier — big enough now to have earned maternity leave from the university library for its, or rather (science having recently deprived the foetus of its last secret) for *her* porter-provider. North to Whangarei, where Hugh's grandmother Charlotte's ancient but still viable relative is signalling that she has come upon 'a few more scraps — probably nothing of interest to you busy folk' of John Flatt's papers. Hugh suspects the old lady, Miss Gladys McDermott, likes these visits, this human contact, and that the 'few scraps' may indeed amount to next-to-nothing. (There is a bar-room story he remembers about an old lady found to have a drawer full of clasp knives, who explained, 'There's nothing a boy scout won't do for a clasp-knife' — but he decides against repeating it.) They think the sortie worth it — just in case; and later, if Jean-Anne's doctor permits, they intend to make another to the south, this time to the Wairere Falls where Tarore was murdered.

So they are talking about bees and bee-keeping; or rather,

he talking, she listening. Drones, queens, workers. Pollination of pasture ('the national economy depends on it') and the consequent damage an imported bee disease could do. Manuka honey. Clover/pohutakawa/honeysuckle honey. Australian competition (could they make a eucalypt honey for colds? — slogan: 'it clears the nose while it soothes the throat'). And the news of a new spread — 'honeycheese'.

He tells her about the farmhouse he once saw, in the north, invaded first by one swarm, and over time, in peaceful coexistence, by several — the house almost derelict but still lived in by the cousin of a cousin of a cousin; old cars and farm machines overgrown, blackberried, in the paddocks; chooks straying in and out, laying in pillows and mattresses; the house-turned-hive humming, droning, a sort of aeolian didgeridoo, down the inner linings of which sometimes, in hot weather, ran stains of molten gold. And the cousin's cousin's old-man Maori cousin, living mostly on eggs and eels and potatoes and puha, saying honey — he never ate the stuff, but that he didn't mind the bees, enjoyed the company — 'them and the dog and the friendly kehua'.

And telling Jean-Anne of the bees in his hair, the mad ride that it was, making the difference between Hugo and Wolf seem something invented and foolish, the pain of it was so equally and horribly shared by them both . . .

And (straying from the subject but not from the region) his father's unsafe safety catch and consequent gnarled and blasted arm with its inoperable (and inoperable) hand and fingers . . . And Josie's voice, and Linny's missing fingers, and Greta's cake that was not a cake; and Frank Mangold's binder-twine moustache; and leathery-brown Willis riding by to 'give a hand' (indeed) at the milking.

They have serious things to talk about, Hugh and Jean-Anne: facts to exchange. She would like to know more about those parts of the whakapapa which it is not in her power to investigate. Carl Christianson, for example — she would like Hugh to tell her more about him. And they are to tell one another what they have discovered about how Heke's war in the north affected, or may be supposed to have

affected, John and Caroline Flatt. But there's time for all that
— time (or that is the feeling today) for everything.

So they arrive at Kaiwaka and go, not through it, direct
on the main road north, but along the back road to Hakaru,
past the farm whose layout so matches and yet fails to match
the precise and unwavering map Hugh will carry in his head
as long as life lasts, and perhaps (though he doesn't believe
it) beyond — a Platonic sketch of how things stood before
the serpent entered the Garden and Time began. This is the
old road where the buggy once lumbered, Hugo up Wolf
down, Hugo down Wolf up, and where they were both,
Hugo-and-Wolf, unloaded to help with haymaking. These are
the fields he walked after the plough went over them,
collecting kauri gum in a sugar bag to be taken back to
Auckland and sold at a shilling a pound. Those are the slopes
on which he was once dangerously and triumphantly let
loose with an oil-burner to clear gorse and blackberry,
emerging at the end of a day, two days, blackened like the
landscape and breathless at his own success. Down there in
the scrub-filled gullies run the streams where he fished for
eels and kokopu; and up there the ridge where he set his traps
and killed his catch, always with a single blow. Somewhere
along this fence line, long since renewed, must have stood
the box in which bees held a public meeting and resolved
to make an example of the next ten-year-old horseman who
dared to put a hand into their shelter . . .

At the little wooden church they stop and get out. They
linger over the Beaumont graves and beside the mound, as
yet without a stone, that is Frank Mangold's — Gilbert Mair's
direct descendant, Hugh reminds her, knowing that she has
encountered Mair's name often in her researches.

He tells how the local chemist read the 'Our revels now
are ended . . .' speech; and because she asks him to, he quotes
it for her under the macrocarpa, one hand lightly, Prospero-
like, on Miranda's shoulder, forefinger, fore- and middle
fingers, twirling a lock, locks, of her hair. And then, because
she likes the poetry, and likes (she is Lydia's daughter) the
touch, he quotes as much as he can remember of

Ye Elves of hills, brooks, standing lakes and groves,
And ye that on the sands with printless foot
Do chase the ebbing Neptune and do fly him
When he comes back; you demi-puppets that
By moonshine do the green sour ringlets make
Whereof the ewe not bites; and you whose pastime
Is to make summer mushrooms . . .

When he runs out of memory they stand as they were. She has put a hand over his, lightly, not inhibiting the twirling of the locks. He listens to the silence of the surrounding landscape and hears the immeasurably small sounds, near and distant, that fill it. He looks up through branches to sky and says, 'I was eight or nine when I climbed this tree. Or ten.'

Looking down at her shape he says that pregnancy is physically becoming and philosophically interesting. Does she think 'I', or think 'we'.

She says sometimes she thinks 'I', sometimes 'we'. 'But that's so even when I'm not pregnant.'

He quotes Nietzsche: 'You say "I" and you are proud of this word. But greater than this is your body and its superior intelligence, which does not say "I", but performs "I".'

She nods, tells him she likes that; says, 'I know why my mother fell in love with you. It wasn't your face.'

He says, 'My face wasn't bad in those days.'

She says, 'It's not bad now.'

'But it was . . .'

'Your voice.'

'Ah.'

SHE'S DRIVING NOW. Fast and furious — or so he says. Over the limit — which gets them on to the subject of the law. He tells her about a case Hat presided over last week — a simple charge of 'common assault', which she expected would be over in an hour. It lasted all day and she had in the end to reserve her decision and bring home notes of legal submissions and photocopies of related cases. It concerned a thirty-year-old homeopathic doctor who believed his trees, which were looking unwell, were being poisoned by a sixty-year-old neighbour because the neighbour had asked if they could be trimmed so sunlight would get through to his house in winter, and the doctor had refused. Finding the neighbour lingering, looking up at the trees on the unfenced edge of his property, the doctor attempted to arrest him. The neighbour, who had seen the doctor performing strange rituals which were meant to protect the trees (chanting spells, blessing them with arms spread wide, encircling their trunks with magic rings of shells), became alarmed, declined to be arrested and fought free — in fact (according to the complainant) punched him in the mouth. In court there was produced a police photograph of the doctor wearing dark glasses and with a swollen and bleeding lip, and one of the accused's knuckles, with an abrasion perhaps caused by the punch. In the photograph, Hat said, the doctor looked like a blowfly; in court he behaved like an abused prima donna. But prima donnas and blowflies have their feelings; and having made her own translation of the laborious and sub-literate cop-speak which, together with the doctor's theatrical account of the incident, constituted the chief evidence for the prosecution, she was ready to convict. Probably, she thought, a conviction and discharge under Section 19, since the sixty-year-old was a solid citizen with no record.

But now into the picture come the defendant's two daughters, acting for him, a pair of young lawyers, beautiful yes, but (more important) formidable. They put their punching-père in the box and he is plausible and civilised, denying damage to the trees but not to the complainant's face, at which (in its photographic form) he even smiles with mild satisfaction. Despite Hat's impatient questioning of relevance, these siblings, duo-Counsel for the Defence of the Patriarch, take a great deal of time extracting from their father his impression of the homeopath's rituals — the point of which the senior of the pair insists will emerge later. Then it's the prosecution's turn to cross-examine, and the patriarch bats the cop-questions dextrously.

When it comes to legal submissions the two young women refresh Hat's memory on some points of law which they seem to think may have grown hazy in the thick of her daily skirmishes at the lower levels of legal argument. The complainant in these circumstances had no lawful right to make a citizen's arrest. Nor was the defendant committing trespass in stepping across the boundary unless, having been asked to leave, he had declined. But he was not asked to leave; on the contrary, he was detained. The attempt to arrest him was therefore an assault. He had lawful right to defend himself against it with reasonable force; and the degree of force considered 'reasonable' was partly to be measured according to the circumstances 'as the person assaulted deemed them to be' — hence his counsels' emphasis on his alarm at the homeopath's incantations and magic circles.

Then come the cases — most of them High Court decisions overturning an initial conviction in the lower court . . .

Hat gives in, reserves her decision and brings it all home to tell to Hugh over several gins and tonic. She has already phoned Richard about it and been told to 'Stop being big-Mother and apply the law' — by which he means 'Acquit.' She wants to know what Hugh thinks. He tells her he thinks a thirty-year-old who loses a fight to a man twice his age and then runs to the police is a wimp.

Hat smiles, murmurs something about male violence, sips her gin, and tells him again how much the young women impressed her.

Hugh reflects — it's the first time in many years that the thought has crossed his mind — how much Hat would have liked one of their children to be a daughter. How much he, too, would have liked it.

THE BRYNDERWYNS. You cross them going north to Waipu, the Scots settlement. (Didn't the settlers go first to Nova Scotia, Jean-Anne asks, then come south to New Zealand?) In this car, and at her speed, she doesn't even need to change down, except from overdrive to top. Hugh finds it hard to believe it's the same gradient on which he remembers the Rover with the green leather pockets labouring, boiling before they reached the summit . . .

James Grady getting out to lift the bonnet and look at it ('It helps to look, Hughie. You don't have to do anything.') Jacket off, shirt sleeves held back from wrists by springy silver bands, tight on the withered right biceps, bulging on the left. The big engine hissing and steaming. They were on their way to the Waipu Highland Games, where Hugh (as Hugo Wolf had by then become) won the high jump . . .

Jean-Anne is asking how it is he's able to quote so much Shakespeare so effortlessly. And Nietzsche. And Wordsworth. And Whatnot ('Whatnot especially.')

He says it's because he's educated. Young people these days are not educated; they're indoctrinated.

She laughs at him (he laughs at himself) and says he sounds like her father.

She means, does she? — his name is . . . Hugh doesn't have to dig long or deep to bring it up. *Bernie?*

She laughs again. It's a lovely musical two-tone laugh that reminds him of Lydia. Was he Bernie in those days? He's Bernard now. Has been for as long as she can remember. A lawyer. 'Saint Bernard', her mother calls him sometimes — rescuer of the snow-bound, the lost-in-the-frost; and sometimes 'S.D.', short for Shaggy Dog.

That's my Lid, Hugh thinks, but doesn't say it. He asks about the family.

Jean-Anne is the oldest. There are three more — two boys and another girl. They live in Napier — 'Sunrise city . . . International capital of Art Deco . . .'

He asks, she answers: Yes, she had a happy childhood. Yes, her father has been successful down there — a solid practice — and he's on the City Council. Yes, her mother works — she's a teacher of remedial reading. Yes, Jean-Anne thinks her parents have a good marriage. No (this after an awkward pause), Lydia doesn't talk about Hugh.

Not ever?

She's silent, steering carefully into a bend as if Hugh's car has suddenly become the ancient Rover, about to boil and steam. And then, 'Did Hat convict?'

He shakes his head. 'Case dismissed.'

After a long silence in which Hugh asks himself whether he is sulking or simply embarrassed, she says carefully, 'The fact that Mummy doesn't talk about you doesn't mean she never thinks about you. Of course she does.'

THEY SPENT PART OF AN AFTERNOON with Miss Gladys McDermott in an old wooden bungalow on a quarter-acre section around which the town of Whangarei had grown, and which its owner had refused, against ever-growing inducements, to sell for commercial development. She seemed unimaginably old and improbably spry. As a child she had known Hugh's grandmother Charlotte, who was her cousin, and Charlotte's daughter, Ethel Elena. She remembered Vincent Flatt in his uniform going off to the First World War, and the pain of the news of his death (his decapitation? — yes, she had heard that) in France. She had met and been charmed by Charlotte's husband, Captain Christianson, and had talked to him about his work in the islands.

She made tea and offered scones and jam, told them family stories she had heard during her childhood, and as they were leaving handed over two shoeboxes full of letters, photographs and documents.

That evening Hugh and Jean-Anne ate in a restaurant in the town and then retired, each to a motel room with a box of papers. Hugh worked as long as he could, and gave up only because his eyes were falling shut and he was no longer taking in what he read. When he put out his light he could see that Jean-Anne was still reading. Their rooms were adjoining, but at right angles to one another. She had not drawn the heavy curtain across the windows, and he could see her through the gauze, sitting at a table, turning page after page. Once while he watched she got up, put hands on hips, and arched her back.

Much later he seemed to wake to the sound of his door

sliding open. In his dream Lydia Lawrence came across the floor, a shadow, vaguely blue in the darkness, and got into bed with him. But there was something prevented their making love — something in the dream that was not so much a physical obstacle as a pressure in the mind, an essential fact temporarily forgotten, which finally woke him.

It was still dark, but with the first pale light creeping into the piece of sky he could see through a gap in the curtains. He brought the dream with him into wakefulness and as he did so recognised that the obstacle had been the knowledge that the person who had come to him had not been Lydia but Jean-Anne; or rather, a combination, but one in whom Jean-Anne predominated.

Remembering the dream again over breakfast with her he felt a moment of embarrassment, as if she might know, or guess, what this elderly scholar's ageless dream-self had almost done with her in the night. Then he wondered what her dream-self might have done with him. Most likely nothing; or nothing more than talk — and that would be flattering enough. But he would never know.

WHAT WERE THE CAUSES OF — the French Revolution? the First World War? the War of Jenkins' Ear? — no, not those, but of Hone Heke's war in the North. (And what were the causes of the Causes?) Driving back to Auckland, having returned some papers to Miss Gladys McDermott and kept others, promising to report on their findings, Hugh and Jean-Anne are trying to put the events of 1844–45, in which John Flatt found himself caught up, into an orderly sequence.

They have found (and that is where they begin) the record of an ill-tempered exchange between Flatt and Henry Williams on the foreshore at Paihia in 1844, Williams telling Flatt that he had been 'impudent' and deserved his financial failure, and suggesting with heavy irony that he might now enlist the help of his 'grand friends in London'; Flatt replying that he had friends nearer at hand, and that they would never confuse truth-telling and impudence.

Both men had been tetchy. Everyone was that year, not least the noble chief Hone Heke, married to his cousin Harieta Rongo, daughter of the great Hongi Hika, and by that marriage confirmed and advanced in his chiefly mana. Heke, who was believed, at least by some, to have supported the treaty at Waitangi, and who when called upon to be first to sign, had certainly come forward and made his mark, now set his face against it — against, therefore, his great Ngapuhi kinsman on the Hokianga coast, Tamati Waka Nene. In part it was because the Bay of Islands trade, once a healthy flow that had made Ngapuhi rich and powerful among the tribes, was declining. Customs duties imposed by the new authority kept some ships away; others went to Auckland because it was the capital. Tribal enemies on the Tamaki isthmus and south of it were profiting while Ngapuhi's mana (or so Heke argued) was damaged.

First to sign could be first to sign off. Heke no longer accepted the treaty. He had opposed the handing over of the murderer Maketu to the British authority, believing that if he deserved punishment for killing Mrs Roberton and the children it should have been at the hands of his own people — and that would have meant one stony blow to the head, not undignified hanging from a rope. Heke had talked to American traders — Mayhew, Smith, Watford, Jack Williams — men who considered their own operations to have been damaged by British rule, and who told him how their people had had to fight for freedom from perfidious Albion. Now Heke flew an American flag, Mayhew's gift, at the prow of his canoe, objected to the British flag that flew over Kororareka, and threatened to bring down the flagstaff.

AFTER THE PAINFUL EXPERIENCE of being 'sold up' as a trader, John Flatt was living in a raupo cottage on Busby's land, growing vegetables and fruit for sale, keeping domestic fowls, hunting pigs in the fern. Sometimes there was paid work for him as a carpenter. There was a second child now. They were never short of food, and had usually a little money to spare;

but everything that belonged to 'civilisation', and especially good shoes and clothing, was in short supply or beyond their means.

Busby's financial problems were huge and complicated and Flatt did not understand them — did not try to. He felt safe under the wing of the former British Resident, even if it was a wing that had been clipped. Only a very rich and powerful man, Flatt told his wife, could have such debts.

The land was nominally Busby's, but the new commissioners were questioning his right to parts of it, arguing that his purchases had been excessive, or inadequately paid for, and threatening to take some of it, not for return to the tribe but to be kept by the Crown. This too angered Heke. What right had these commissioners to question a sale he had made to his good friend Busby? It had been his land, Heke's, and now it was Busby's. Heke did not want it back. He had made an agreement and it should be honoured. That it might be taken away from them both and given to the Crown only proved what the Americans said — that the authority represented by that flag flying over Kororareka was not, and would never be, true to its promises.

Heke visited his English friends in the Bay often, talking long and late. He had no grudge against the Pakeha, whose presence he welcomed so long as they treated him with respect. His objection was only to the new authority asserted by those representing Queen Wikitoria. His intention of cutting down the flagstaff was always mentioned, but in ways which left those who heard it uncertain. The Maori way, they knew, was to talk figuratively. Perhaps Heke did not mean that he would take to the staff with an axe.

And then there were those times when Heke went further. After the flag was gone, he said once, but in the tone some thought unserious, he might march on Auckland, take the capital, and make a new and better treaty with the good Government of America.

These threats, if they were threats, were delivered at different times in the hearing of Flatt, of Gilbert Mair, of Henry Kemp, of missionaries Burrows, Davis, Williams. It was always Williams who was given, or took upon himself, the responsibility of answering them. The treaty, Williams told Heke, would be the salvation of the native New Zealanders. It had saved them from the civil but pitiless French, from the unscrupulous New Zealand Company, from the chaos of unregulated settlement and lawless visitors.

Heke listened to Te Wiremu, as Williams was known to his Maori flock. But to Flatt, after one of these harangues, he said that he grew tired of 'Te Karu Wha', who had 'four eyes but only one song'.

In June of 1844, when there was not a lot to be done in his market garden, Flatt took work in Kororareka as a builder. Whether he stayed in the town or crossed the water each day from the Paihia side is not recorded; but he noted that Heke's men were coming into the town in groups, acting in ways which seemed intended to provoke.

There were stories of the time which Gladys McDermott told, and which Hugh, hearing them, believed he too had heard in his childhood.

Returning home on one occasion, Flatt found Caroline upset and frightened. She had been stewing pork in an iron pot over the open fire when a group of armed natives had arrived at her door. She recognised them as some of Heke's men, and though alarmed by their unfriendly faces she had contrived a neutral demeanour — firm, enquiring, neither unpleasant nor fearful nor yet welcoming. Since she could not speak more than a few words of the language little had been said on either side. The leader of the group had looked around the house, stood a moment over the fire, and then without word or warning had taken a knife from the table, stabbed the piece of pork and pulled it from the simmering pot, and gone off with it, followed by his friends.

It was the same now in the town. Heke's warriors arrived in canoes. They camped on the foreshore, swaggered about the town, stole, challenged, threatened. Once they set an empty house on fire. Among the settlers the women were anxious, the hard men wanted to fight, the cooler heads and the missionaries warned against it. There were incidents, stories, rumours, exaggerations. Heke was looking now for an excuse, a trigger, and everyone believed that if one was not presented to him, he would invent it.

It came, in July, in the form of an insult. A Mr Lord, a Kororareka butcher, was married to a native woman who had been, and so far as the chief was concerned was still, Heke's slave. He claimed her back and sent men to bring her to him. She refused to go, pointing to a carcase in the shop and saying, 'Ina a Heke!' (That is Heke!) The insult was reported to Heke, who claimed utu. It was refused. Several days of what seemed to John Flatt absurd and petty negotiations passed without result, at the end of which Heke's men climbed the hill above the town and cut down the flagstaff. And here another of Gladys McDermott's stories found its place.

Caroline at Paihia did not know what had happened that morning on the other side of the Bay. Recent rains had passed over, the sun was shining, and she had carried the baby down to sleep under trees at the water's edge, allowing Joseph, now aged four, to play in the sand. She was dozing beside the sleeping baby when Joseph ran to her and shook her arm. Two canoes full of armed warriors were coming over from Kororareka.

The canoes were beached, and the warriors, carrying their weapons, gathered in a long line on the foreshore and performed a haka, directed at the mission house and meant to express their triumph. The slapping, stamping, chanting, the rolling eyes and poking tongues, aroused fear in Caroline; but because it frightened Joseph and made him cry, it aroused anger as well.

As the warriors returned to their canoes she shouted at them that they should 'go away to their homes and make themselves useful'. They glanced at the Pakeha wahine, her face red, her hair falling down out of the clip that held it in place, and did not respond. In a matter of minutes the winter sun was glinting on their strong bronze backs bent to the paddles, receding across the calm waters of the Bay.

NOW CAROLINE WAS INDEED READY to leave the Bay of Islands. The idyll of their sojourn at the Treaty House — the fine furniture, the evenings around the piano, the established garden with flowers, vines, fruit trees and vegetables, the huge lawn and beyond it that view of the Bay with its islands seeming to float and drift, the presence of the Governor and naval officers with their symbols of power and authority, the compliance of the natives — all of that peace and beauty and seeming security was gone from their life, replaced by the hard realities of pioneer existence.

Caroline could stand hardships and privations. The Bay was as beautiful as ever, and her pleasure in it was constant. She loved her nuggety and resourceful husband, whose devotion to his new family and willingness to work himself to a standstill for it aroused in her a corresponding strength of purpose. But to follow in the wake of those who had already made the move south to the capital seemed now only prudent.

But when, and how, should it be achieved? While they debated, the flagstaff was restored and the plants in Flatt's garden grew. It was announced that Governor FitzRoy had sent to Sydney for troops. In September he arrived with them, to be met by Waka Nene who claimed to speak for the Ngapuhi tribe. Nene assured the Governor that Heke's anger would fail because it lacked a 'putaki' (a root, or foundation). He begged that the troops should be removed, promising that Heke would be kept in order, and laying ten muskets at FitzRoy's feet as a sign of good faith. The promise was accepted and the troops withdrawn.

Heke was insulted by this guarantee. He mocked the 'ten rusty muskets' and said Waka Nene should keep to the Hokianga coast, which was his territory, and leave the Bay to those whose business it was. But there was no sign of action from him. Optimists among the settlers believed that having made his symbolic gesture he would now be content. It had satisfied his honour, the troops had been removed, and no more would be heard from him.

The mild wet winter turned to balmy, occasionally

torrential spring and glowing summer. John Flatt's garden was (as he meant it to be) a demonstration, to any who cared to look, of what he might have done at the Waimate mission ten years before, and a reproach to those who had prevented him. The settlers were kind to one another — more so since the recent disturbances had thrown them together. There was a new informality, a casting aside of social restraints which at home would have kept them apart. Another summer-Christmas was celebrated, saddened for the Flatts by the memories that came with the birthday of Mary-Anne's little girl, named after her, and now in the care of Reuben Haslip and his wife Margaret.

There were still troubles in the Bay — threats, insults, demands for utu, thefts of horses; but Flatt, absorbed once again in the work on his garden and the sale of its produce, let them pass him by. They would move south — that was their intention — but each day was crowded and the weeks passed uncounted.

Then, early in January, Hone Heke struck again. The flagstaff came down, was restored, and a week later again was cut down. Henry Williams urged the Governor to take care. The settlement lacked forces sufficient to defend its symbol of British power, and the missionaries thought it best that Heke should be allowed his small triumph. Some settlers agreed. Others argued that if there were no show of force, Heke, and the chief Kawiti who supported him, would extend their rebellion. The time had come for Governor FitzRoy to act.

BEES IN THE WEATHERBOARDS. Eggs in the mattresses. The whole honey-running hen-infested house a hive and a nest; and the old man Ngapuhi cousin of a cousin's cousin standing out by the fence where his eels were hung out in a long line, drying in the sun, telling young Hugo and his cousin Hilly what Auntie Wi in the long house remembered she had been told by her Granny Ripeka about how Granny Ripeka's Grandpa Matiu was there with Heke when their diversion brought most of the soldiers (they were from the 96th Regiment) running out of the blockhouse and down the hill into an ambush; and how he and Heke and others rushed in and killed the four remaining guards (and the signalman 'by mistake'); and what a long time it took them to hack through the new iron and chain casing around the base of the flagstaff; and how they laughed and yelled when it came down. And how Granny Ripeka's Grandpa Matiu had a half-brother over at Hokianga who as the war heated up fought for Waka Nene on the Pakeha's side; and how the half-brothers used to get together in between battles when nothing much was happening and compare notes and tell stories, each one boasting about how well his side was fighting, and what it might do next . . .

Hugh and Jean-Anne are heading south again, back to Auckland, stopping at Warkworth for lunch by the bridge where the stream runs, as streams do, seaward-and-the-same whatever History may be doing; and on the table Jean-Anne has spread a photocopy she has made at the Whangarei library of a sketch of Kororareka, 'ordered to be printed by the House of Commons, London 1845' under the heading 'Correspondence on the Attack at the Bay of Islands, New Zealand'. There they can see represented what John Flatt saw bringing Caroline and Joseph and baby Robert over the water from the Paihia side on 10 March 1845: the houses and stores clustered along the Kororareka shore line; to the right, the pa of 'friendly' Maoris (but how securely 'friendly'? — all of them in the Bay admired Heke) surrounded by palisades; and further to the right, Bishop Pompallier's house. Up the slope above the pa can be seen the Anglican church and Mr Dudley's house; and higher still, up what is marked as the 'Matavia Pass', Heke's camp. On the pass the place is shown where a one-gun battery was mounted, and near it the position taken by Captain Robertson and his sailors from the *Hazard*, intending to block Heke's path into the town. At the other end of the town, close to the foreshore, Mr Polack's house and stockade, where the ammunition was stored, are sketched in. Directly above it looms the hill, with one blockhouse halfway up, and a second, newly built at the top, protecting the new flagstaff. In the foreground can be seen the *Hazard* and the *Victoria*, anchored offshore, guns at the ready.

During February Heke's threats had been more explicit, less easy to ignore, and the unpredictable, usually aggressive, actions of his followers had become more difficult for Heke himself to limit or control. Isolated holdings like the Flatts' had been subjected to harassment and thefts. Horses had been stolen, barns burned.

There were now troops in the Bay; a new blockhouse had been built to guard the flag over Kororareka, and the pole had been reinforced. But these precautions, and the fact that £100 had been offered for anyone arresting Heke (such a small sum, Heke had said, was an insult to his mana), only seemed to increase his determination. The new defences were a challenge which he assured his friends he and his ally Kawiti would find ways to overcome.

Early in March the prospect darkened. Word that Heke was about to attack seemed more than rumour. It was confirmed for the Flatts by Gilbert Mair, whose sources of information were always good. The missionaries also believed it, though they continued their attempts to prevent it. Finally came a message from Governor FitzRoy, sent through police magistrate Beckham to all Europeans at the Bay, promising that in the event of an attack Kororareka would be protected, but pointing out that the safety and property of 'out-settlers' could not be guaranteed, and adding that 'no compensation for loss or damage could be made by the Government'.

On 9 March Flatt decided to take his family across to Kororareka where the men were being armed and drilled, the women and children were being housed in the safety of Mr Polack's stockade, and marines had come ashore under Captain Robertson of the *Hazard*, intending to guard the town against Heke's attack.

On the afternoon of 10 March the Flatts loaded into their dinghy four flax kits of treasured objects (including her sheet music and his journals) and a bundle of spare clothing tied in a blanket. Caroline, once again pregnant, holding baby Robert in her arms, and with Joseph beside her, took her place in the stern while Flatt, smiling encouragement, telling her she looked lovely, and glancing now and then, but without admitting what he was feeling, past her to the raupo cottage and the market garden they were leaving behind, pulled out towards the *Hazard*_and the *Victoria* riding at anchor, and on towards the little town of Kororareka which twenty-four hours later would be burning.

TEN MILES AWAY AT WAIMATE the Rev Robert Burrows woke on the morning of 11 March without feeling he had slept, there had been, during the night, so much movement and chatter among the natives. Alarmed at news of Heke's and Kawiti's coming attack on the Pakeha, many had set up camp inside the mission perimeter, hoping that the tapu which protected it would also protect them.

Burrows rose early and was eating his breakfast when he heard the guns of the *Hazard* firing in the Bay. The Rev Richard Davis was visiting what had been in effect, until the posting to Kaikohe which had so upset him, his private domain. Edward, son of Henry Williams, was also there. The three men with a number of the mission natives set off at once for a hill less than a mile away which on a good day, as this was, gave a clear view of the Bay. There with the aid of a spyglass they were able to pick out the puffs of smoke from the ship's side, which seemed to be directed towards the flagstaff hill. Try as they might none could pick out the flagstaff; it appeared already to be gone.

As the day went on they moved back and forth between the mission, where they expected news would be sent, and the hill which gave them that unsatisfactory ten-mile view. The sound of big guns firing and the sight of smoke from the shore continued. About one o'clock they heard an explosion; and as the afternoon wore on more and more smoke rose from the town, until a huge pall of it was drifting all the way across to the Paihia shore.

By the time a messenger reached them his news came only as confirmation of what they feared. Some hundreds of Heke's and Kawiti's rebels had divided into three groups, one of which had taken the blockhouse on the hill and cut down the flagstaff, while another fought a desperate engagement, hand-to-hand, with Captain Robertson's marines at the Matavia pass. The marines had prevailed, beating the rebels back; but at least a dozen had been killed, and twenty of Kawiti's men, including his son. Captain Robertson, who had fought Kawiti cutlass-against-axe (an encounter both had survived with honour), had later been shot twice and was among the severely wounded.

In other places the defenders had had the greatest difficulty engaging the attackers because (as the messenger reported) 'their mode of warfare is entirely strange to us'. The rebels had remained under cover of the bush and seldom allowed themselves to be drawn from it, making it impossible for a regular field engagement to take place. Yet at times it had seemed as if the whole range of hills surrounding the town was full of armed warriors waiting in ambush.

Late in the morning as the battle flared up and died away in different places around the town it had been decided to remove the women and children from Polack's stockade to the safety of ships anchored in the Bay, and this had been accomplished without any hindrance from the rebels. It was even said that during a temporary truce there had been cases where Heke's men had helped settlers get their belongings together.

Around one o'clock the ammunition in Polack's stockade had blown up, destroying everything there, including a great deal of the settlers' most prized possessions brought in for safe-keeping — but no one could speak of anything but the Providence which had determined that the women and children should have been removed in time.

As more and more settlers were taken on board, and the fighting men drew back towards the ships, the attacking warriors had hesitated, as if suspecting an ambush. Then, accepting that the town was theirs, they had moved into it in large numbers, looting houses and stores. When the *Hazard*'s gunners, thinking perhaps to drive them off, had fired on the town, the attackers, many of them now excited by victory and rum, had set about burning it. Fires were still being lit. Only the churches and mission houses were being spared. All the rest, the messenger feared, would soon be burned to the ground.

JOHN AND CAROLINE FLATT are standing together in a line on the foreshore, waiting for the approaching boat that will take her and the children out to the ships. Flatt holds the baby. Joseph, who has sat quiet beside her for three hours on the stairway to Mr Polack's cellar, stands, holding her hand, exhausted, still quiet. She and her husband stare out ahead of them, tears in their eyes. Behind them the town burns.

As the boat beaches and the queue begins to shuffle forward, they gather up their flax kits and blanket-bundle. Unable to control her fears, she throws her arms around his neck and begs him again to take care; to remember that if he dies she will be alone in this wild land with two children and a third on the way.

He assures her again he will look after himself. But he must stay. Her brother Reuben is missing, said to have been taken by Heke's men. Flatt has promised Reuben's wife, who is already on board the American ship, the *St Louis*, that he will find Reuben and bring him to Auckland. He reminds Caroline that he speaks the native language, understands their ways, has still some of missionary mana to protect him, and carries no weapon.

An officer urges her to hurry. She is handed into the boat with little Joseph. The baby, the kits, the blanket-bundle are passed to her. The boat fills and begins to move, the oarsmen reversing it as they go so that it is stern-on to the shore.

John Flatt watches it all the way to out to the ship, waving from time to time and throwing kisses.

TWO DAYS LATER he was across the water on the Paihia side, standing at the door of their raupo cottage looking at what had been his garden. Nothing remotely edible in it was left, and the soft soil was trampled, marked with the prints of bare feet and horses' hooves. From inside the cottage everything usable had been taken — furniture, mirrors, utensils, clothing. What little remained was broken.

His friend Gilbert Mair waited some yards away, saying nothing. As they walked back to where they had tied their horses Mair put a hand on his shoulder. 'Don't be depressed,' he said; 'starting again is always daunting; but it's seldom something you regret.'

─── TWELVE ───

PARNELL, PONSONBY, MT EDEN — Hugh Grady, sixty years old, pulls at the threads of family history that cross and recross a centre which is the Auckland isthmus, hoping for pattern, colour, harmony, a warp and weft, but recognising that in the end there may be only a great granny knot of time and circumstance. He looks from his westward desk towards the Waitakeres where the sun goes down, listening to the CD he has put on his machine of songs by Ravel. Somewhere below his line of sight there is the house where he grew up, boy soprano Hugo Wolf with sister Aida Norma who did not sing; and nearby, the one in which their grandmother Charlotte Christianson (née Flatt) spent her declining years.

Being, like all the Gradys, inveterately ambulant, he could walk from this place eastward all the way to the little lane at the top of the Parnell Rise where his great-great-grandparents John and Caroline Flatt rented a house in 1845 after Heke's war had driven them from the Bay of Islands; or to the triangle of land just below it where the old Parnell School once stood and where, before the First World War, his mother Ethel Elena first learned her spelling and times tables; or (still in Parnell) to the house on Brighton Road above Hobson Bay where she lived for three years with a German family while her parents were away on Ocean Island; or (taking a different, more northerly route) to the house in Ponsonby where they lived, Ethel and her parents, when Carl and Charlotte Christianson returned.

When Ethel went to the Parnell School she did not know

(would never know) that she was passing every day the lane where her great-grandfather had first lived in Auckland. Nor does Hugh's son Richard, lawyer-like-his-mother and not burdened by more than passing thoughts about history, know (he will be told) that his house on the edge of Hobson Bay lies across a path his grandmother Ethel used to take down to the water when, stricken with a six-year-old's longing for her absent parents, she took her grief there and found it a place to hide among the mangroves.

Place-to-place, person-to-person, person-to-place — these connexions that bind his family, his singing whakapapa, to the Auckland isthmus, historian Hugh now holds in his head. He turns each of them over (as the poet has it) 'like a dead bird in his hand', wondering how it is that they should seem at once so empty of meaning and full of significance.

He remembers that after the death of James Grady and when, ailing, she had given up writing *Venus is Setting*, Ethel Elena one day asked him to drive her to Ponsonby, to what had been Disraeli Street and was now Dickens Street. They cruised along it until she picked out the house she had lived in with her parents after their three years without her in the islands. Parked outside it, she told Hugh how clear the memory was of waking there, aged eight or nine, opening her eyes and recognising where she was by the ornate moulded ceilings, and feeling once again the pleasure, the immense relief that she was back with her mother and father.

She had been left behind, aged five, partly because they feared for her health in the tropics; but also so she could go to school, and so her talents in music could be fostered by the German family who took her in, all of whom sang and played at least one instrument. The music had been a solace. Grief, she said, had made her a musician — hence her affinity with the composer after whom her son was named. The Germans had been kind to her. She remembered the Herr making a special soup when she was ill; the girls lending her hats and dresses; the boys helping her to lace her boots before school. But in all those three years, so long when they are the years from five to eight, the sense of loss had never gone away, and the sense of a recovery had been correspondingly immense.

She had been with the Germans a year or more when her photograph was taken in best white dress, best black shoes and white socks to the knee, standing beside an ornate carved chair. It was sent to her parents on Ocean Island. They in turn were photographed, seated out of doors below their verandah on either side of a table on which a cloth had been laid and the photograph of her placed in the centre. Carl was smoking a cigar, and on his side of the table could be seen a cigar box, a tobacco tin and tobacco pouch, and his pipe parked in a glass horseshoe. On her side Charlotte was doing crochet work, and one of her completed pieces was displayed, laid over something so it could be seen. They were both — but Carl in particular — bronzed by the tropical sun, and they smiled seriously out of the picture as if to say to their daughter, 'Here we are with our picture of you. All is well.' Ethel Elena used to stare at that photograph until it became unreal and lost its intended significance.

Once, much later, she had reproached her father, asking how someone who had been abandoned by his own mother could have done such a thing to his only daughter. Carl Christianson had winced at the accusation and seemed so pained it had been difficult for him to answer. They had meant well, he said. He was sorry if it had been a mistake. They too had suffered. And he told her how Charlotte had gone to the Parnell school on the day of their departure, hidden herself behind the fence, and through anguished tears watched her little girl, whom she was not to see for three years, playing in the school yard.

Parked in Dickens Street staring at the picturesque villa with wisteria in flower over its verandah, Hugh could feel what his mother was feeling. Though she seemed not to know it, he was sure it was the loss of her husband that had brought her back to this place where the wound inflicted by the first loss had been healed.

She pointed out to him the upper floors of what had been an orphanage in the next street. As a child she had been able to look over her back fence into its grounds and feel pity for the children who lacked mother and father.

She remembered her mother sitting on that verandah during the First World War, going through the daily casualty lists in the *Herald*, fearing the worst, regretting that she had encouraged Uncle Vincent when he had said he wanted to join up; and Charlotte's grief and guilt when the news came that her brother had been killed in France.

'I'd like to die in that house,' she said, as they drove away.

It was as if (Hugh now recognised) his mother had grown up without family and without history. She had no brothers or sisters. Her father had come out of Sweden, all ties of blood seemingly shameful or unknown or severed. Her mother's two sisters had died in infancy, and the brother as a young soldier. Even Charlotte's father, Robert Flatt, who might have provided lines back into the past, had died while his three daughters were infants and his son, Vincent, unborn. When Charlotte's mother died on Malden Island it had meant Ethel was to grow up without grandparents.

So the Christianson trio, mother, father, daughter, had seemed to Ethel Elena almost the beginning and end of her world of blood relations. With the German family in Parnell, and later with her husband's extended family, especially the Beaumont tribe in the north, she learned how big and blowsy, how rough and ready and casual and consoling a family could be. But that was not her own experience. Her extended family was self-made and of the mind, like a child's imaginary friends. Her first cousins were Verdi and Bellini; later she joined the kinsfolk of Wagner and Wolf against the tribe of Brahms and Hanslick. And when her son and daughter were born she connected them by name and ambition (hers) to that family of the mind.

Charlotte Flatt had known that her late father's father, John Flatt, had been (as she would always say) 'an early missionary who fell out with the church because he criticised its purchases of Maori land'. She remembered visiting him in Te Aroha when he was an old man; but that was all of his story she had heard or all that Hugh remembered hearing from her. After his involvement in events that were part of what became public record John Flatt had faded into obscurity; had died singing but unsung, remembering but unremembered — a jolly old man who read the newspaper at ninety without glasses, and was renowned for his green fingers.

Denied family history, and untrained in the academic variety which knows how to ask, if not how to answer, questions that begin 'What were the causes of . . .', Ethel Elena Grady was nevertheless her historian-son's mother. For her there was a path back through space and time which was marked by the different ways composers arranged notes on a page. Listening to a piece of music unknown to her, or unremembered, she would identify, by its style, first the country of origin, then the approximate date, and by those measures the likely composer. She knew history by ear, and thus by heart, but did not know what she knew. That knowledge belonged to her son.

THE FIRST WORLD WAR came and went. New Zealander Vincent Flatt's head was severed from his body, and both were buried in France. What the 'causes' of this severance were, apart from the immediate one of an exploding shell, and the proximate one of a young man's appetite for adventure, were unknown to its victim; and the question was one which his great-nephew would consider lacked, would always lack, a meaningful answer. What the point or practical usefulness of his death might have been was also obscure — made more so, not less, by the confidence with which dawn speeches commemorating it, and all those like it, would be annually delivered in front of Anzac cenotaphs and memorials.

Vincent's death brought into that Disraeli Street villa a heavy, circular and beautifully cast bronze plaque showing a bare-bosomed woman holding aloft an olive wreath above the inscription 'He died for Freedom and Honour'. Vincent's country, the plaque and the memorials seemed to imply, had with his help come of age. He had participated in one of the great blood-lettings which constitute 'History'.

While the war continued Carl Christianson remained prudently silent and inconspicuous. His accent, his blue eyes, and the name Carl, made him vulnerable as long as the fervour of blood-fuelled patriotism continued. Once he was told he could not command a ship because the sailors believed he was a German disguising himself as a Swede. He didn't argue, but found another, more modest command. His friends, the undisputedly German family who had looked after his daughter, fared worse. They played and sang bravely, declaring loyalty to King not Kaiser; but there were times when bricks flew through their windows, when daughters were chased home from school and sons beaten in alleys.

When the war ended Carl was appointed Overseer of Deep Sea Moorings on the tiny equatorial phosphate island of Nauru. And this time they would not leave Ethel Elena behind.

THE MOORINGS WERE TO BE LAID OFFSHORE, beyond the coral reef, so that ships which came to collect the phosphate could tie up there in all weathers; and 'offshore', shelving instantly down hundreds of fathoms, meant 'deep sea'. The Nauruans themselves did not work — that seemed to be accepted — but received their modest phosphate royalties, spearfished from the reef or took their outrigger canoes beyond it in pursuit of bonito and yellowtail, grew coconuts and pandanus, played games, made love.

Inland on the plateau which the Nauruans had always neglected, preferring to live on and cultivate the coastal strip, some hundreds of Chinese labourers worked at the phosphate deposits — so effectively that at times, when no wind blew from the sea, a cloud of flour-pale dust hovered over the island.

Carl Christianson was in charge of the island's 'kanakas' — Fijians and Banabans, mainly, who built roads, and laid the rail-tracks on which the phosphate jiggers ran down to the sea and back to the plateau. But the largest part of his work with them was the moorings for buoys, each buoy a riveted cast-iron sealed barrel as big as a good-sized room and attached to anchors on the sea floor by chains as thick as a man's head.

They were his 'boys' and he was their 'Boss'. Their bodies were black under ragged clothes, and their feet were bare. His face, out of which the blue eyes shone startlingly when he trimmed his beard in the morning mirror, was dark-tanned above its white suit and under its white topee. The 'boys' were also pearl-divers, some of them, and could stay down at great depths for long useful minutes. They were far from home, poorly paid, and sometimes unhappy; but Carl Christianson reminded himself that he had not been born into a perfect world. He could not change it; but he could improve it by kindness — and even, by way of bonus, find himself loved.

Charlotte, her now fifteen-year-old daughter considered, was made 'indolent' by the island life. Chinese servants cooked and cleaned for her, laundered her clothes and laid them out, fresh every morning and again in the evening when the men and women gathered for drinks. Charlotte's particular friends among the hundred or so Europeans on Nauru were more often French than English and Australian, and more often German than French. She took tea or coffee with them on their enormous verandahs open to the air but closed against the worst harshness of the light by trellising and rattan through which, nevertheless, a glare was filtered sufficient for the photographs which Ethel Elena liked to take of them.

There the women sit in their cane chairs, wearing white ankle-length dresses of silk or finest cotton and lace, their luxuriant hair engineered into loops and swirls, their eyes smiling or choosing not to, the elegance of hands and fingers casually displayed in the holding of fine cups and plates, their gross-cake (Schwarzwald Kirsch Torte, for example, with almonds and whipped cream) laid waste in mid-table beside a small graceful potted fern, while the equatorial light pushes and probes through the trellising, and those harsh sounds which the camera can't record, iron-on-iron, iron-on-rock, come to them from far off, like the occasional pale cloud of phosphate dust, reminding that their husbands are overseeing the profitable business of the island.

Was it a sense of irony or merely accident that made the young Ethel Elena attach, on the facing page of the album she was keeping, a photograph of a group of Nauruan women and girls, all in short coconut-leaf skirts beginning below the navel and ending above the knee, wearing necklaces of dark shells and coronets of white coral, the older women with big bare breasts hanging flat and empty against protuberant stomachs, and all drinking, as if joining in a toast, from coconut shell cups?

In her diary Ethel wrote with teenage disapproval of her mother's passive indulgence; and with a sort of forgiving disappointment of her father's tolerance. His response, when she complained to him of her mother's overeating, had been to remind her that Charlotte 'had sailed always with Death in the next cabin'. Before she was thirty she had seen, one by one, her father, two sisters, mother, brother, all taken. She was 'sole survivor of a shipwreck'. If a time had now arrived when she found it possible to subside, to take comfort, know security, even a degree of luxury, why should she not be indulged? It was a precarious world. Today there was cake and friendship. Today there were calm seas — and Charlotte deserved them.

But today there was no sibling, brother or sister, for Ethel — and there would be none tomorrow; and that too, perhaps, with its consequent sense of failure, or anyway of disappointment, helped to explain Charlotte's willingness to accept idleness. Years later she would tell Ethel Elena who would tell Aida Norma who would tell Hugo Wolf (a lapse of years between each telling) that she had inadvertently sterilised herself on Malden Island by using potassium permanganate douches as her means of birth control.

And there was one respect in which, trim or cake-logged, Charlotte never changed. On Nauru, as everywhere, she sang.

Her voice was an acknowledged marvel of the island. The Chinese in their compound, the Kanakas in theirs, the Nauruans in their thatched houses — all knew the Overseer's lady for her singing as well as for her kindness, and would stop along the paths among the coconut palms to catch the sound of her voice on the wind.

The Europeans in their airy bungalows all spoke of it too, the British admiring, the French analysing, the Australians wanting to teach her their bush ballads. But it was the Germans who never tired of the subject, asking one another how it could be, as if her singing voice, or its presence in mid-Pacific, required an official explanation.

IN THE OLD TRIBAL DIVISIONS of the tiny island there was one micro-region, Buada, the only one which did not touch the sea, and which contained the Buada lagoon — not a true salt-water lagoon of the kind found on most Pacific atolls, but really a brackish lake a mile or so inland from the road (hardly more than a wide pathway) which ran around the island's coastal strip. Buada lagoon was sheltered by surrounding uplands and by a dense forest of coconut palms, and in all but storm weather was the most perfect water surface imaginable, everything on its edge repeated, the palms reaching once up into the sky and a second time down into the same blue element, mirrored underfoot. When a bird or a cloud sailed over another sailed under. And its echoing silence was as stunning as its reflections. Buada's language was signs. Every statement it made bore repeating, and was repeated.

Ethel went there sometimes to sing and hear herself singing. She had a small true voice and knew, by the measure of that instrument of her mother's which cake could not smother and coffee could not drown, that she would never be privileged to throw tantrums and break hearts in the world's great opera houses. A little drawing room lieder was the best she might offer; and she would not offer it while it drew the inevitable comparison. Let her mother, all things to all tastes, do 'Land of Hope and Glory' full-bellow for the British, followed (exquisitely — Ethel conceded that) by 'O Dieu! Que de bijoux!' for the French, or 'Dove sono?' for the Germans, and then 'Waltzing Matilda' heartily for the Australians; and finally, when the crowd had dispersed, something gentle and sentimental for Swedish Carl. That was her way. She enjoyed crowds, performances, parties, jokes, as she enjoyed the occasional riot of weeping and regret. Alone at the lagoon's edge Ethel Elena sang not to be listened to, but to listen; and leaned out over the mirror water not to be seen, but to see. Buada was her place of self-discovery.

But she was not always alone there. Sometimes Nauruan men came with nets to catch ibija fish which they farmed, having taken them as fry on the reef and acclimatised them to fresh water. Sometimes there were boys shinning thirty and more feet up the bare trunks to cut coconuts and send them hurtling down. And there was a young Nauruan who lived in a thatched house close to the water's edge who sometimes came down when she was there and squatted gravely nearby, saying nothing.

When they did begin to speak it was only to exchange names and facts about their lives. His name was Anatok, and he was, he told her, a temonibe — a Nauruan noble. He told her he had heard her singing, and liked it. She sang him some German lieder and he sang her some of the chants of his tribe. After several meetings she wrote in her diary that she was 'in love with a brown prince', that it was only a matter of time before she was found out, and then 'the skies would fall'.

But before this prophecy could be fulfilled, Anatok was lost. Outside the reefs ran strong currents, and when the Nauruan men took their canoes out in pursuit of big fish they had always to judge how far they could go and be sure of safe return. Sometimes they would come back exhausted, having battled the current and the winds for many hours. Among the younger men, outrigger risk-taking was a way (especially since tribal warring had come to an end) of challenging death, a kind of initiation — forbidden but indulged in, as it had always been by youths wanting to prove themselves, including those who were now elders and forbade it. Anatok was one of three young men whose canoe did not return. There was no ship tied up that could be sent in search of them. Radio messages went out. It was said they might be picked up; or they might reach another island five hundred miles away and return by the next ship — sometimes it happened that way. Much more likely they would be lost in the vast ocean and would die.

Ethel Elena concluded that Anatok would die, and that this was intended by Fate. She wrote a poem about him, and wept by Buada lagoon.

THE CHRISTMAS SEASON CAME and there was the annual carnival including aquatic sports on Boxing Day, the Fancy Dress Ball on New Year's Eve, and the Athletic Sports on New Year's Day.

The aquatic sports included the One Hundred Yards Swimming Race (by which was meant the race for Europeans) and the One Hundred Yards Swimming Race for Kanakas. There was the Canoe Race (crews of three), the Nauruans' Canoe Race (crews of three); the Cargo Boat Race for Kanakas (crews of five), and the Whale Boat Race (crews of seven). Other events were the 440 Yards Swimming Race, the 50 Yards Breast Stroke Race, the Neatest Dive, and the Longest Swim Under Water.

Tea was served on the jetty at 3 p.m.

The New Year's Eve Ball was preceded by a performance by the Nauru Pierrots, five men and five women of whom Ethel Elena was the youngest. They wore black clown suits with white collars and white pom-poms. The men juggled and mimed and told funny stories; the women sang songs like 'Lead me to Love', 'Romany Lass', 'Heart-Breaking Baby Doll', 'Oh Mother I'm Wild', and 'Alice Blue Gown'.

Ethel's days now were full of purposeful order. There was no school for a fifteen-year-old to attend, but she read every morning, kept her diary, and spent most of the afternoon practising at the piano and studying theory for examinations she would take when they returned to New Zealand. In the Belgian chemist's darkroom she learned to develop her own photographs and, incidentally, how to signal that a man's hands were unwelcome while pretending she had not noticed they were touching her. Nevertheless, since the chemist was teaching her French and she was finding him 'quite attractively Gallic', she gave him on his birthday a photograph of herself, inscribed 'A mon ami dans le cabinet noir — joyeux anniversaire — E. E.'

In the evenings she rehearsed her parts in plays put on by the Kookaburra Club at a little theatre called the Yangor. Her poem about the death of Anatok had grown to six poems, then to ten, in which she imagined her 'brown prince', first buffeted by a cyclone, then lost on a burning, windless ocean, knowing he must die, ready to give up his life, but still clinging sadly to the memory of beautiful Buada lagoon and of the blue-eyed white girl who had exchanged songs with him.

The months passed and there were no seasons, only faintly perceptible variations. What mattered most was water, and the behaviour of rain-clouds was unpredictable, even to the islanders. Once when water tanks were low and the native crops wilting, a huge cloud was seen to approach the island and then to divide and pass. At sea on either side heavy rain fell, while the twelve square miles remained dry. Two weeks later there was a storm which drove them all indoors for a day and a half, bent the coconut palms double, flattened some small shelters, wrecked a few of the Nauruan houses, but refilled the island's tanks and replenished the lagoon.

Carl Christianson's work was progressing favourably. The moorings and the huge buoys attached to them had been put to the test by the storm and survived. Soon the Christiansons would return to New Zealand.

Seven months after their disappearance Anatok and his two friends were returned to Nauru. Exhausted and ill from lack of water they had been picked up by one ship and taken some distance south before being handed over to a second which landed them at Rarotonga. After some delay they had been shipped to Ocean Island, and finally home to Nauru. Ethel Elena burned her tragic poems, which she had already begun to tell herself were juvenile. She had stopped visiting the lagoon, and wrote in her diary that though she was glad Anatok had survived, she had 'no wish to revisit the past'.

BACK IN AUCKLAND FROM NAURU, Ethel passed her musical examinations with ease, moving through the grades until she had qualified for her 'Licentiate' and the right to put letters after her name. Before she was twenty she was a professional 'teacher of pianoforte and theory'.

Carl Christianson, Master Mariner once again, came and went, mostly on vessels sailing between Auckland and Australian ports. But the island life called to him. When a post as Harbourmaster was offered on the French island of Makatea, he took it. This time his wife and daughter remained in Auckland.

On Makatea, Carl wrote, he had a beautiful little house perched among trees and flowers on a cliff above the boat harbour. A Chinese 'boy' prepared his meals and looked after his clothes. But the post was in some ways a disappointment. 'They simply will not let me do anything,' Carl wrote, 'except sign an order now and then and prepare a monthly report. I do not have to run any labour — only give orders to the Lieutenant de Port and he carries out all the work with the help of a native foreman. When a ship arrives I board her, see her safely moored, give information and instructions about the method of working and the port regulations, and need trouble no more as long as the weather keeps fine and the moorings hold.'

So he had renamed his little house 'l'Hermitage', was reading more than he had done since he was a young man — books in French, English and Swedish — was often lonely, and having to let out his buttons because he was 'growing a bow-window'. The English books included some of his old favourites by Robert Louis Stevenson, whose grave in Samoa he had taken them to visit, and by Joseph Conrad. The books in Swedish had made him think about the country of his birth. And as he wrote, he told them, there was a large ship, the *Rio Clara*, nearly loaded. 'We had to stop yesterday because of surf or she would have sailed by now. She is taking a cargo to Sweden, to within a few miles of where I was born, and if it had been summer at home instead of winter I think I might have stowed away.' It was the first time his wife and daughter could remember him expressing such a thought and referring to Sweden as 'home'.

'I wish you could see me sitting here at my table,' he wrote in another letter, 'in a gentle cooling breeze on my verandah. The weather is beautiful, the sea all blue out there with a snowy fringe of breakers on the reef.' It was Bastille Day 1924, he had been to a ball the night before, and had had 'quite a busy time saying agreeable nothings to French ladies'. But it was the 'Tahitiennes' who had impressed him most, beautiful in their 'silks and satins' and dancing to the music of a band bizarrely composed of an accordion, a trombone, a guitar and a mandolin. It had made him want to dance; but instead he had left early and made his way along the beach in the moonlight 'to spend the night with a couple of books for company'.

This was a letter to his daughter and she reread it more than once. Yes, she could imagine her father alone and melancholy in the moonlight. Equally she could imagine him in that romantic perch of a house, moon on the verandah, the sound of breakers floating up from the reef, one of those beautiful Tahitiennes removing her clothes, helping him off with his. Might it not have been guilt that had made him add an uncharacteristic postscript: 'Dearest girl I hope that you will be able to keep your poor Mummy cheerful. Be good to her, my darling, she has not had a very happy life. I have been a failure and never been able to keep at home as I should have liked.'

These were the years when Ethel was beginning to make her own life. She had her pupils. Opportunities came to perform at private occasions. One by one she was perfecting the Beethoven sonatas, adding them to her repertoire of Liszt and Chopin and Rachmaninoff. The great Paderewski came to Auckland and she was fired with the idea that she might become a concert pianist. It was not something she could believe in for long. She was a fine pianist, but she knew she would never be a great one.

And then there was what her father had taught her to call the zeitgeist. She was a young woman of her time and her time was the twenties. She and Irma, one of her German 'sisters' from the family she had lived with as a child, were now going every week to dances at the Ngaire Club in Devonport. They wore short skirts and white stockings and hats like decorated helmets, and their charleston was said to be formidable. And they were meeting two brothers, James and Joseph Grady. James, the older, impressed Ethel as handsome, intelligent, self-mocking and funny. He paid her constant attention and always made her laugh. He kept his right hand in his pocket or behind his back, and was reluctant to go swimming. A few years earlier he had accidentally shot himself on a farm at Kaiwaka, north of Auckland, and his right arm was badly scarred and the hand paralysed.

AFTER MAKATEA IT WAS AGREED there were to be no more island adventures, no more going to sea. Carl Christianson was not a wealthy man, but comfortable, having earned good money and invested it while living mostly at the Company's expense. On half an acre in Mt Eden he built the house that was to be his and Charlotte's retirement home, and spent many months landscaping it, building rock walls, rockery gardens, ornamental pagodas over which roses were trained, planting fruit trees and laying out flower and vegetable gardens. This was Hugh's grandmother's house, the playground of his earliest years.

But Carl's wife and daughter could read the signs. As time passed and he made more frequent visits into town where he roamed the docks taking note of the shipping, talking to captains and first mates, his family knew it would not be long before he signed on again.

So we move forward a number of years. Ethel Elena is married to James Grady, living close to her parents' house in Mt Eden, and their first child, Aida Norma, has been born. Carl Christianson, aged sixty, has signed on for yet another 'last' island adventure. He has been engaged by a French company to sail out of New Caledonia prospecting for phosphate deposits along the coasts of the New Hebrides. His last message has been from Noumea. It is unclear when the next is to be expected.

The next, when it comes, some months later, is from the Company. Captain Christianson is back in Noumea, in hospital. He has suffered a serious bout of malaria, has managed to bring his ship back to port, but as a consequence of this effort is now gravely ill. There are complications . . . Fears are held . . .

Charlotte sets off for Wellington where a ship is about to leave for New Caledonia. The day before it sails the news reaches her that he is dead and already buried. In the confusion and distress of her grief, she takes the night train back to Auckland.

A headstone must be ordered, and this simple duty seems all at once to concentrate the mystery of the man who came out of nowhere and filled their lives. Names, place-names, dates will put on record but not to rest the unanswered question of his birth, and will bring together, in a place which is neither, the opposite ends of the earth — Auckland/Helsingborg — which he called home. When Ethel, with the help of James and the acquiescence of the distraught Charlotte, has set out the necessary facts in suitable abbreviation, it is decided that the stone should be crowned with a line of R. L. Stevenson's: 'Home is the sailor home from the sea'. That Carl Christianson is not really at home in Noumea seems to Ethel only appropriate. His home was nowhere, or everywhere, or wherever he happened to find himself.

NOT MANY YEARS LATER, when Hugo Wolf Grady was arriving at the first infant consciousness that all about him were other egos at least as capable as he was of pain and sorrow, he became aware that the subject of his late grandfather, Swedish Carl, was one which could bring tear-filled eyes and sudden exits. His mother still mourned, his grandmother grieved. But grief and silence were not necessary companions. Nothing short of her own death would silence Charlotte's singing.

THIRTEEN

G RAVES. THE GRAVE. GRAVESTONES. We began with, or at,
one; or among some — it was Hakaru (remember?) near
Kaiwaka, Hugh with Hat sheltering under the macrocarpa,
he fifty years older, it fifty years taller, with the Beaumont
cousins among the Beaumont stones, and down the slope
at the end of the family line the flower-surrounded open clay-
mouth receiving Frank Mangold, late advocate of the study
of our New Zealand history, friend and mentor of the long-
since amalgamated Hugo-and-Wolf, great grandson or great-
great-nephew or otherwise descended of Gilbert Mair whose
whaleboat brought Hugh's great-great-grandparent ashore
from the becalmed *Blackbird* with Colenso and the Wades in
January 1835 . . . These paths we have trodden, these
mysteries we have explored, in the intervening months
during which already, and in Hugh's unwitting absence, the
Hakaru clay has been disturbed again and cousin Linny who
made him his Indian head-dress of pheasant and Black
Orpington feathers, Linny of the two lost fingers and the
two-horse (Hugo up, Wolf down) buggyride, the elderly
elegant one at Frank's graveside assisted in walking by her
two daughters, has gone down beside her brother-in-law into
the last darkened room.

Graves. Tarore's at Waharoa, strangely rediscovered,
rededicated ('whose Gospel of St Luke brought peace to the
Tribes of Aotearoa') by the Maori Queen in 1977. Annie
McDermott's and the young Norwegian seaman's, side by
side, abandoned, exchanging the language of silence on
Malden Island. Annie's son Vincent, who lost his head

among the poppies, lying now in a forest of white crosses on the wrong side of the world. Carl Christianson ('Home is the sailor') still unvisited by any of his kin in the graveyard at Noumea. James and Ethel Grady, together like lovers discreetly behind a hedge, passed from time to time (left to rest in peace? neglected?) by their son Hugh on his way to and from the airport. And John Flatt's grave, lost somewhere, untraceable, its stone broken and buried with him in the graveyard beside the racecourse at Te Aroha.

Hugh and Jean-Anne are heading south again, this time to the Wairere Falls where the attack on Flatt's party happened and where Tarore was murdered. It will be their last journey into the past before Jean-Anne is delivered of her burden of the future. They mean to talk about history while driving but have been silenced by a Wagner tape which at this moment, coming at them from four speakers, front and back on either side, is plundering the deepest reaches of the soul with the *Siegfried* death music. Nothing more splendid, more stirring, in the repertoire and Hugh is splendidly stirred while thinking that such an assertion of individual grandeur and uniqueness belongs only to gods and heroes, and that in reality something simpler (why not 'The Carnival is over'?) would better serve the termination of this mixed blessing, this fluky aggregation of cells that constitutes a human life.

Is this the spirit of his grandmother Charlotte alive in him, asserting itself, as her dominating voice once did, over the sensibility of his mother Ethel Elena? Something of that, no doubt; and also of his one-arm bandit of an Irish-style father, who in the days when business was booming used puckishly to ask Charlotte to sing 'the Darwin number'. Hugh imagines, and quite enjoys the idea of it, something brilliant and loud at a funeral, Viennese perhaps (is there a soprano aria from *Die Fledermaus* that would serve?) followed by torte and strudel and champagne. But then (Ethel Elena asserting herself in him) if you can't bear the weight of Wagner on your frail shoulders there is always Richard Strauss. The Four Last Songs, for example. Hugh acknowledges there have been times when he thought them the most beautiful music ever written; only wonders whether he would want at his burial (and yes, it is the thought of his own obsequies, in conjunction with the *Siegfried* death-krieg, that is driving this interior dialogue) an in-built ceremonial sadness.

Now he is remembering his and Jean-Anne's first run south, so early in their researches — how they climbed (her pregnancy at that time invisible and undeclared) above the town of Te Aroha and looked out over and beyond it to the plain, and understood why this region stretching away west of the mountains had so called to John Flatt through the long years of his separation from it.

Remembering also how they drove to the Te Aroha cemetery, and the full hour they spent hunting for Flatt's grave, knowing it was there, not finding it, deciding its stone, which would have been in the part that sloped down to the river, must long since have gone underground to join him in anonymity. And then while Jean-Anne waited by the car, Hugh climbed an observation tower on the edge of the racecourse and again, in the unglaring yet everywhere-exposing light, experienced that sense of the vast, river-patterned, spirit-level plain running away as far as the eye could run with it; and of how in just a few generations it had been transformed from a wilderness to a richly productive garden.

That was the journey which took them further south, to the grave of Tarore. They knew then only that she was the young Maori killed in the attack on Flatt's party at the Wairere Falls; and that the grave was still to be found at Waharoa. They knew nothing more, and expected another probably unsuccessful hunt among gravestones.

It was a Sunday morning. Outside the little township of Waharoa they found a graveyard, could see it from the main road on the far side of the railway track, but with no obvious way to reach it. In the empty main street they stopped a Maori man carrying a Bible and asked for directions, explaining that they were looking for the grave of a young Maori murdered at the Wairere Falls in the 1830s.

271

Immediate recognition. Tarore. Cross the railway line here in the town. Go past the dairy factory ('Can't miss it. Biggest in the world when it was built in the 1940s') and straight along the road, past both cemeteries, Maori and Pakeha. Go on maybe half a mile. To the left across an open field they would see . . .

And they did. A white cross in the distance. It was Maori land, neglected, full of dock and thistles, but with the remains of some turnip crops and some corn. Further up the road they could see Maoris arriving in cars and utes, on horseback and on foot, going along a rough track and disappearing among trees. What was there to draw them together was hidden by the trees and by a sudden dip down to what must have been a river.

There was no way to the grave except to climb the fence and stumble over the rutted fields. Hugh reached it first.

TARORE
aged 12 years
whose Maori Gospel of St Luke brought peace to the
tribes of Aotearoa
daughter of Ngakuku . . . & great-niece of Te Waharoa of Matamata
died at Wairere Falls 19th October 1836

— those lines inscribed on the front of the white wooden cross. On its back the information that the new memorial had been unveiled by the Maori Queen, Dame Te-Ata-i-Rangikaahu, on 16 October 1977. Already grass and weeds were invading the little picket fence around the grave. A rose thorn was growing up and beginning to throw a casual arm around the cross. Fifteen kilometres away across the plain rose the wall of the Kaimai Range, and down its face could be seen the silver trace of the falls where she had died.

Tarore ('aged 12 years'? — more likely fifteen) whom Flatt had described as 'mature, thoughtful and intelligent', her eyes 'sometimes grave, sometimes sparkling with fun' . . . Who had been the first to call him by his Maori name, Parati . . . Whose Luke Gospel had provided his texts to the

Tauranga natives during his weeks of banishment there . . .
Whose cleverness had troubled Brown . . . Who had been
shot, then hacked down, outside Flatt's tent, her young heart
torn out . . . Whose death he had written of in such distress,
and then failed to mention in his evidence to the Lords . . .

'Hear my prayer, O Lord,' Flatt had chanted that morning
of her death, 'and let my cry come unto thee. Hide not thy
face from me in the day when I am in trouble . . .' Stripped
almost naked, riding saddleless over the Kaimais . . .

Hugh and Jean-Anne (we are with them still in Hugh's
present remembering of that earlier journey) stared at the
inscription, and at one another, surprised to learn that the
death Flatt had been witness to had acquired a significance
of its own, quite separate from him. Flatt had vanished into
the dustiest corners of the Pakeha record, and his grave was
lost; Tarore had survived in the word-of-mouth which was
Maori history, and here was her grave restored. Her father,
Ngakuku, influenced by the Matamata missionaries, had
forgiven her killers. Her Gospel (Hugh and Jean-Anne were
to discover) had been taken back to Rotorua by her
murderers, and was said to have influenced the Arawa chiefs
towards Christianity and peace; and then, by some accident
or design of fate, it had gone to the camp of the great warrior
Te Rauparaha, with the same effect.

It was hard to believe; it did not have to be believed —
but that was the story, and there is a sense in which stories
will not be denied. In death Tarore had become martyr,
symbol and reconciler — the one who had brought the
beginning of the end of the last great intertribal war.
Thenceforth, when the Maori went to war it would be with
the Pakeha.

Jean-Anne took photographs. Hugh took one of her
beside the grave. She wrote some notes in a little notebook.
He stood looking across the plain towards the mountains.
Voices came up — children laughing and shouting. The level
land came to an end not far beyond the grave, dropping
sharply to a river. He went to the edge and looked down. The
water after recent rain was flowing fast and brown. The voices

were coming from beyond a bend in the river. It was, he decided, a waterhole, a swimming place, a picnic spot, below what had once been Waharoa's pa. Somewhere on this ground had been the Matamata mission. Here the Rev Brown had read his gospel and preached his sermons; here John Flatt had made gardens, put down floors in raupo houses, built fences and given his Maori workers their morning classes in reading and writing. Here the first of Flatt's scattered party had come back to report the Arawa attack and Tarore's death; to be followed by others, including her father, Ngakuku, bringing her mutilated body in a box.

Every trace of the missionaries' work was gone now, along with the Maori palisading and trenches, the ornamental carved gateway, the kumara pits, the whares, the meeting house, the huts on poles for storing vegetables. But it was not that thought, or impression, which took strongest hold of Hugh's imagination. It was the memory of something told to him by his grandmother about one of her few meetings with her grandfather. The memory did not come back to him all at once and complete, but rather in fragments, at first like a word on the tip of the tongue, an atmosphere, a dream recovered with difficulty, reforming into fragments which, with patience and concentration and passivity, would form a picture. What took hold was the certainty that as a young woman Charlotte Flatt had stood where he was standing now, with the sound of Maori children's laughter and shouting coming up from the waterhole; and that with her in this place had been her grandfather, John Flatt, an old man who had returned to it for one last visit.

But before we explain Hugh's recollection we must return to Flatt where we left him last, in 1845 at his raupo house on Busby's land near Waitangi, its contents stripped by Heke's men, its garden laid waste, the smoke of what had been the settlement of Kororareka still drifting across the Bay. The words are Flatt's own, written several days later to his wife Caroline and preserved in Miss Gladys McDermott's house in Whangarei among those boxes of family papers.

'YOU MUST FORGIVE ME, my dear wife, and I know that you will, for the way in which I was forced to abandon you (or, should I say, to have you abandon me?); but I could see no way to deal with the events of that terrible day than to send you ahead of me into safety while staying here to find, and if need be rescue (or ransom, or whatever the circumstances should demand), our brother Reuben. And I should say first and at once that in that endeavour I have been successful. Indeed I would not be sending these pages ahead of myself by the *North Star* but would have been aboard her myself with Reuben if it had not been for an injury to his knee and ankle, not serious, one a brief few days will see repaired, but sufficient, especially now that we have no horse, to prevent him making his way to the Bay from the Waimate Mission where he is now resting and where I am writing you this letter. So while I must pass the time in idleness, and while I have, by the kindness of the Rev Burrows, found a place of comfort, I will tell you what I can of events and circumstances here, which will be of interest to you and may even be of use to those needing intelligence on which to base their decisions for the future.

'I am told that all of our people driven from the Bay by Heke's action have one way and another been looked after in Auckland by the Governor, who has made their care and comfort his own responsibility, and I trust that this is true and that you will be safe until my return, which I assure you will be soon. And I should tell you also that you and I and our little family will not be returning to the Bay when the danger is past. There is nothing to return to. Our raupo house (and forgive me for telling it baldly, but you will have expected it) was first stripped, including my garden, and I am told, though I have not been back, has since been burned to the ground. We will start again in Auckland, my dear love, and there in the new capital I know we will prosper.

'This war of Heke's, if it is properly so-called, is strange and most difficult for an Englishman to understand. There is a strong anticipation, and determination, among the few remaining settlers scattered around the Bay that it must only be a matter of time before the Governor sends an effective military force to punish Heke for the destruction wrought upon the town. The missionary brethren, knowing the native mind better than most of the settlers do, but still, I think it fair to say, not really understanding that mind (and indeed, my dear, though I claim experience of it, I do not pretend to understand it either), also believe that the military retaliation must come, and that it will not be undeserved; but they caution against the idea that a truly vigorous and damaging blow against Heke would be either possible or desirable; or, indeed, that Heke's kinsman, Tamati Waka Nene, though he supported the treaty at Waitangi and stands by it, and though he has been and remains our defence against any further excesses on Heke's part, would permit Heke to be simply routed.

'Waka Nene, it seems, who is the key to this mystery, is determined to assert his seniority among the Ngapuhi by curbing Heke's pride and limiting his movement. There will be no march on Auckland while Waka is strong; nor will he let Heke and his men simply retire north to Kaitaia where they would probably be content to go, claiming the sack of Kororareka as a great victory. Waka blocks their path home, and will not let them pass. But to destroy Heke's force, as Waka might try to do if they were of different tribes, is out of the question. What we are seeing is a curious kind of skirmishing, like children playing at war, a serious, deadly "play" in which every day men are wounded and some few die (including even a son of Kawiti), but nothing like I saw in my days in Matamata and the Bay of Plenty, nothing of that furious blood-letting, cold-hearted cruelty, unspeakable barbarism. And this, I think, is what the missionary brethren fear: that if the soldiers should come and fight it like a "real" war, then an older and darker savagery could be unleashed.

'Heke himself has said to me there was no need for the settlers to abandon the town. You may well ask how I come to have spoken to him since his attack on the settlement, but that was necessary if I was to discover what had become of Reuben; and though the prospect frightened me, there was, I found, neither danger nor difficulty in approaching him. He remained as he used to be when he visited us at the Bay: proud, suspicious, his mood sometimes veiled; but also wise, sensible, and not unfriendly. It was difficult to remember that he was the man who had burned our town.

'Though the warrior parties keep on the move (laying waste to crops and gardens and livestock as they go), I was always able, with Mr Mair's help, to locate Heke's camp, and that of Kawiti; Waka Nene was never far distant; and to my surprise (until I saw that each side was constantly hungry for news of the other) I found them always willing, and usually eager, to talk. When fortifications were being built we talked beyond the outer palisade, they liking to keep secret whatever traps and pits and cover they are preparing. But to korero is what the native New Zealander does better than anything, better even than fighting, at which (and pray God the Governor remember it when deciding how he should commit the young men at his command) they excel.

'To Heke's remark that the settlers need not have left Kororareka, and to his show of displeasure that they should have done so, I replied by asking whether he expected them to sit in their houses while they burned. He replied that if they had been in their houses there would have been no burning. Nor would any settler who kept away from the fighting have been harmed. His only quarrel, Heke insisted, was with the Pakeha soldiers who represented the Queen and her flag and her treaty.

'I asked him how those of us with wives and children to protect should be expected to know that he could be relied upon not to do us harm, and he replied that he was a Christian, and knew that I had been a missionary of the Church: did I not, then, trust the power of my own faith and the good will of those who have been converts to it?

'I could not answer this question frankly. Even now I believe it would have been too great a risk to have taken him at his word. I have seen the native as savage, and as duplicitous savage; they love to make promises and keep them, just as they love to make and break them, and to laugh at the fool who believed the promise would be kept. And though it is true Heke acted on the whole honourably at Kororareka, releasing prisoners and allowing his enemies to recover and bury their dead, it might not have been so. A mere whim might have made it otherwise.

'I could not say it to Heke, but I have come to believe that our missionary work has been for the most part no better than a coat of paint. I am glad to have been released from it, however painful the injustice of the removal, and however difficult it has been for me to accept. Working in my garden on Mr Busby's land I came to think, dearest Caroline, that this was the true labour God intended for my hands, "the one true talent" I have which, as the most Christian of poets says, "is death to hide". And how fertile and beautiful a land He has given us in which to live and work and bring our children to manhood and womanhood! Let us be full of gratitude for all that has befallen us, and of hope and confidence for our future in the new capital!

'But I have not told you of Reuben (though he will be telling his own story in the letter he is now writing to Margaret). He was not involved in the fighting on the day of the attack on the town, but the evening before was drawn into a war of words with Kawiti's men who were pulling down his stake-fences to make their fire, and in the course of the argument, his anger growing larger as his fence grew smaller, he called them cannibals and attempted to push one of them away, whereupon he was struck a blow on the head, and woke at some time during that night trussed up in something like a hen-coop. He did not know where he was nor how he had been taken there, but was fed by two native women throughout the next day and the two following, being told each time that he was being fed because he was too thin to eat, but that when he was fatter the "cannibals" were going to make a feast of him.

'During these days I had been asking where he was and had met with those deliberately blank faces and denials by which I know (again from old experience) the native New Zealander lies to you and lets you know he is lying. I could get nothing from Heke, nor from Kawiti, nor from any of their men, except the suggestion which I knew to be absurd that my brother-in-law had been taken by Waka Nene.

'And then one night Reuben stumbled into the Waimate, still confused, uncertain where he had been or who had been holding him. He had been told that they had given up hope of ever making him fat enough for good eating and were turning him loose. "Run home, long pig", they had said to him; with much loud laughter. I suppose it had all been a joke, and a punishment for calling them cannibals, but how is one to know? In the dark the poor fellow had taken a bad tumble which left one leg very sore that night, and the following morning so swollen he was not able to put a foot to the ground. But as I have said, it is an injury which will soon heal, and when there is next a ship making ready for Auckland, he will hobble (with my assistance) the twelve miles to the Bay and we will pray for a fair wind to carry us both to our dear wives and darling children.

'That is all for now, my dear love. The *North Star* (a propitious name for a ship, is it not?) will carry this to you, with all assurances of your husband's love.'

THE WAGNER IS LEFT BEHIND somewhere just south of the Bombay Hills. They have gone left, which is to say east, off the main highway south, through Mangatawhiri and Maramarua on the Hauraki plain. Ngatea is just ahead, and beyond that Paeroa, where they will turn south again, down the Waihou River, which Captain Cook absurdly and unsuccessfully named the Thames, towards Te Aroha.

Also left behind now, but for a few scraps and a death certificate, is the written record. In Auckland John Flatt became a private citizen, disengaged from that 'New Zealand History' which, though Hugh still puzzles over what it properly includes and excludes, he never regrets having been urged by his Mangold mentor to make the lifetime object of his studies.

There are records showing Flatt's residency in Parnell

before the end of 1845, and that he was employed by one Caleb Robinson as a gardener on Colonial Government land. There are records of sons and a daughter, of their marriages, of the family move in the 1860s to the Thames goldfield, and finally, in Flatt's old age, to Te Aroha. These, Hugh and Jean-Anne agree, seem only to increase his anonymity. He has faded into the unrecorded, or if recorded, unspecific and general, life of the nation, and they have only in two instances been able to find later echoes of his early days in New Zealand: once a letter of 1849, not sent, but tucked into what remains of his journals, taking pleasure at the news of the dismissal of his old enemy Henry Williams; the other, a note recording his last meeting with Colenso, which took place in 1855.

Where the two former catechists met is not shown, though Jean-Anne believes it was at Colenso's home in the course of a journey Flatt made down the east coast; and it was probably family matters (their wives being related by marriage) as much as their old association which brought them together.

Flatt's note (also found among Gladys McDermott's papers) comments on the strain apparent in Colenso's face. It records his fall from grace, his having been dismissed from holy orders for fathering a child with a young native woman, Ripeka, who had been (Colenso was strangely at pains to point out) 'given' to him by her parents while she was still a little girl. Flatt's note expresses full sympathy not only for his old friend's misfortune, but for the fact that he had taken it so hard. But it observes with surprise that Colenso seemed to have expected his superiors in the Church ('hard men', Flatt commented, 'unyielding, all of them') to overlook the matter; to understand and forgive him. And Flatt concluded, 'The truth is that for all the affection aroused in me by the memory of the time when we were young together and united in pious hope and ambition, there is no longer, between me and Colenso, a real meeting of minds. The old intensity of missionary zeal has quite gone from me. In him, and despite his fleshly transgression, it remains strong. He wanted my sympathy, and had it, but not *as* he wanted it. I could hardly think about the consequences of his act for thinking about the act itself. There my imagination stuck (should I be ashamed to say?) almost as if I looked upon the picture of a beautiful landscape remembered from long ago.'

TE AROHA AT LAST, and they stop at a place they remember from their previous visit for the savage splendour of its toasted cheese and onion sandwiches and the dark intensity of its accompanying pot of tea. They order the same and are refreshed by this rural repast, cheered by it, catching one another's eyes, wanting to laugh when there is nothing in particular to laugh at.

And then, Jean-Anne tucking her heavy belly behind the wheel to take a turn at driving, they head straight on south, not stopping at the racecourse road that leads to the cemetery and the unfindable John Flatt grave, but on down the old road, running parallel to the main one but east of the river, nearer to the wall of the mountain range. This is the landscape through which Brown and Fairburn and Flatt drove cattle overland from Puriri to Matamata — beautiful country, everything presenting itself dramatically to the eye, which perhaps explains why Hugh and Jean-Anne forget history for some kilometres and talk about what they have seen and missed seeing in the recent film festival.

Jean-Anne asks did he see *Voyager*, with Sam Sheppard in the leading role. No, Hugh says, he didn't; and she begins to tell the story. It's about an older man who has an affair with a young woman and then discovers that she is the daughter of the woman he was in love with when he was a young man. They quarrelled and separated and she married someone else — a man he now knows is dead. The daughter knows nothing of this. She brings her mother and her lover together, and he discovers that his young friend — his mistress — is his own daughter. Before he and the mother can decide how to deal with this the daughter is killed in an accident. She is bitten by a snake and falls among rocks, striking her head. She is recovering from the snake bite, but the head injury causes her to die.

'Symbolic, I suppose,' Hugh murmurs, and feels foolish. He has had to curb his responses, since he too has seen the movie, and remembers some of the details Jean-Anne has forgotten; but having told her he has not seen it, he must either keep silent or explain his denial.

GRAVES AGAIN. THE GRAVE. GRAVESTONES. Zarathustra's Funeral Song beginning, 'Yonder is the grave-island, the silent island; yonder too are the graves of my youth. I will bear thither an evergreen wreath of life.'

What had come back to Hugh Grady on that previous visit to this region, when he had stood with Jean-Anne at Tarore's grave, surprised to find that in death the young Maori woman killed in Flatt's presence had acquired such significance among the tribes, was the recollection of something told him by his grandmother. As a girl of fifteen she had joined children and grandchildren of John Flatt who had travelled to Te Aroha, where he was living with his son Joseph, to celebrate his ninetieth birthday. Some of them had made a day-trip with him in two horse-drawn traps, south to Matamata and Waharoa where he had once worked as an Anglican missionary, and where he had seen the Maori tribes at peace and at war in the manner of their pre-European days.

There had been a lot of singing as they went along, a picnic at the hot springs, a stop for tea in one of the little towns; and then Charlotte had gone with him, just the two of them, on a ramble across paddocks to a grave, marked then only by a single stone, like a very large pebble, set in the ground, and with a name or word on it she did not afterwards remember. It had not been a designated graveyard, but an ancient Maori burial place, a wahi tapu, and at that time a few other graves had been marked by stones and wooden carvings. John Flatt had told her that this stone marked the grave of someone he had loved very much.

While he stood looking down at it, silent, lost in his memories, the young Charlotte had wandered away, her attention drawn by the sound of laughter and shouting coming up from the river. She had gone to the edge and, seeing nothing but the river, had followed where it curved away among trees, until she was able to look down on a place where it widened and deepened. There Maori children were playing, swimming, diving, swinging out over the water on a rope.

As they walked back across the fields to join the others — and it was this that had made the recollection stay with Charlotte — her grandfather had thanked her for coming with him and had told her that for many years he had wanted to revisit that place. He would, he told her, rest easier in his own grave for having looked on it one last time.

MOUNTAINS TO THE LEFT, plains to the right, while the road, straight as an arrow (almost) and (almost) without rises and falls, runs them south from Te Aroha. And now they have their first view of the Wairere Falls, two drops — eighty and seventy-three metres their research has told them — seeming to come straight off the wall of the hills, as if the river flowed uphill on the far side where in fact, to gather so much water, the mountain range must go on ridging back, out of sight from the road which runs so close to its base.

The off-road angles left, takes them through pasture land, heavy, damp, intense green, with patches of bush and cabbage trees. Cows look up and stare as they pass. There is no human eye to see them. They find a rough carpark, with signs to the falls. In their heavy boots they climb a stile, Jean-Anne with Hugh's help bravely heaving her bulk over, and make their way into the bush. They must be a kilometre or more from the falls, but keep catching sight of the upper cascade and its fine aureole of spray rising and deflecting the light.

The bush track, climbing always, follows the river which dashes down, a huge volume of brilliant clear impatient water, so loud and voluble among boulders that Hugh and Jean-Anne must shout to one another to be understood.

They arrive at the sign marking the start of the old Maori

track, curving away from the river and up the hillslope to cross the mountain range. They will come back to it; but first they press on along the river track, through heavy bush, crossing bridges over and then back across the rushing water, until they are brought into full, magnificent sight of the falls.

They stop there, rest, take photographs. Ahead there are steep paths and wooden staircases that would bring them closer, but in Jean-Anne's condition it would not be possible — nor, Hugh adds, at his age wise. And in any case, sight-seeing is not their purpose.

So now they turn and walk back to the sign marking the start of the old track. It is here that Maoris from Waharoa's pa, and Pakeha traders and missionaries, stopped for the night on their journey from the plains to the coast. It is here that Flatt made camp with his party; here that the Arawa taua attacked, and Tarore was murdered.

The stopping place is on a wooded ledge, perhaps four metres wide, and five or six above the river. There is a grassy space among the trees where the raupo whare must have stood. Some distance from it there is another flat space, the only one on which Flatt could have pitched his tent. The trees close overhead, the land lifts steeply on one side and drops almost vertically on the other, straight down to the river. The attackers must have come up from the river; and Flatt's mission Maoris, woken at or just before first light by the barking of their dogs, must have made their escape up into thick bush covering the slopes above.

Hugh and Jean-Anne sit in the soft grass. There is no wind, no birdsong. The rushing of the river among boulders directly below is white noise, loud and ebullient, insistent and unvarying.

How long do they remain like that, not speaking, not needing to speak? Until she moves closer to him and takes his hand. 'I know now what happened,' is what she says.

He nods. It's as if they both have known, but until this moment, forced by the place itself to imagine in detail, they have not known what they knew.

Why else did Flatt write first of Tarore's murder in such

distress, and then later, recounting in evidence to the Lords the attack on his party, make no mention of any death? Why, after the attack, did he send his party of natives back to their pa, and himself ride on alone to Tauranga? Why did Tarore's father, Ngakuku, twice ask whether his daughter's soul would go to Heaven or to Reinga, saying to the Rev Brown, 'She has heard the Gospel with her ears, and read it with Mother Brown, but I do not know whether she received it in her heart'? Why else did little children in the party escape and not the fit and strong Tarore? Why else did Flatt tell his granddaughter that the grave they visited belonged to someone he had loved? And write of Colenso's transgression with a young Maori woman that he could 'hardly think about the consequences of the act for thinking about the act itself', which was like 'looking upon the picture of a beautiful landscape remembered from long ago'? What else could have been referred to in the missing half page of the Rev Thomas Chapman's postscript of 15 March 1837, declaring Flatt unsuited for further catechetical duties?

On the night of 19 October 1836 all had happened as Flatt recounted it. He had fixed his tent. They had prepared supper and eaten it and he had called them together for family prayers. Then they had retired, he to his tent, they to their raupo whare. But in the night Tarore had come to Flatt's tent — probably not for the first time.

Woken by their dogs that morning the Maori group had fled into the bush. Flatt and Tarore had not woken until the taua was outside the tent. In one of the missionary accounts it was said she had been killed in the raupo house; but Flatt himself said she was shot and hacked down outside his tent. He must have remained inside with her, hoping to protect her there. In his evidence to the Lords he said the attacking party called to him, asking was he Tapsell. When he said he was not, they began to tear down the tent. It must have been then that Tarore took fright and ran. She was shot, then axed, while Flatt struggled to get out from under the canvas. He was in time to see her lying dead, a warrior hacking at her chest.

Ngakuku had seen his daughter rise in the dark and go to Flatt's tent, and had known she was there in the morning when the attack came. In his concern for what would become of her soul he must finally have told Chapman what he had seen. Still shaken by the Yate scandal and other transgressions, the missionaries had thought it best to drop Flatt from their ranks without enquiry or explanation. Even Flatt himself may not have known what they knew. By the time he reached London he was no longer willing or able to talk about the savage murder of someone he had loved, and there is no evidence that he ever spoke of it again.

But at the age of ninety he had remembered her still, and had returned with his granddaughter to her grave.

'Yonder is the grave-island, the silent island . . . I will bear thither an evergreen wreath of life.'

THEY ARE LYING PROPPED on their elbows in the grass, considering sex and death, death and sex. Hugh thinks, but cannot make the effort to raise his voice and say it aloud, that this bullying/ebullient water-music has gone on, unchanging, through the 160 years that have passed since his forebear first heard it. That it was there before . . . will be there after . . .

Jean-Anne pushes herself up suddenly. Her hands go down, as if she is supporting the burden of her belly. Her expression is distressed, or perhaps embarrassed. She throws some words at him which the river catches and swallows. He sees that her trousers are wet. She is saying something about an accident. She has wet herself . . .

It takes them a minute or two to decide it is the waters that have broken. She says she thinks she has felt something like a contraction. The birth is not due for two or three weeks. They are both nervous, alone in this remote place among dark trees by rushing water. They put together their fragments of knowledge. They have some idea that if the waters break early the baby is not protected — that Jean-Anne must move carefully.

He helps her back along the track, over fallen branches,

down slippery slopes. What seemed a short walk seems now a very long one. At the stile he goes ahead of her, helps take her weight as she goes over it. At the car they decide she should lie on the back seat while he drives. She says that something is going on down there — something between a wave motion and stomach cramps — maybe the beginning . . .

He drives, fast but carefully, carefully but fast, caught between two contrary impulses. The road which seemed so flat and straight now seems to rise and fall and sway to left and right. The distance back to Te Aroha seems huge, his efforts at the wheel making no impression on it, as if the town is moving away from them faster than he can safely ask the car to go. Everything, he tells himself, is subjective; most things which happen happen in the mind.

Now he contradicts himself. Everything is far from subjective. Babies are safely delivered, or not; they arrive decorously in hospital theatres, or messily on litters or in the backs of cars.

He glances over his shoulder at her. She smiles to reassure him, and fails.

And later, at a further enquiry: Yes, she says; they do need to hurry. Something is definitely happening.

Keep calm, he tells himself, and stops the car to look at a map. Gordon? They must have gone through Gordon without seeing it. Shaftesbury lies just ahead.

But when they reach Shaftesbury there is nothing except a house or two and a name on an AA sign.

Off to the left — and Hugh registers it with a sort of irritation, as if it were inopportune — the sun is going down over the plain with a display of long orange and yellow rays and angled cloud-spearing.

Jean-Anne is breathing now in little gasps. Hugh knows about this. It is something they learn at antenatal classes, meant, he thinks, to slow things down, to keep the baby indoors until the world is ready to receive it. Over his shoulder he asks again is she okay. She says she is; but she thinks she will need help soon.

Darkness has rushed over the plain. Only the tops of the mountain range are in sunlight. The shadow rises, pushing the last of the light up to the eastern peaks and off them. In the west, low down in the sky the sun has finished with the clouds which lie about like victims of a terrible fire.

Jean-Anne is humming a tune, moaning at intervals; humming, then moaning, then humming again. Now the lights of Te Aroha West appear. A stop, an enquiry, the information that the young woman in the back is in labour, produces a flurry of rural excitement and help. Hugh is led into the grounds of the Te Aroha hospital by a tow-truck flashing its emergency lights.

Now he is in a pale blank corridor, walking up and down. He has been here before, twice, once for John, a second time for Richard, in exactly this neutral nowhere, sick with anxiety. He tells himself there is no need to feel so involved — this is not his responsibility — but that makes no difference. He is experiencing once again the male's consummate moment of uselessness, the always shocking discovery of his irrelevance when the doors of new life are opening.

There must be something he can do. The faceless female persons smilingly present and in charge on these occasions let him use a phone in the front office. He calls Jean-Anne's number, hears her voice on the answerphone, and leaves a message for Philip.

He calls Hat and tells her what is happening. She asks for details, tells him to stay calm, says reassuring things, reminds him of the births of Richard and John. She promises to keep phoning Philip at home and hospital until she's sure the message has reached him.

Hugh says he will call again as soon as there's anything to report.

Now he is invited into the theatre — Jean-Anne has asked for him. She is sweating and huge in there, pink and red and white, a human balloon about to be popped. She is attended by three women, a Pakeha, a Maori and an Asian. The Asian is the doctor. There is no sense of panic. He's told to relax; this is not a traffic accident, it's a birth.

He dabs Jean-Anne's brow. Her eyes are squeezed shut, her teeth clamped tight on pain. She puts her hand to her face, drops it, heaves, relaxes, says something to him which he doesn't catch, except his name, Hughie.

'That's looking better,' the doctor says, a gloved hand vanishing between Jean-Anne's legs.

Jean-Anne throws her head back and groans. The groan doesn't die away. It swells in volume and becomes something like a shout, in which Hugh seems to catch an echo of cousin Greta's voice calling down from the ridge into the back paddock. But it's *Fuck!* Jean-Anne shouts; and again, 'Oh Jesus. *Fuck!*'

'Push,' the women say, crowding around her so that Hugh is bundled out of the way. '*Push!*'

FOURTEEN

WHEN HUGH AND HAT RETURNED with Richard and John from their end-of-the-Sixties journey to Europe they could say to one another truthfully that they were reconciled. Hugh's sexual misadventure had been put firmly into the past. They had been away from New Zealand almost a year; and even if the visit to Sweden, or rather Hugh's curious lack of response to what they had learned there, had been disappointing, Hat's 'Swedish card', as he called it, had served its purpose in persuading him to come with her on a journey which in every other respect had fulfilled her hopes. They had grown closer as a family. The boys had learned more from their travels than school could have taught them. Hat had improved her knowledge of the law, and Hugh had extended his of libraries and historical research. It was from that journey Hat dated the earliest stirrings of an ambition to be among the first New Zealand women appointed to the bench. And London had given Hugh access to colonial papers he had not had the chance to study before.

But most of all there had been long hours alone and at leisure together, Hugh and Hat enjoying one another's company, talking, sharing pleasures, recovering their marriage in all its aspects.

So the episode of Lydia Lawrence was put behind them; and when, on their return, Hat made discreet enquiries and found that she had left the university without completing her degree and was now living somewhere out of Auckland, that seemed an end to it.

For Hugh it was less simple. Yes it was over; and that,

he acknowledged within himself, was as it should be. Lid had to be free of an emotional tie which would prevent her from making a life of her own. He had to be free of one which would confuse and undermine his love for Hat.

All that was accepted. Sincerely. But self-denial did not change Hugh Grady. He was the same person, with the same appetites, dreams, desires. Thoughts of Lid still came to him. He still wished it were possible to see her, talk to her, hear her laugh and say witty things, fuck her. She existed in his mind as something possessed and lost. He wanted to possess her again, and by that possession to feel his own strength, the greater certainty she had given him that he existed.

From time to time, though only on impulse, never purposefully, he enquired about her. She had done a good job in covering her tracks, but late in the year after his return he learned from a student friend that she was living in Napier, married, and with a baby daughter.

He got her telephone number from the directory service. There was at first a fear, or nervousness — something he didn't properly understand — about making the call. Days passed while the intention lay in his mind, incubating. One morning, without thought or conscious decision, he put through a toll call from his library office.

Lydia answered. He recognised her voice at once; but she recognized his, and put down the receiver.

Twice more this happened, at intervals of several weeks, and he knew he must stop or put himself in a very bad light.

At about this time a collection of his essays on New Zealand history (he had given it the title *Without Cause* and dedicated it to Frank Mangold) was published. It was a book of modest size put out by an academic press, and he wanted Lid to see it. He inscribed a copy and sent it to her. It came back unopened.

Now he wrote her a letter. He understood, he told her, that she did not want any further contact. That was painful, but understandable. He loved Hat, and no doubt (he added without quite believing it) she loved Bernard; and marriages, especially marriages with children, had to be protected. All of that was acknowledged. But did it mean that they, he and Lydia, couldn't also love one another? Couldn't even exchange news and greetings? Had to behave as if what had happened between them had not happened, or was of no importance? Wasn't it a sign that their affair was *not* over if they couldn't even say or write an occasional word to one another?

It was all reasonable — plausible; but not, or not in any simple way, quite truthful. Hugh's motives, he recognised, were predatory, and the recognition gave him no sense of shame or guilt. To be male, he had decided, was to be predatory; all pretence to the contrary was window-dressing. If Lydia possessed one kind of strength she would respond; if she possessed another kind, she would not.

There was no reply.

And then, two years after his return, three since he had last seen her, he caught sight of her in Queen Street. She saw him and turned away; then turned to face him when she saw she was being followed.

'Hullo Hugh,' she said, and he saw that she was pregnant. She told him that she and Bernard were visiting Auckland briefly, that Bernard wasn't far away, that to find them talking would upset him, and would Hugh please go away.

Hugh refused unless she promised to write to him. She promised, and when pressed, promised again. Yes, she would write to him if he would only go.

When her letter came, a week or so later, there was no address or date. It said,

'Dear Hugh,
'Here is a letter as promised, and only *because* I promised. Please don't reply. *Please*, Hughie, just let me get on with my life, and you get on with yours. D'accord?
'Love,
'L.
'PS: I have a little girl, and another (g or b) on the way.
'PPS: Here is a Zen story which contains a message for you —
'Two monks, Tanzan and Ekido, were travelling together.

It was raining and they came to a swollen river. Standing at the water's edge there was a beautiful young girl in a fine silk kimono, wanting to cross. "Let me help you," Tanzan said, and he picked her up and waded across with her in his arms. Ekido said nothing. All day the two monks travelled on, but at evening Ekido could contain himself no longer. "You know the rule of our order which is that we do not touch women, and especially women who are young and beautiful. Yet at the stream you allowed yourself to pick up that girl and carry her." To which Tanzan replied, "Yes, but I left her there. You, it seems, are still carrying her."'

That second postscript was a small, but to Hugh a significant, sign — not of weakness quite, but of vulnerability. The door was shut, yes; but it wasn't locked. He had lost her physically — he knew that; but the mind, too, is predatory. In reply he wrote:

'Very dear L,

'Thank you for keeping your promise, and for the Zen story and its message, which I accept. Here is one for you:

'In ancient China there were two friends, a man and a woman, he who played the harp exceptionally well, and she who was especially appreciative, finding always the right words to express the innermost qualities of the music. When the one played thinking of a mountain or a forest, the words "mountain" or "forest" would be somewhere in the friend's comments. When he played thinking of running water she would say, "Here is the stream." But she fell sick and died, whereupon he cut the strings of his harp and never played again. Since when the cutting of the strings of a harp has always been a symbol of friendship.'

'I'm also sending you my little book of essays again. Please don't return it. Read it. Or at least keep it so I can let myself believe it's being read. I don't want to have to cut the strings — not yet. But I will leave you in peace.

'Your

'Hugo Wolf'

There was no reply — and it was the last communication between them. But this time the inscribed copy of *Without Cause* had not not been returned.

HUGH GRADY WAS WALKING up and down the empty whitely lit main street of Te Aroha — town of the toasted cheese and onion sandwiches and the strong colonial tea, where his great-great-grandfather, laid to rest beside the racecourse, had found peace, reconciliation, anonymity.

Aroha, Hugh thought — it meant love. Love was what he felt. Arohanui. He had seen the latest life slither headfirst and bloody into Te Ao Marama — the world of light.

Hat had phoned the hospital to say that she had got through to Philip Devantier and he was on his way — would arrive some time during the night. She sent her love and warm congratulations to Jean-Anne. She told Hugh to stay as long as he felt needed, and to take extra care, driving back late, that he didn't fall asleep at the wheel. If need be he should hole up at a motel and drive back in the morning.

Later Jean-Anne had wanted Hugh to call her parents with news of the birth. She had given him the number; and when he returned to say that the front office of the little hospital was locked up for the night, she had given him a phone card and sent him out into the empty neon streets to find a call-box.

He pressed the numbers and waited. To Hugh's ear every voice was distinct — he prided himself on recognitions; but this one, which he had not heard in more than twenty years, played a chord that seemed to take the strength out of his limbs.

He explained who he was.

Lydia knew. She too still had her ear for voices — even, or especially, long-lost ones.

She was impatient to know why he should be calling late at night. Was something wrong? Was Jean-Anne alright?

'Yes, fine,' he said. 'Absolutely. She has a daughter, Lid. A lovely baby, born this evening. Ten fingers and toes. Everything intact. Sings in tune. And Jean-Anne's well. She's fine. Awfully pleased with herself. A few stitches, but otherwise no problems at all.'

He explained that they were in Te Aroha, and how they came to be there. And that Philip was on his way.

'Good. Oh I'm so glad. What a relief.' His recital of the facts was punctuated by expressions of pleasure from Lydia.

Now she laughed. 'Hugh, this is absurd. We don't exchange a word for more than twenty years and then you're the one who phones to tell me . . .'

Yes, absurd, he agreed. But nice. She knew, didn't she that they . . .

Were working together? Oh yes, she'd been told. 'And you, Hughie, you knew that Jean-Anne . . .'

'Was your daughter? Not at first. But she told me . . . She's lovely, Lydia. Beautiful. Intelligent. She's helped me so much. You wouldn't believe . . .'

There was a moment's pause. The silence that had lasted so long between them opened again before Hugh Grady like a landscape in which it would be easy to be lost, or injured. Without quite intending to, he asked whether the new baby was his grandchild.

There was silence at the other end. 'What I mean,' he began.

'I understand what you mean,' Lydia said. 'You mean is Jean-Anne your daughter.'

He tried to say yes to that, but his voice failed.

Her voice too was faint. 'Yes, she is, Hughie.'

Now there was a longer silence, into which he breathed almost inaudibly that he was glad.

'I think it's right it should be acknowledged,' Lydia murmured. 'Between us. Not to be . . .'

'Talked about. No, of course not.' He was still swallowing his words. And then: 'Does Jean-Anne . . .'

'Know? Yes she does.'

'I'm glad. And Bernard?'

'Of course.'

'I've so much to apologise for,' Hugh said.

'Not to me, Hugh. Not at all.'

'Which means, I guess, that you've had — you're having

. . .' He hesitated. 'A good life? It's been so long, but the years pass so quickly, don't they? It seems only yesterday. I think often about, you know, us, and . . . Have you . . . This is something I shouldn't ask . . .'

She seemed to laugh. 'Then don't.'

'I wondered whether you've thought of me sometimes.'

'Don't be wet Hughie. Of course I have.'

He was reaching out, he wasn't sure for what — for the all that was no longer possible; for the everything he had renounced; for the return of the past. While his mind floundered, recognising the absurdity of his own desires and finding no words that could make them seem otherwise, Jean-Anne's card ran out. They were cut off.

He banged the phone with the heel of his hand, uttered a stifled wail, and pushed out into the empty Te Aroha night, walking fast and without any idea of where he should go. At the dark end of the street where the lighting ran out he looked up into the brilliance of the Milky Way, remembering Lydia's letter that had ended 'I look at the stars and tell God to fucking lay off me.'

But what more could he have hoped for? Their conversation had to end. Life was like that, wasn't it? Your card ran out, and that was it.

'I have a daughter,' he said, still walking into the dark, still staring heavenward.

He did not know what to do next. He felt restless, wide awake, excited. No reason now to stay in this town. Jean-Anne would sleep, and wake to find Philip beside her, there to look after her and to get his first sight of their baby girl.

But Hugh was not quite ready to leave. He looked at his watch. It was almost midnight. He would drive out to the racecourse and walk once around the track under the stars, thinking about John Flatt, lying somewhere nearby in a grave now unmarked, and about the 'singing whakapapa' that had just issued its latest challenge to the universal silence which would always defeat it.

Then he would put a tape on the stereo and drive home through the night.

GLOSSARY

for Australian readers

aroha	love
arohanui	great love
bobby	unweaned calf sent to meatworks to keep cow in milk
bowyangs	cords for tying trouser legs below the knee so cuffs don't trail in mud
Ehara, ko te tamaiti o Ngakuku, ka mate i Te Wairere	Certainly she was struck down — Ngakuku's daughter — at the Wairere Falls
fight (n)	missionary literal translation of 'taua' meaning 'war party'
haere ra	farewell
haka	war dance
hangi	oven-pit and food cooked in it
hongi	greeting by pressing noses
kauri	species of New Zealand conifer
karakia	charm, spell, incantation, prayer
kehua	ghost
kokopu	small freshwater fish
korero	talk, parley
kumara	sweet potato
long pig	human flesh for eating
mana	reputation, standing
manuka	scented flowering shrub
matakite	seer, prophet
mere	hand-held sharp-edged stone club
moko	tattoo

pa	fortified village
Pakeha	European New Zealander
pohutukawa	coastal flowering tree
puha	edible thistle
pipi	edible shellfish
rangatira	chief or person of rank
raupo	reed, bullrush, used for thatch
taiaha	carved wooden spear
tapu	sacred, bewitched, forbidden
taua	war party
te ao marama	the world of light
te karu wha	four eyes
toetoe	pampas/Prince of Wales feathers
tohunga	priest, sage
tui	bird
utu	revenge or recompense for wrong
wahine	woman
wahi tapu	sacred place
whakapapa	genealogy
whare	Maori house or hut